PACEMAKER®

Basic
Mathematics

Third Edition

TEACHER'S ANSWER EDITION

GLOBE FEARON EDUCATIONAL PUBLISHER
Upper Saddle River, New Jersey
www.globefearon.com

Contents

Reviewers

We thank the following educators, who provided valuable comments and suggestions during the development of this book:

Rosemarie Estok, Woodbridge Public Schools, Woodbridge, New Jersey
Audris Griffith, Glen Bard West High School, Glen, Illinois
Dorie Knaub, Downey Unified School District, Downey, California
Christine Sweat, Highland Middle School, Jacksonville, Florida

Subject Area Consultant: Kay McClain, Department of Teaching and Learning, Vanderbilt University, Nashville, Tennessee
Pacemaker Curriculum Advisor: Stephen C. Larsen, formerly of The University of Texas at Austin

About the Cover: Mathematics is a way to help people understand and deal with their environment. The images on the cover of this book show how an understanding of basic mathematics is relevant in everyday life. Runners need to calculate their speed over distances. Architects use geometric structures and formulas to build cities. Newspapers and magazines display data visually in graphs. Mechanics use gearing ratios to repair machines such as cars and airplanes. How do you use mathematics in your everyday life?

ISBN 0-835-95747-0

Printed in the United States of America

3 4 5 6 7 8 9 10   03 02 01

GLOBE FEARON EDUCATIONAL PUBLISHER
Upper Saddle River, New Jersey
www.globefearon.com

Proven Solution for Today's Classrooms from Globe Fearon

As we approach the 21st century, students and educators alike face increased challenges. Students need preparation for the rigors of more difficult standards and proficiency tests, as well as the ability to successfully apply learning to daily challenges—including the challenges of the workplace. Educators must meet the needs of diverse classrooms, keep learning up-to-date and relevant, and create supportive learning environments for a range of learning styles. Both students and educators will need teaching and learning tools to meet the challenges of the 21st-century classroom.

Globe Fearon's *Pacemaker Basic Mathematics* has always supplied educators and students with materials and techniques that are accessible, predictable, age-appropriate, and relevant. This new third edition continues to provide a solid, well-balanced approach to teaching math content and building math skills.

The Third Edition of Basic Mathematics retains these successful features:

- small, manageable lessons
- lessons focused on a single skill or concept
- concepts presented in a predictable format
- frequent opportunities for review and practice
- pre-taught vocabulary and controlled reading level
- a high-interest, age-appropriate design
- solid teacher support
- NCTM-based curriculum

The new edition of Basic Mathematics is enhanced with features teachers asked for:

- a FULL COLOR student edition
- new life-skills and workplace features that make relevant connections
- a Workbook that parallels the student edition
- even more predictable lesson formats
- more comprehensive coverage—correlates to standards
- Everyday Problem Solving lesson features
- opportunities to practice and prepare for standardized tests
- more visuals to address a variety of learning styles
- MORE teacher support—new *Teacher's Answer Edition* with answers and notes on the student pages, *Teacher's Planning Guide* saves time, and an improved *Classroom Resource Binder* with plenty of teacher support

The careers of the 21st century demand a strong foundation of mathematics and problem solving. To meet this challenge and take advantage of this opportunity, the *Algebra for All* movement has drawn attention to the importance of *all* students succeeding in an algebra course. As a result, many states and districts require that students successfully complete an algebra course to graduate and to prepare for the future.

Pacemaker® BASIC MATHEMATICS — THE FIRST STEP ON THE LADDER TO SUCCESS

Facing more challenging math requirements, many students need a firm grounding in the concepts and skills prerequisite to subsequent courses that are more algebra specific. Many students need to develop confidence by taking that first step—and succeeding. *Pacemaker® Basic Mathematics* bridges the gap between the varied abilities of students and the ladder to success in algebra.

What is Basic Math? It is . . .

- Using the four operations with whole numbers, fractions, decimals, and integers.
- Using ratios, proportions, and percents.
- Interpreting information from graphical displays.
- Using measurement and geometry.
- Applying basic statistics and the meaning of probability.
- Solving problems.
- Learning elements of introductory algebra.
- Applying concepts and skills to problems of daily living and the workplace.
- Thinking critically.
- Working cooperatively.
- Using a calculator.
- Communicating mathematically.
- Writing about math.

THE OTHER STEPS ON THE LADDER TO SUCCESS

- *Pacemaker® Basic Mathematics* is the first step to the other Globe Fearon math products developed specifically for student success in algebra.
- *Pacemaker® Pre-Algebra* takes the arithmetic, geometry, statistics, and other topics of basic math and relates them to such algebra fundamentals as evaluating expressions, solving equations, writing equations, and graphing.
- In turn, *Pacemaker® Algebra 1* extends the presentation of algebra to such areas as linear equations in two variables, systems of equations, functions and their graphs, and to more work on geometry, probability, and statistics.

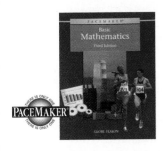

BASIC MATHEMATICS
Contents

Understanding Whole Numbers
Adding Whole Numbers
Subtracting Whole Numbers
Multiplying Whole Numbers
Dividing Whole Numbers
More About Numbers
Fractions and Mixed Numbers
Adding and Subtracting Fractions
Multiplying and Dividing Fractions
Decimals
Percent
Ratios and Proportions
Graphs and Statistics
Customary Measurement
Metric Measurement
Geometry
Integers
Algebra

PRE-ALGEBRA
Contents

Whole Numbers
Number Expressions, Equations, and
    Properties
Variable Expressions
Variable Equations
Decimals and Algebra
Factors and Multiples
Fractions and Mixed Numbers
Adding and Subtracting Fractions and
    Mixed Numbers
Multiplying and Dividing Fractions
    and Mixed Numbers
Ratios, Proportions, and Percents
Integers
Integers and Algebra
The Coordinate Plane

ALGEBRA 1
Contents

Numbers for Algebra
Tools for Algebra
Solving Equations
Introducing Functions
Linear Equations and Functions
Writing Linear Equations
Inequalities
Systems of Linear Equations and
    Inequalities
More About Data and Data Analysis
Exponents and Functions
Quadratic Functions and Equations
Polynomials and Factoring
Radicals and Geometry
Rational Expressions and Equations
Topics from Probability

PRACTICAL MATHEMATICS FOR CONSUMERS

This life-skills math course teaches and reinforces basic math concepts that prepare students for independent living. For more information about this or other Globe Fearon titles, call 1-800-848-9500.

Complete Support for Every Lesson!

STUDENT EDITION
- unit opener activities introduce and motivate
- chapter openers pre-teach vocabulary and give hands-on projects
- single-concept lessons
- stepped-out examples
- variety of practice for every lesson
- everyday problem solving
- problem-solving strategies
- *In Your Life, On the Job,* and *Using Your Calculator* features
- Extra Practice section in student book
- chapter reviews for vocabulary and quiz
- unit reviews for standardized test practice
- meets national and state standards

TEACHER'S PLANNING GUIDE
- plans and customizes every lesson
- detailed objectives
- activities for groups and individuals
- options for reteaching, reinforcement, enrichment
- addresses ESL and language development
- addresses learning styles
- workplace and life-skills connections
- diagnostic and placement tools
- alternative assessments

WORKBOOK
- complete parallel practice for every lesson
- examples, review skills, and content
- critical thinking questions and word problems

TEACHER'S ANSWER EDITION
- answers in place on student pages
- notes on avoiding errors and common errors
- ESL tips
- teaching suggestions for projects and opening lesson activities

CLASSROOM RESOURCE BINDER
- chapter-by-chapter reproducibles
- vocabulary practice
- ample lesson practice and mixed practice
- pages for reteaching, reinforcement, and enrichment
- real-life and workplace applications
- two parallel chapter tests
- test-prep section
- organization and planning charts
- visuals and math tools

SEPARATE ANSWER KEY
- all answers for all components also available in a separately bound key

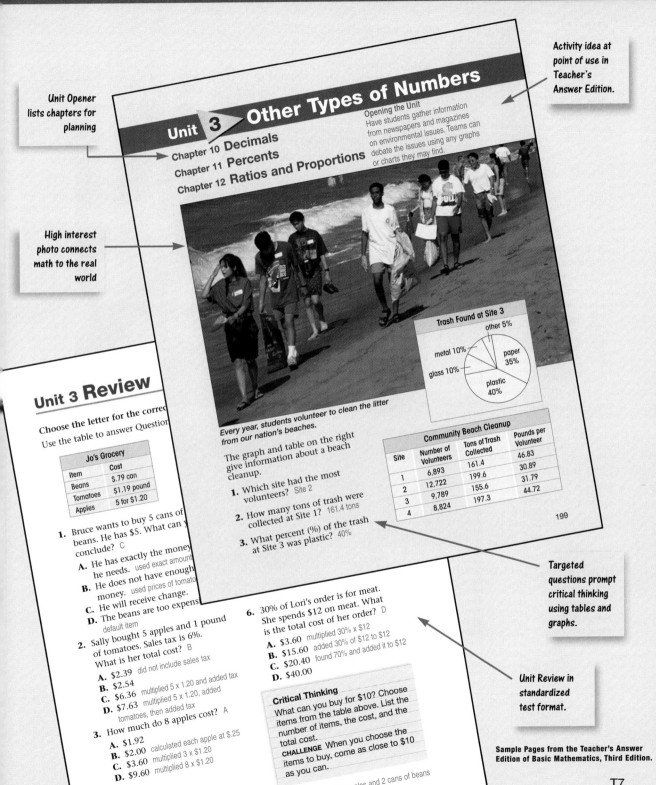

Unit Opener lists chapters for planning

High interest photo connects math to the real world

Activity idea at point of use in Teacher's Answer Edition.

Unit 3 **Other Types of Numbers**

Chapter 10 **Decimals**
Chapter 11 **Percents**
Chapter 12 **Ratios and Proportions**

Opening the Unit
Have students gather information from newspapers and magazines on environmental issues. Teams can debate the issues using any graphs or charts they may find.

Every year, students volunteer to clean the litter from our nation's beaches.

The graph and table on the right give information about a beach cleanup.

1. Which site had the most volunteers? Site 2

2. How many tons of trash were collected at Site 1? 161.4 tons

3. What percent (%) of the trash at Site 3 was plastic? 40%

Trash Found at Site 3

other 5%
metal 10%
paper 35%
glass 10%
plastic 40%

Community Beach Cleanup			
Site	Number of Volunteers	Tons of Trash Collected	Pounds per Volunteer
1	6,893	161.4	46.83
2	12,722	199.6	30.89
3	9,789	155.6	31.79
4	8,824	197.3	44.72

199

Targeted questions prompt critical thinking using tables and graphs.

Unit 3 Review

Choose the letter for the corre[ct]
Use the table to answer Question[s]

Jo's Grocery	
Item	Cost
Beans	$.79 can
Tomatoes	$1.19 pound
Apples	5 for $1.20

1. Bruce wants to buy 5 cans of beans. He has $5. What can y[ou] conclude? C
   A. He has exactly the money he needs. used exact amount
   B. He does not have enough money. used prices of tomato[es]
   C. He will receive change.
   D. The beans are too expens[ive]
   default item

2. Sally bought 5 apples and 1 pound of tomatoes. Sales tax is 6%. What is her total cost? B
   A. $2.39 did not include sales tax
   B. $2.54
   C. $6.36 multiplied 5 x 1.20 and added tax
   D. $7.63 multiplied 5 x 1.20, added tomatoes, then added tax

3. How much do 8 apples cost? A
   A. $1.92
   B. $2.00 calculated each apple at $.25
   C. $3.60 multiplied 3 x $1.20
   D. $9.60 multiplied 8 x $1.20

6. 30% of Lori's order is for meat. She spends $12 on meat. What is the total cost of her order? D
   A. $3.60 multiplied 30% x $12
   B. $15.60 added 30% of $12 to $12
   C. $20.40 found 70% and added it to $12
   D. $40.00

Critical Thinking
What can you buy for $10? Choose items from the table above. List the number of items, the cost, and the total cost.
CHALLENGE When you choose the items to buy, come as close to $10 as you can.

Possible answer: 35 apples and 2 cans of beans cost $9.98.

Unit Review in standardized test format.

Sample Pages from the Teacher's Answer Edition of Basic Mathematics, Third Edition.

T7

...d Proportions

Application Idea at point of use in Teacher's Answer Edition.

Photo Present possible finish times. Discuss why decimal numbers are important for determining a winner.
USA 4 minutes 10.53 seconds **Oceania** 4 minutes 10.58 seconds

Captivating color photo sparks students' interest and connects content to real life.

These runners are at the end of a close race. Only .01 of a second may separate the winner from the runner in second place! How else are decimals used in sports?

Detailed caption supports understanding and prompts critical thinking.

Caption Decimals may also be used in weights, distances, or scores.

200   Chapter 10 • Decimals

Sample pages from the Teacher's Answer Edition.

Additional activities and strategies to customize lessons can be found in the *Teacher Planning Guide*.

Point-of-use teacher support for opening the chapter.

Chapter **10** ▷ **Decimals**

ESL Note In many countries, a comma is used instead of a decimal point.

Key vocabulary previews the words students will encounter in the lessons.

Words to Know

decimal	a number that names part of a whole
decimal point	the dot in a decimal; a decimal has digits to the right of its decimal point
decimal places	the places to the right of a decimal point
mixed decimal	a number with a whole number and a decimal

Words to Know Point out that the word *decimal* is the basis for all the terms in the chapter.

Decimal Search Project

Look for decimals in different places. Try the newspaper, a magazine, or another textbook. For example, your science or social studies book might contain decimals. Tell the class what is described by the decimals you found. Write two problems using your decimals.

Learning Objectives

- Read and write decimals.
- Compare and order decimals.
- Add, subtract, multiply, and divide decimals.
- Change a decimal to a fraction.
- Change a fraction to a decimal.
- Round decimals.
- Solve problems using decimals.
- Apply knowledge of decimals to shopping and banking.

Concise learning objectives aid goal-setting and assessment.

High-interest project engages students and gears them up for the lessons ahead.

Project The project can be done in small groups or as homework assignments. Have students store the examples they find in folders or envelopes. Students can use these decimals to practice the skills in the chapter.

Chapter 10 • Decimals   201

Step-by-Step lessons make content accessible.

Clear, visual presentation of concepts

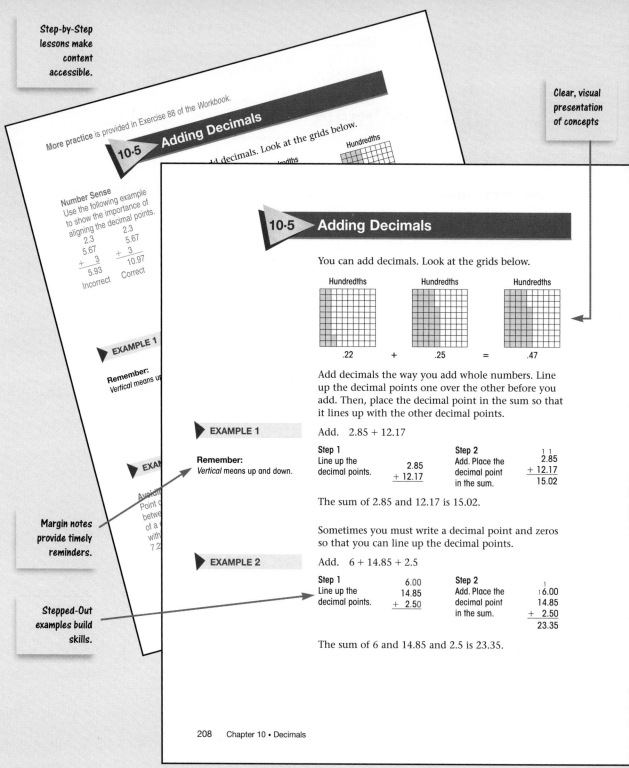

More practice is provided in Exercise 88 of the Workbook.

10·5 ► **Adding Decimals**

Number Sense
Use the following example to show the importance of aligning the decimal points.

2.3	2.3
2.3	5.67
5.67	+ 3
+ 3	10.97
5.93	Correct
Incorrect	

Margin notes provide timely reminders.

Stepped-Out examples build skills.

10·5 **Adding Decimals**

You can add decimals. Look at the grids below.

Hundredths   Hundredths   Hundredths

.22   +   .25   =   .47

Add decimals the way you add whole numbers. Line up the decimal points one over the other before you add. Then, place the decimal point in the sum so that it lines up with the other decimal points.

► **EXAMPLE 1**

Remember:
Vertical means up and down.

Add.   2.85 + 12.17

Step 1
Line up the decimal points.

2.85
+ 12.17

Step 2
Add. Place the decimal point in the sum.

1 1
2.85
+ 12.17
15.02

The sum of 2.85 and 12.17 is 15.02.

Sometimes you must write a decimal point and zeros so that you can line up the decimal points.

► **EXAMPLE 2**

Add.   6 + 14.85 + 2.5

Step 1
Line up the decimal points.

6.00
14.85
+ 2.50

Step 2
Add. Place the decimal point in the sum.

1
1 6.00
14.85
+ 2.50
23.35

The sum of 6 and 14.85 and 2.5 is 23.35.

208   Chapter 10 • Decimals

Sample pages from the Student Edition.

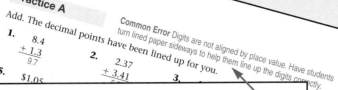

Practice A

Add. The decimal points have been lined up for you.

1.   8.4
  + 1.3
	2. 2.37
	  + 3.41
		3. 5.232
		  + .627
			4. 5.1
			  + 6.8

5. $1.05
   3.96
  + 2.15
	6. 16.155
	   4.073
	  + 2.009
		7. $3.28
		   5.00
		  + .50
			8. 1.050
			  4.000
			  + 2.103

Teacher's Answer Edition provides point-of-use annotations on the student pages, such as strategies, error analysis, and answers.

Practice B

Add. Remember to line up the decimal points. Write a decimal point and zeros if needed. Show your work in vertical form.

9. 3.4 + 5.1 + 8.2   **10.** .112 + .03   **11.** $159 + $.28

12. 5.51 + .2 + 8.5   **13.** 8 + 9.3 + .502   **14.** 65 + 5.1 + .81

15. 1.7 + .02 + 5.8   **16.** $.03 + $3 + $87.50   **17.** .01 + .001 + .0001

18. 5 + .05 + 5.005   **19.** 4 + 42.2 + .08 + .03   **20.** $25 + $.15 + $49

A variety of practice sets build skills and confidence. For more on practice, see page T16.

Everyday Problem Solving

Jen went shopping. Look at the receipt on the right. Some of the information is missing.

1. How much will Jen spend before tax? Add the prices to find the subtotal.

2. What is the total she needs? Add the sales tax to the subtotal to find out.

3. Jen has $128.35. Does she have enough money to pay the total you found in question 2?

```
CLOTHES PLACE
ITEM            PRICE
SWEATSHIRT     $39.95
JEANS           45.39
DRESS SHIRT     29.79

SUBTOTAL
TAX             8.76
TOTAL
```

Real-life practice makes math relevant.

Chapter 10 • Decimals   209

Problem-solving lessons follow a natural progession throughout the book.

Examples with models build problem-solving skills.

Consistent problem-solving method from chapter to chapter.

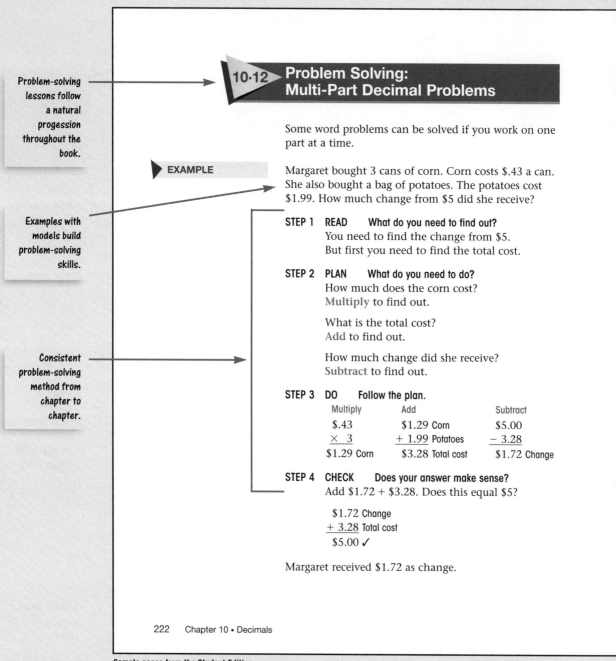

10·12 Problem Solving: Multi-Part Decimal Problems

Some word problems can be solved if you work on one part at a time.

▶ **EXAMPLE**

Margaret bought 3 cans of corn. Corn costs $.43 a can. She also bought a bag of potatoes. The potatoes cost $1.99. How much change from $5 did she receive?

STEP 1 READ   What do you need to find out?
You need to find the change from $5.
But first you need to find the total cost.

STEP 2 PLAN   What do you need to do?
How much does the corn cost?
Multiply to find out.

What is the total cost?
Add to find out.

How much change did she receive?
Subtract to find out.

STEP 3 DO   Follow the plan.

Multiply	Add	Subtract
$.43	$1.29 Corn	$5.00
× 3	+ 1.99 Potatoes	− 3.28
$1.29 Corn	$3.28 Total cost	$1.72 Change

STEP 4 CHECK   Does your answer make sense?
Add $1.72 + $3.28. Does this equal $5?

$1.72 Change
+ 3.28 Total cost
$5.00 ✓

Margaret received $1.72 as change.

222   Chapter 10 • Decimals

Sample pages from the Student Edition.

Problem Solving

READ the problem. Answer the questions under PLAN.
DO the plan to solve the problem.

1. Al bought 5 pounds of apples. The apples were $.39
   a pound. He also bought a bag of grapes. The grapes
   were $2.58. How much change from $10 did he receive?

   PLAN
   How much did the apples cost? What was the total
   cost? How much change did he receive?

2. Helen bought 1 ear of corn and cabbage. Ten ears of
   corn cost $3.50. The cabbage was $.99. How much
   change from $2 did she receive?

   PLAN
   How much did 1 ear of corn cost? What was the
   total cost? How much change did she receive?

3. Bill bought 2 pounds of butter. Butter costs $1.78 a
   pound. He also bought 1 roll. Rolls cost $4.80 for
   12 rolls. What was the total cost?

   PLAN
   How much did the butter cost? How much did the roll
   cost? What was the total cost?

Guided problem-solving practice uses real-life situations to promote skill building.

Problem Solving Strategy

Problem-solving strategy builds students' proficiency in solving word problems.

Often, problems can be solved by working backward.

Cathy bought tomatoes for $3.50. She also bought lettuce.
Cathy gave the store clerk $5.00. Her change was $1.00.
How much did the lettuce cost?

Fill in the blanks below to find the cost of the lettuce.

$1.00 Change	$3.50 Tomatoes
+ ▨▨▨ Total cost	+ ▨▨▨ Lettuce
$5.00	▨▨▨ Total cost

Sample Page from Chapter 1 of the Student Edition.

Students practice math skills in the context of real-life situations.

MATH IN YOUR LIFE
Understanding Computer Memory

Did you ever try to play a computer game but found out your computer did not have enough memory? To play games and use software, you need to know about memory.

Memory is the space something takes up on a computer or disk. Memory is measured in bytes. A *byte* is a unit of information. A *megabyte* is the same as 1,000,000 bytes. Megabyte is abbreviated as MB.

You can change megabytes to bytes by writing six zeros to the right. Then you can compare sizes of memory.

1 MB	is the same as	1,000,000 bytes
10 MB	is the same as	10,000,000 bytes
64 MB	is the same as	64,000,000 bytes

This tiny chip stores computer memory.

Relevant photos and realistic graphics make content accessible.

Look at the computers below. Decide if each computer has enough memory to fit the software.

1. Memory: 68MB

2. Memory: 13MB

3.

Every chapter has either the "On-the-Job" or "In-Your-Life" feature.

Real job focus provides school-to-work connections.

ON-THE-JOB MATH
Bank Teller

Carmen Soleteri works for a bank. She is a bank teller. Carmen helps customers every day. They ask her to cash checks. They also ask her to make deposits and withdrawals. She also counts cash.

This is a good job for Carmen because she likes math and meeting people. She also stays calm under pressure.

To make a deposit, a customer must fill out a deposit slip. Carmen must make sure the total on the slip is correct.

Look at the deposit slips below. Tell whether or not the customer added correctly.

1.
DEPOSIT TICKET
J. J. SUMMERS
One Eastway Road
New Town, ST 00000
DATE
| 1 3 8 , 4 3 |
| 3 2 , 4 7 |
| 2 4 5 , 6 3 |
Total **$** | 4 1 6 , 4 3 |

2.
| 2 3 , 6 4 |
| 6 , 2 8 |
| 5 4 , 7 6 |
Total **$** | 8 4 , 6 8 |

3.
| 2 1 1 , 2 4 |
| 1 3 0 , 0 0 |
| 4 7 , 5 0 |
Total **$** | 2 6 0 , 0 4 |

Critical Thinking
What do you think Carmen should say to a customer if the deposit slip is incorrect? Work with a partner to decide what she should say. Share your answer with the class.

Chapter 10 • Decimals   215

Critical thinking provides prompt for communicating mathematically.

Sample page from Chapter 10 of the Student Edition.

Sample page from Chapter 1 of the Student Edition.

Calculator functions and skills applied to chapter content.

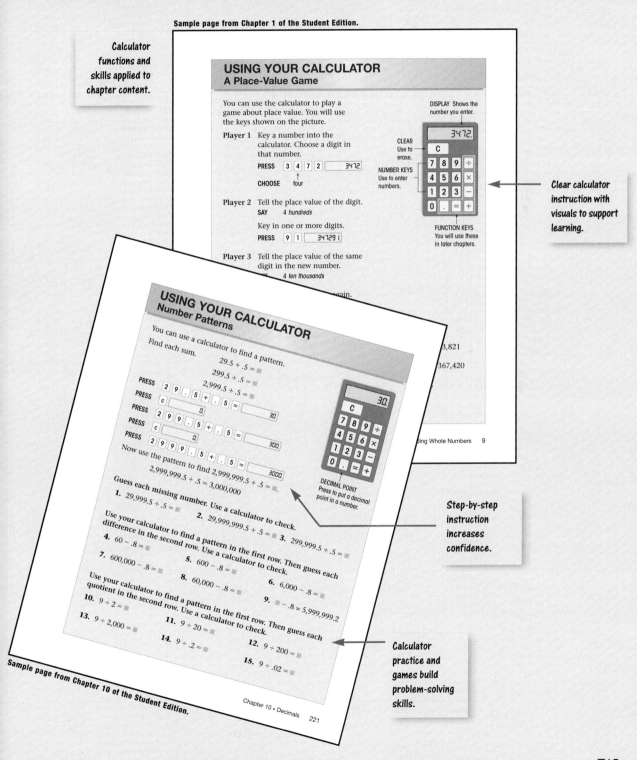

USING YOUR CALCULATOR
A Place-Value Game

You can use the calculator to play a game about place value. You will use the keys shown on the picture.

Player 1 Key a number into the calculator. Choose a digit in that number.

PRESS 3 4 7 2   3472.

CHOOSE four

Player 2 Tell the place value of the digit.

SAY 4 hundreds

Key in one or more digits.

PRESS 9 1   34729 ۱

Player 3 Tell the place value of the same digit in the new number.

4 ten thousands

DISPLAY Shows the number you enter.

CLEAR Use to erase.

NUMBER KEYS Use to enter numbers.

FUNCTION KEYS You will use these in later chapters.

Clear calculator instruction with visuals to support learning.

ing Whole Numbers   9

USING YOUR CALCULATOR
Number Patterns

You can use a calculator to find a pattern. Find each sum.

$$29.5 + .5 = ■$$
$$299.5 + .5 = ■$$
$$2,999.5 + .5 = ■$$

PRESS 2 9 . 5 + . 5 =
PRESS c   0.
PRESS 2 9 9 . 5 + . 5 =   30.
PRESS c   0.
PRESS 2 9 9 9 . 5 + . 5 =   300.

Now use the pattern to find 2,999,999.5 + .5 = ■.

$$2,999,999.5 + .5 = 3,000,000$$

Guess each missing number. Use a calculator to check.

1. $29,999.5 + .5 = ■$

2. $29,999,999.5 + .5 = ■$ **3.** $299,999.5 + .5 = ■$

Use your calculator to find a pattern in the first row. Then guess each difference in the second row. Use a calculator to check.

4. $60 - .8 = ■$ **5.** $600 - .8 = ■$ **6.** $6,000 - .8 = ■$

7. $600,000 - .8 = ■$

8. $60,000 - .8 = ■$

9. $■ - .8 = 5,999,999.2$

Use your calculator to find a pattern in the first row. Then guess each quotient in the second row. Use a calculator to check.

10. $9 \div 2 = ■$

11. $9 \div 20 = ■$ **12.** $9 \div 200 = ■$

13. $9 \div 2,000 = ■$

14. $9 \div .2 = ■$

15. $9 \div .02 = ■$

3,821

367,420

DECIMAL POINT Press to put a decimal point in a number.

Step-by-step instruction increases confidence.

Calculator practice and games build problem-solving skills.

Sample page from Chapter 10 of the Student Edition.

Chapter 10 • Decimals   221

▶ Workbook Provides Practice for Every Lesson . . .

Fosters retention via a "review, reinforce, apply" method.

Offers clear examples to refresh key concepts.

Lesson-by-lesson practice parallel to student edition.

Critical thinking or word problems with every lesson.

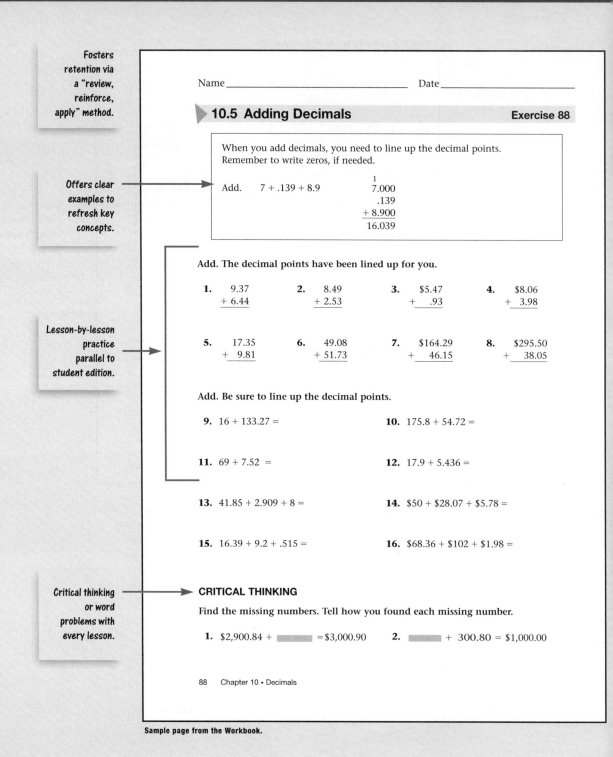

Name ____________________ Date ____________________

10.5 Adding Decimals — Exercise 88

When you add decimals, you need to line up the decimal points.
Remember to write zeros, if needed.

Add. 7 + .139 + 8.9

```
   1
 7.000
  .139
+ 8.900
16.039
```

Add. The decimal points have been lined up for you.

1. 9.37 + 6.44

2. 8.49 + 2.53

3. $5.47 + .93

4. $8.06 + 3.98

5. 17.35 + 9.81

6. 49.08 + 51.73

7. $164.29 + 46.15

8. $295.50 + 38.05

Add. Be sure to line up the decimal points.

9. 16 + 133.27 =

10. 175.8 + 54.72 =

11. 69 + 7.52 =

12. 17.9 + 5.436 =

13. 41.85 + 2.909 + 8 =

14. $50 + $28.07 + $5.78 =

15. 16.39 + 9.2 + .515 =

16. $68.36 + $102 + $1.98 =

CRITICAL THINKING

Find the missing numbers. Tell how you found each missing number.

1. $2,900.84 + ______ = $3,000.90

2. ______ + 300.80 = $1,000.00

88 Chapter 10 • Decimals

Sample page from the Workbook.

Sample pages from the Student Edition.

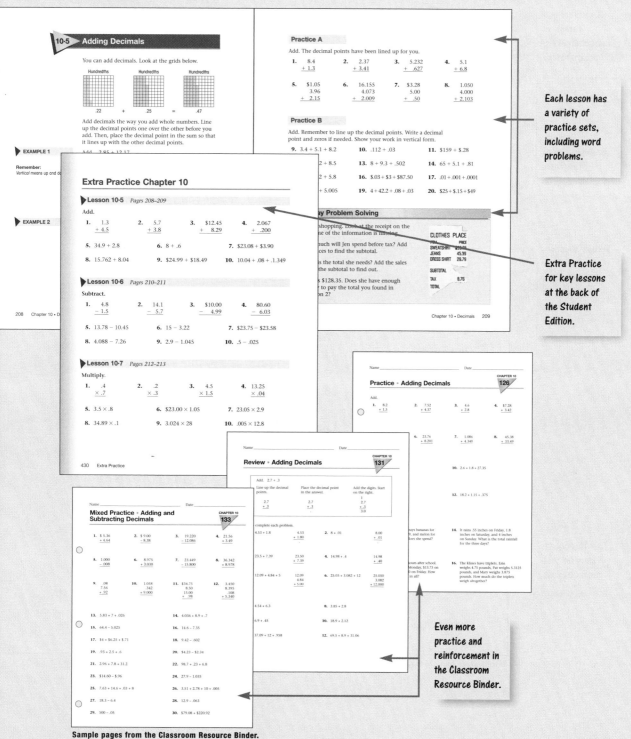

10-5 ▸ Adding Decimals

You can add decimals. Look at the grids below.

Hundredths   Hundredths   Hundredths

.22   +   .25   =   .47

Add decimals the way you add whole numbers. Line up the decimal points one over the other before you add. Then, place the decimal point in the sum so that it lines up with the other decimal points.

EXAMPLE 1

Add. 2.85 + 12.17

Remember:
Vertical means up and d

EXAMPLE 2

208   Chapter 10 • D

Practice A

Add. The decimal points have been lined up for you.

| 1. | 8.4 + 1.3 | 2. | 2.37 + 3.41 | 3. | 5.232 + .627 | 4. | 5.1 + 6.8 |

| 5. | $1.05 3.96 + 2.15 | 6. | 16.155 4.073 + 2.009 | 7. | $3.28 5.00 + .50 | 8. | 1.050 4.000 + 2.103 |

Practice B

Add. Remember to line up the decimal points. Write a decimal point and zeros if needed. Show your work in vertical form.

9.	3.4 + 5.1 + 8.2	10.	.112 + .03	11.	$159 + $.28
	2 + 8.5	13.	8 + 9.3 + .502	14.	65 + 5.1 + .81
	2 + 5.8	16.	$.03 + $3 + $87.50	17.	.01 + .001 + .0001
	+ 5.005	19.	4 + 42.2 + .08 + .03	20.	$25 + $.15 + $49

ay Problem Solving

shopping. Look at the receipt on the ne of the information is missing.

uch will Jen spend before tax? Add ces to find the subtotal.

s the total she needs? Add the sales the subtotal to find out.

$128.35. Does she have enough to pay the total you found in on 2?

CLOTHES PLACE

ITEM	PRICE
SWEATSHIRT	$39.95
JEANS	45.99
DRESS SHIRT	29.79

SUBTOTAL
TAX   8.76
TOTAL

Chapter 10 • Decimals   209

Each lesson has a variety of practice sets, including word problems.

Extra Practice Chapter 10

▸**Lesson 10-5** *Pages 208–209*

Add.

| 1. | 1.3 + 4.5 | 2. | 5.7 + 3.8 | 3. | $12.45 + 8.29 | 4. | 2.067 + .200 |

| 5. | 34.9 + 2.8 | | 6. | 8 + .6 | | 7. | $23.08 + $3.90 |

| 8. | 15.762 + 8.04 | | 9. | $24.99 + $18.49 | | 10. | 10.04 + .08 + .1.349 |

▸**Lesson 10-6** *Pages 210–211*

Subtract.

| 1. | 4.8 − 1.5 | 2. | 14.1 − 5.7 | 3. | $10.00 − 4.99 | 4. | 80.60 − 6.03 |

| 5. | 13.78 − 10.45 | | 6. | 15 − 3.22 | | 7. | $23.75 − $23.58 |

| 8. | 4.088 − 7.26 | | 9. | 2.9 − 1.045 | | 10. | .5 − .025 |

▸**Lesson 10-7** *Pages 212–213*

Multiply.

| 1. | .4 × .7 | 2. | .2 × .3 | 3. | 4.5 × 1.5 | 4. | 13.25 × .04 |

| 5. | 3.5 × .8 | | 6. | $23.00 × 1.05 | | 7. | 23.05 × 2.9 |

| 8. | 34.89 × .1 | | 9. | 3.024 × 28 | | 10. | .005 × 12.8 |

430   Extra Practice

Extra Practice for key lessons at the back of the Student Edition.

Name _____   Date _____

Practice • Adding Decimals

CHAPTER 10
126

Add.

| 1. | 8.2 + 1.5 | 2. | 7.52 + 4.37 | 3. | 4.6 + 2.8 | 4. | $7.28 + 3.42 |

| 6. | 23.76 + 8.201 | 7. | 1.086 + 4.340 | 8. | 45.38 + 33.49 |

| 10. | 2.6 + 1.8 + 27.35 |

| 12. | 18.2 + 1.15 + .375 |

Name _____   Date _____

Review • Adding Decimals

CHAPTER 10
131

Add. 2.7 + .3

| Line up the decimal points. | Place the decimal point in the answer. | Add the digits. Start on the right. |
| 2.7 + .3 | 2.7 + .3 . | 1 2.7 + .3 3.0 |

complete each problem.

| 4.53 + 1.8 | 4.53 + 1.80 | 2. | 8 + .01 | 8.00 + .01 |

| 23.5 + 7.39 | 23.50 + 7.39 | 4. | 14.98 + .4 | 14.98 + .40 |

| 12.09 + 4.84 + 5 | 12.09 4.84 + 5.00 | 6. | 25.05 + 3.082 + 12 | 25.050 3.082 + 12.000 |

| 4.54 + 6.3 | | 8. | 3.85 + 2.8 |

| 6.9 + .45 | | 10. | 18.9 + 2.12 |

| 37.09 + 12 + .958 | | 12. | 69.5 + 8.9 + 31.06 |

ays bananas for 9, and melon for oes she spend?

14. It rains .55 inches on Friday, 1.8 inches on Saturday, and 4 inches on Sunday. What is the total rainfall for the three days?

ours after school. Monday, $13.75 on 0 on Friday. How in all?

16. The Klines have triplets. Erin weighs 4.75 pounds, Pat weighs 5.3125 pounds, and Mary weighs 3.875 pounds. How much do the triplets weigh altogether?

Name _____   Date _____

Mixed Practice • Adding and Subtracting Decimals

CHAPTER 10
133

| 1. | $5.36 + 4.64 | 2. | $9.00 − 8.38 | 3. | 19.220 − 12.086 | 4. | 21.56 + 3.49 |

| 5. | 1.000 − .008 | 6. | 8.975 + 3.030 | 7. | 23.449 − 15.800 | 8. | 36.342 + 8.978 |

| 9. | .08 7.56 + .92 | 10. | 1.058 .342 + 9.000 | 11. | $34.75 8.50 15.00 + .98 | 12. | 3.450 8.395 .108 + 5.340 |

| 13. | 5.83 + 7 + .026 | | 14. | 4.036 + 8.9 + .7 |

| 15. | 64.4 − 5.025 | | 16. | 14.6 − 7.35 |

| 17. | $4 + $6.25 + $.71 | | 18. | 9.42 − .602 |

| 19. | .93 + 2.5 + .6 | | 20. | $4.23 − $2.34 |

| 21. | 2.96 + 7.8 + 31.2 | | 22. | 98.7 + .23 + 6.8 |

| 23. | $14.60 − $.96 | | 24. | 27.9 − 1.035 |

| 25. | 7.63 + 14.6 + .03 + 8 | | 26. | 3.51 + 2.78 + 10 + .005 |

| 27. | 18.3 − 6.4 | | 28. | 12.9 − .063 |

| 29. | 500 − .05 | | 30. | $79.08 + $220.92 |

Even more practice and reinforcement in the Classroom Resource Binder.

Sample pages from the Classroom Resource Binder.

Assess concept
retention.
Build study skills.
Prepare to take
tests.

Chapter

10 ▷ Review

Essential
vocabulary review
reinforces
word power.

| decimal |
| decimal point |
| decimal places |
| mixed decimal |

Vocabulary Review

Complete each sentence with a word from the list.

1. A __?__ is the dot in a decimal.

2. A number that names part of a whole number is a __?__.

3. A __?__ contains a whole number and a decimal.

4. __?__ are to the right of the decimal point.

Writing questions
challenge
students to
communicate
mathematically.

5. Writing Show that you understand these words. Write a sentence for each word. Do not use the sentences above.

Chapter Quiz

LESSONS 10-1 to 10-4

Test Tip
When comparing decimals, first compare the whole number parts.

Writing, Comparing, and Ordering Decimals
Write each number as a decimal.

1. three hundredths

2. seven and five tenths

3. twenty-two thousandths

4. fifty and five hundredths

Compare each pair of numbers. Use >, <, or =.

5. 15.03   9.03

6. 1.52   1.63

7. 8.6   8.61

8. 7.23   7.203

9. 6.3   6.25

10. 45.03   45.03

LESSONS 10-5 and 10-6

Test Tips provide
hints for test-
taking success.

Test Tip
Line up the decimal points when adding or subtracting decimals.

Adding and Subtracting Decimals
Add or subtract.

11. $8.65 + 9.37$

12. $5.8 + 26.98$

13. $16.25 - 9.7$

14. $6 + 4.59 + .729$

15. $14.05 - 8.59$

16. $7 - 3.075$

Sample pages from the Student Edition.

Two additional
chapter tests are
provided in the
Classroom
Resource Binder.
See page T21.

LESSONS 10·7 to 10·11

Test Tip
Be sure to place the decimal
point correctly in the product or
quotient.

Multiplying and Dividing Decimals
Multiply. Show your work in vertical form.

17. 1.2×4 **18.** $.7 \times .06$

19. $2.5 \times .5$ **20.** 8.09×1.7

21. $38.5 \times .29$ **22.** 478×6.05

Divide. Show your work in vertical form.

23. $36.4 \div 24$ **24.** $448.7 \div 35$

25. $6 \div 12$ **26.** $37.95 \div 4.6$

27. $5 \div .09$ **28.** $.453 \div .15$

Review sections
correlate to
lesson objectives.

Lessons are
clearly labeled
for quick and
easy reference.

LESSON 10·12

Test Tip
If the word problem has many
parts, solve one part at a time.

Solving Problems with Decimals
Solve each problem.

29. Greg buys 3 pounds of cheese at $1.29 a pound
and bread for $2.29. How much change from $10
does he receive?

30. Janine has $20. Does she have enough money to
buy socks for $2.99 and a T-shirt for $12.95?

LESSONS 10·13 and 10·14

Test Tip
The last place value of a
decimal is the denominator of
the equivalent fraction.

Changing Decimals and Fractions
Rename each decimal as a fraction.

31. $.2$ **32.** $.25$ **33.** $.03$

Rename each fraction as a decimal.

34. $\frac{3}{5}$ **35.** $\frac{5}{8}$ **36.** $\frac{3}{4}$

High-interest
group activity
fosters
collaborative
learning.

▶ Group Activity
With your group, use a grocery store flyer to shop for a family of three for
a week. You have $125 to spend. Make a list of the items you want to buy
and the cost. Decide on the items to purchase and explain your choices.

Chapter 10 • Decimals   229

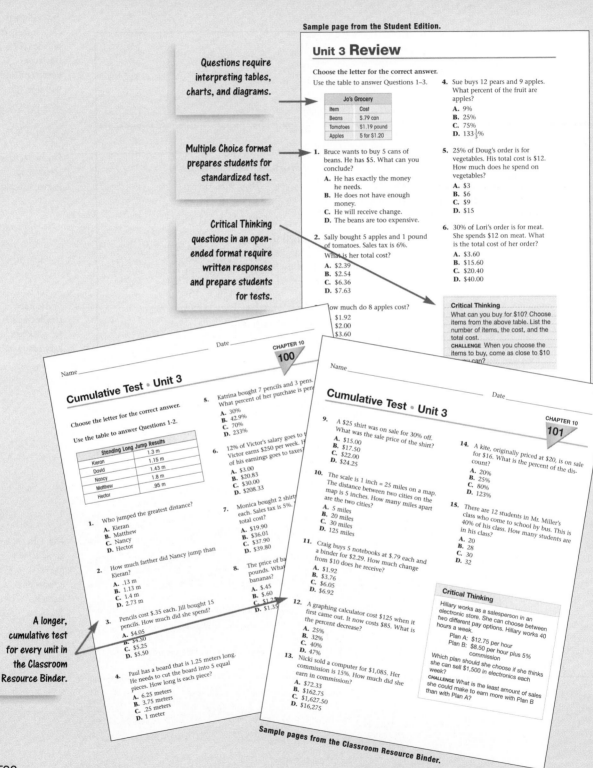

Sample page from the Student Edition.

Unit 3 **Review**

Choose the letter for the correct answer.
Use the table to answer Questions 1–3.

Jo's Grocery	
Item	Cost
Beans	$.79 can
Tomatoes	$1.19 pound
Apples	5 for $1.20

1. Bruce wants to buy 5 cans of beans. He has $5. What can you conclude?

- **A.** He has exactly the money he needs.
- **B.** He does not have enough money.
- **C.** He will receive change.
- **D.** The beans are too expensive.

2. Sally bought 5 apples and 1 pound of tomatoes. Sales tax is 6%. What is her total cost?

- **A.** $2.39
- **B.** $2.54
- **C.** $6.36
- **D.** $7.63

ow much do 8 apples cost?

$1.92
$2.00
$3.60

4. Sue buys 12 pears and 9 apples. What percent of the fruit are apples?

- **A.** 9%
- **B.** 25%
- **C.** 75%
- **D.** $133\frac{1}{3}$%

5. 25% of Doug's order is for vegetables. His total cost is $12. How much does he spend on vegetables?

- **A.** $3
- **B.** $6
- **C.** $9
- **D.** $15

6. 30% of Lori's order is for meat. She spends $12 on meat. What is the total cost of her order?

- **A.** $3.60
- **B.** $15.60
- **C.** $20.40
- **D.** $40.00

Critical Thinking
What can you buy for $10? Choose items from the above table. List the number of items, the cost, and the total cost.
CHALLENGE When you choose the items to buy, come as close to $10
u can?

Questions require interpreting tables, charts, and diagrams.

Multiple Choice format prepares students for standardized test.

Critical Thinking questions in an open-ended format require written responses and prepare students for tests.

Name _____ Date _____

CHAPTER 10

100

Cumulative Test • Unit 3

Choose the letter for the correct answer.

Use the table to answer Questions 1–2.

Standing Long Jump Results	
Kieran	1.3 m
David	1.15 m
Nancy	1.43 m
Matthew	1.8 m
Hector	.95 m

1. Who jumped the greatest distance?
- **A.** Kieran
- **B.** Matthew
- **C.** Nancy
- **D.** Hector

2. How much farther did Nancy jump than Kieran?
- **A.** .13 m
- **B.** 1.13 m
- **C.** 1.4 m
- **D.** 2.73 m

3. Pencils cost $.35 each. Jill bought 15 pencils. How much did she spend?
- **A.** $4.05
- **B.** $4.50
- **C.** $5.25
- **D.** $5.50

4. Paul has a board that is 1.25 meters long. He needs to cut the board into 5 equal pieces. How long is each piece?
- **A.** 6.25 meters
- **B.** 3.75 meters
- **C.** .25 meters
- **D.** 1 meter

5. Katrina bought 7 pencils and 3 pens. What percent of her purchase is pen
- **A.** 30%
- **B.** 42.9%
- **C.** 70%
- **D.** 233%

6. 12% of Victor's salary goes to t Victor earns $250 per week. H of his earnings goes to taxes
- **A.** $3.00
- **B.** $20.83
- **C.** $30.00
- **D.** $208.33

7. Monica bought 2 shirt each. Sales tax is 5%. total cost?
- **A.** $19.90
- **B.** $36.01
- **C.** $37.90
- **D.** $39.80

8. The price of ba pounds. Wha bananas?
- **A.** $.45
- **B.** $.60
- **C.** $1.2
- **D.** $1.3

A longer, cumulative test for every unit in the Classroom Resource Binder.

Name _____ Date _____

Cumulative Test • Unit 3

CHAPTER 10

101

9. A $25 shirt was on sale for 30% off. What was the sale price of the shirt?
- **A.** $15.00
- **B.** $17.50
- **C.** $22.00
- **D.** $24.25

10. The scale is 1 inch = 25 miles on a map. The distance between two cities on the map is 5 inches. How many miles apart are the two cities?
- **A.** 5 miles
- **B.** 20 miles
- **C.** 30 miles
- **D.** 125 miles

11. Craig buys 5 notebooks at $.79 each and a binder for $2.29. How much change from $10 does he receive?
- **A.** $1.92
- **B.** $3.76
- **C.** $6.05
- **D.** $6.92

12. A graphing calculator cost $125 when it first came out. It now costs $85. What is the percent decrease?
- **A.** 25%
- **B.** 32%
- **C.** 40%
- **D.** 47%

13. Nicki sold a computer for $1,085. Her commission is 15%. How much did she earn in commission?
- **A.** $72.33
- **B.** $162.75
- **C.** $1,627.50
- **D.** $16,275

14. A kite, originally priced at $20, is on sale for $16. What is the percent of the discount?
- **A.** 20%
- **B.** 25%
- **C.** 80%
- **D.** 123%

15. There are 12 students in Mr. Miller's class who come to school by bus. This is 40% of his class. How many students are in his class?
- **A.** 20
- **B.** 28
- **C.** 30
- **D.** 32

Critical Thinking

Hillary works as a salesperson in an electronic store. She can choose between two different pay options. Hillary works 40 hours a week.

Plan A: $12.75 per hour
Plan B: $8.50 per hour plus 5% commission

Which plan should she choose if she thinks she can sell $1,500 in electronics each week?

CHALLENGE What is the least amount of sales she could make to earn more with Plan B than with Plan A?

Sample pages from the Classroom Resource Binder.

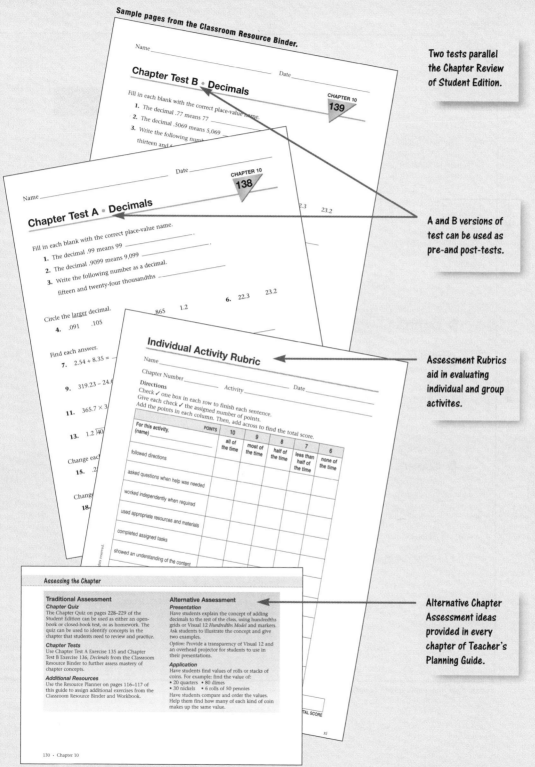

Sample pages from the Classroom Resource Binder.

Name _____

Date _____

Chapter Test B • Decimals

CHAPTER 10
139

Fill in each blank with the correct place-value name.

1. The decimal .77 means 77 _____
2. The decimal .5069 means 5,069 _____
3. Write the following numb...
thirteen and ...

Date _____

CHAPTER 10
138

Name _____

Chapter Test A • Decimals

Fill in each blank with the correct place-value name.

1. The decimal .99 means 99 _____
2. The decimal .9099 means 9,099 _____
3. Write the following number as a decimal.
fifteen and twenty-four thousandths _____

6. 22.3   23.2

Circle the larger decimal.

4. .091   .105

865   1.2

Find each answer.

7. 2.54 + 8.35 =

9. 319.23 – 24.6

11. 365.7 × 3

13. 1.2)‾40

Change eac...

15. .2

Chang...

18-

Individual Activity Rubric

Name _____

Chapter Number _____   Activity _____   Date _____

Directions
Check ✓ one box in each row to finish each sentence.
Give each check ✓ the assigned number of points.
Add the points in each column. Then, add across to find the total score.

For this activity, (name)	POINTS	10	9	8	7	6
		all of the time	most of the time	half of the time	less than half of the time	none of the time
followed directions						
asked questions when help was needed						
worked independently when required						
used appropriate resources and materials						
completed assigned tasks						
showed an understanding of the content						

2.3   23.2

Assessing the Chapter

Traditional Assessment

Chapter Quiz
The Chapter Quiz on pages 228–229 of the Student Edition can be used as either an open-book or closed-book test, or as homework. The quiz can be used to identify concepts in the chapter that students need to review and practice.

Chapter Tests
Use Chapter Test A Exercise 135 and Chapter Test B Exercise 136, *Decimals* from the Classroom Resource Binder to further assess mastery of chapter concepts.

Additional Resources
Use the Resource Planner on pages 116–117 of this guide to assign additional exercises from the Classroom Resource Binder and Workbook.

Alternative Assessment

Presentation
Have students explain the concept of adding decimals to the rest of the class, using hundredths grids or Visual 12 *Hundredths Model* and markers. Ask students to illustrate the concept and give two examples.
Option: Provide a transparency of Visual 12 and an overhead projector for students to use in their presentations.

Application
Have students find values of rolls or stacks of coins. For example: find the value of:
• 20 quarters • 80 dimes
• 30 nickels   • 6 rolls of 50 pennies
Have students compare and order the values. Help them find how many of each kind of coin makes up the same value.

TAL SCORE

xi

130 · Chapter 10

Sample pages from the Teacher's Planning Guide.

Two tests parallel the Chapter Review of Student Edition.

A and B versions of test can be used as pre-and post-tests.

Assessment Rubrics aid in evaluating individual and group activites.

Alternative Chapter Assessment ideas provided in every chapter of Teacher's Planning Guide.

NEW!

More practice is provided in Exercise 88 of the *Workbook*.

10-5 Adding Decimals

Number Sense
Use the following example
to show the importance of
aligning the decimal points.

2.3	2.3
5.67	5.67
+ 3	+ 3
5.93	10.97
Incorrect	Correct

You can add decimals. Look at the grids below.

Hundredths   Hundredths   Hundredths

.22   +   .25   =   .47

Add decimals the way you add whole numbers. Line
up the decimal points one over the other before you
add. Then, place the decimal point in the sum so that
it lines up with the other decimal points.

▶ **EXAMPLE 1**

Add.   2.85 + 12.17

Remember:
Vertical means up and down.

Step 1
Line up the
decimal points.

2.85
+ 12.17

Step 2
Add. Place the
decimal point
in the sum.

1 1
2.85
+ 12.17
15.02

The sum of 2.85 and 12.17 is 15.02.

Sometimes you must write a decimal point and zeros
so that you can line up the decimal points.

▶ **EXAMPLE 2**

Add.   6 + 14.85 + 2.5

Avoiding Errors
Point out the difference
between a zero at the end
of a decimal and a zero
within a decimal.
7.20 = 7.2 ≠ 7.02

Step 1
Line up the
decimal points.

6.00
14.85
+ 2.50

Step 2
Add. Place the
decimal point
in the sum.

1
1 6.00
14.85
+ 2.50
23.35

The sum of 6 and 14.85 and 2.5 is 23.35.

208   Chapter 10 • Decimals

Practice A

This hardback teacher's book has answers and annotations on the student pages.

Common Error Digits are not aligned by place value. Have students turn lined paper sideways to help them line up the digits correctly.

Add. The decimal points have been lined up for you.

1. 8.4
    + 1.3
    —————
    9.7

2. 2.37
    + 3.41
    —————
    5.78

3. 5.232
    + .627
    —————
    5.859

4. 5.1
    + 6.8
    —————
    11.9

5. $1.05
    3.96
    + 2.15
    —————
    $7.16

6. 16.155
    4.073
    + 2.009
    —————
    22.237

7. $3.28
    5.00
    + .50
    —————
    $8.78

8. 1.050
    4.000
    + 2.103
    —————
    7.153

Practice B

Add. Remember to line up the decimal points. Write a decimal point and zeros if needed. Show your work in vertical form.

Answers at point of use.

9. 3.4 + 5.1 + 8.2 16.7

10. .112 + .03 .142

11. $159 + $.28 159.28

12. 5.51 + .2 + 8.5 14.21

13. 8 + 9.3 + .502 17.802

14. 65 + 5.1 + .81 70.91

15. 1.7 + .02 + 5.8 7.52

16. $.03 + $3 + $87.50 $90.53

17. .01 + .001 + .0001 .0111

18. 5 + .05 + 5.005 10.055

19. 4 + 42.2 + .08 + .03 46.31

20. $25 + $.15 + $49 $74.15

Everyday Problem Solving

Jen went shopping. Look at the receipt on the right. Some of the information is missing.

1. How much will Jen spend before tax? Add the prices to find the subtotal. $115.13

2. What is the total she needs? Add the sales tax to the subtotal to find out. $123.89

3. Jen has $128.35. Does she have enough money to pay the total you found in question 2? yes

```
CLOTHES PLACE
ITEM            PRICE
SWEATSHIRT     $39.95
JEANS           45.39
DRESS SHIRT     29.79

SUBTOTAL

TAX              8.76

TOTAL
```

Additional annotations link practice, assessment, and other support throughout the program.

Extra Practice for this lesson is provided on page 430.

NEW!

More than 225 pages of resources to plan and customize your lessons.

An overview of the lessons and features in the chapter.

Resources to assess prerequisite skills or to remediate.

Diagnostic and assessment tools make it easy to place students in the program.

Concise objectives help you target instruction for individual needs.

Correlations to other program resources make planning easy.

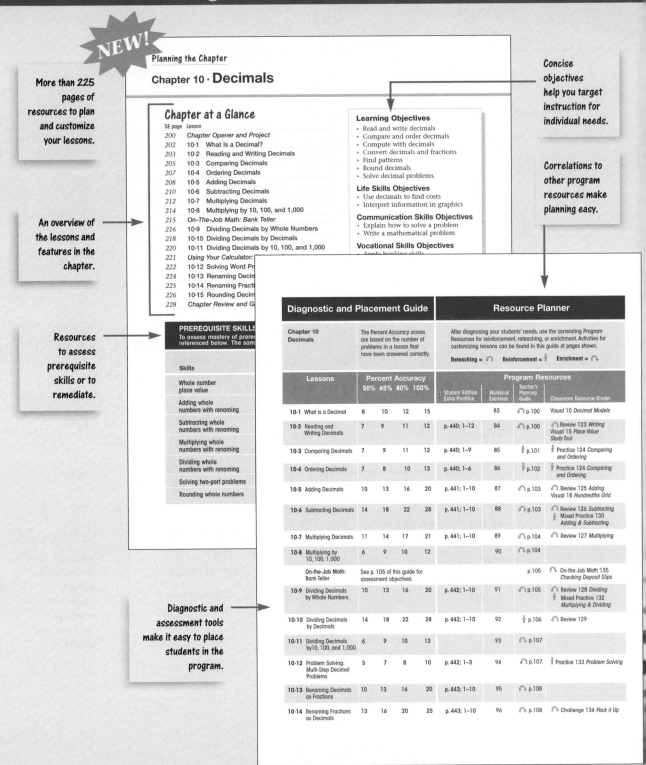

Planning the Chapter

Chapter 10 · Decimals

Chapter at a Glance

Learning Objectives
- Read and write decimals
- Compare and order decimals
- Compute with decimals
- Convert decimals and fractions
- Find patterns
- Round decimals
- Solve decimal problems

Life Skills Objectives
- Use decimals to find costs
- Interpret information in graphics

Communication Skills Objectives
- Explain how to solve a problem
- Write a mathematical problem

Vocational Skills Objectives
- Apply banking skills

PREREQUISITE SKILLS
To assess mastery of prereq
referenced below. The sam

Skills

- Whole number place value
- Adding whole numbers with renaming
- Subtracting whole numbers with renaming
- Multiplying whole numbers with renaming
- Dividing whole numbers with renaming
- Solving two-part problems
- Rounding whole numbers

Diagnostic and Placement Guide			Resource Planner	
Chapter 10 **Decimals**	The Percent Accuracy scores are based on the number of problems in a lesson that have been answered correctly.		After diagnosing your students' needs, use the correlating Program Resources for reinforcement, reteaching, or enrichment. Activities for customizing lessons can be found in this guide at pages shown. Reteaching = ⌒ Reinforcement = ‡ Enrichment = ⌒	

Lessons	Percent Accuracy 50% 65% 80% 100%	Program Resources Student Edition Extra Practice / Workbook Exercises / Teacher's Planning Guide / Classroom Resource Binder

Lessons	50%	65%	80%	100%	Student Edition Extra Practice	Workbook Exercises	Teacher's Planning Guide	Classroom Resource Binder
10-1 What is a Decimal	8	10	12	15		83	⌒ p.100	Visual 10 *Decimal Models*
10-2 Reading and Writing Decimals	7	9	11	12	p. 440; 1–12	84	⌒ p.100	⌒ Review 123 *Writing* Visual 15 *Place Value Study Tool*
10-3 Comparing Decimals	7	9	11	12	p. 440; 1–9	85	‡ p.101	‡ Practice 124 *Comparing and Ordering*
10-4 Ordering Decimals	7	8	10	13	p. 440; 1–6	86	‡ p.102	‡ Practice 124 *Comparing and Ordering*
10-5 Adding Decimals	10	13	16	20	p. 441; 1–10	87	⌒ p.103	⌒ Review 125 *Adding* Visual 18 *Hundredths Grid*
10-6 Subtracting Decimals	14	18	22	28	p. 441; 1–10	88	⌒ p.103	⌒ Review 126 *Subtracting* ‡ Mixed Practice 130 *Adding & Subtracting*
10-7 Multiplying Decimals	11	14	17	21	p. 441; 1–10	89	⌒ p.104	⌒ Review 127 *Multiplying*
10-8 Multiplying by 10, 100, 1,000	6	9	10	12		90	⌒ p.104	
On-the-Job Math: Bank Teller	See p. 105 of this guide for assessment objectives.						p.105	⌒ On-the-Job Math 135 *Checking Deposit Slips*
10-9 Dividing Decimals by Whole Numbers	10	13	16	20	p. 442; 1–10	91	⌒ p.105	⌒ Review 128 *Dividing* ‡ Mixed Practice 132 *Multiplying & Dividing*
10-10 Dividing Decimals by Decimals	14	18	22	28	p. 442; 1–10	92	‡ p.106	⌒ Review 129
10-11 Dividing Decimals by10, 100, and 1,000	6	9	10	12		93	⌒ p.107	
10-12 Problem Solving: Multi-Step Decimal Problems	5	7	8	10	p. 442; 1–3	94	⌒ p.107	‡ Practice 133 *Problem Solving*
10-13 Renaming Decimals as Fractions	10	13	16	20	p. 443; 1–10	95	⌒ p.108	
10-14 Renaming Fractions as Decimals	13	16	20	25	p. 443; 1–10	96	⌒ p.108	⌒ Challenge 134 *Pack it Up*

Sample pages from the Teacher's Planning Guide.

Closing the Chapter
Student Edition pages 228–229

Chapter Vocabulary

Review with students the Words to Know on page 201 of the Student Edition. Have students find the first use of each word in the chapter. Challenge them to write a sentence of their own for each word.

Have students copy and complete the Vocabulary Review on page 228 of the Student Edition. For more vocabulary practice, have them complete Vocabulary 119 *Decimals*.

Test Tips

Test tips with examples can be copied onto index cards. Labels for easy reference for this chapter may include: Reading and Writing; Comparing and Ordering; Adding and Subtracting; Multiplying and Dividing; Solving Problems.

Learning Objectives

Have students review CM6 *Goal*
They can check off the goal th

Assessing the Chapter

Traditional Assessment
Chapter Quiz
The Chapter Quiz on pages 22
Student Edition can be used a
book or closed-book test, or as
quiz can be used to identify c
chapter that students need to

Chapter Tests
Use Chapter Test A Exercise 13
Test B Exercise 136, *Decimals*
Resource Binder to further ass
chapter concepts.

Additional Resources
Use the Resource Planner on p
this guide to assign additional
Classroom Resource Binder an

130 · Chapter 10

Note that each section of the quiz corresponds to a Learning Objective.

Group Activity
Summary: Students shop for a family of three for a week on a $125 budget.

Materials: grocery flyers and circulars; catalogs and brochures; calculators; Visual 16 *Blank Table*

Procedure: Encourage students to brainstorm a list of what they want before looking through the circulars. You might assign roles to group members, such as recorder, money counter, reporter, and researcher.

Assessment: Use the Group Activity Rubric on page *xii* of this guide. Fill in the rubric with the additional information below. For this project, students should have:

• selected healthy foods and necessary supplies.
• spent a total amount within the budgeted $125.

RELATED MATERIALS See the unit overview page for other Globe Fearon books that can be used to enrich and extend the material in this unit.

Activities and assessments to close the chapter.

Traditional assessment tools check understanding of the chapter.

10.11 Dividing Decimals by 10, 100, 1,000
Student Edition page 220

Prerequisite Skills
• Dividing decimals
• Dividing whole numbers by 10, 100, and 1,000

Lesson Objective
• Divide a decimal number by a power of 10.

Cooperative Group Activity

Who Am I?
Materials: none
Procedure: Write 78.2 on the chalkboard. To the right of the number, write 7.82. Allow enough space between the two numbers for students to write "× 10," "× 100," or "× 1,000." Point first to the number on the left and then to the number to its right. Say: "I can turn the number on the left into the number on the right. Who am I?"

• A volunteer comes to the board and writes "× 10" between the two numbers. The volunteer counts the number of zeros in the power of 10. The volunteer counts the number of places that the decimal point moves to change the number on the left to the number on the right. The class verifies that the number of zeros and the number of places that are moved are the same.
• The same volunteer writes a new set of decimal numbers on the board and asks the "Who am I?" question.
• The activity proceeds in the same manner, using different volunteers each time.

Customizing the Activity for Individual Needs
ESL Have students create self-study cards to help them understand the direction for moving the decimal point to the *right* for *multiplication* and to the *left* for *division*.

Learning Styles Students can:

👁 highlight the number of *zeros* in the power of 10 and use the same color to draw scoops to the left.

✋ use a finger to trace the movement of the decimal point.

🗣 say aloud the number of places the decimal point moves and why. For example: "The decimal point moves 1 place to the left

126 · Chapter 10

---

when the number is divided by 10 because 10 has 1 zero."

Enrichment Activity 🎧

Have students make up posters comparing the pattern of dividing by 10, 100, and 1,000 in whole numbers and in decimals. Encourage students to write about similarities and differences.

Alternative Assessment

Students can identify the quotient of a decimal number and a power of 10 from a written set of choices.

Example: Which answer below is 3.5 × 1,000?

.0035   .035   .35   35   350   3,500

Answer: 3,500

USING YOUR CALCULATOR
Number Patterns
Student Edition page 221

Lesson Objectives
• Find patterns to solve problems.
• Life Skill: Compute with decimals on a calculator.

Activity
How Close Can You Get?
Materials: sign with numbers as shown below, calculators
Procedure: Have students work in pairs to play the game.
• A player looks at the directions and target number for each problem, and then chooses numbers from the sign to add or subtract.
• The sum or difference should be as close to the target number as possible.
• The player with the sum or difference that is closest to the target scores 1,000 points.

1. Add two numbers.
   Target: 1.5
2. Add two numbers.
   Target: 3.25
3. Add three numbers.
   Target: 15
4. Subtract two numbers.
   Target: .5
5. Subtract two numbers.
   Target: 5.5
6. Subtract two numbers.
   Target: 3.01

5.6		8.7
	3	
.05		1.5
	8	
6		.5

Alternative Assessment helps check student's grasp of lesson content.

Hands-on activities bring math to life.

Clear prerequisite skills and objectives aid lesson planning.

Activities designed to meet individual needs.

Over 300 pages of
reproducibles are
organized by chapter.

A variety of practice
sets, including word
problems, reinforce
key skills and
concepts.

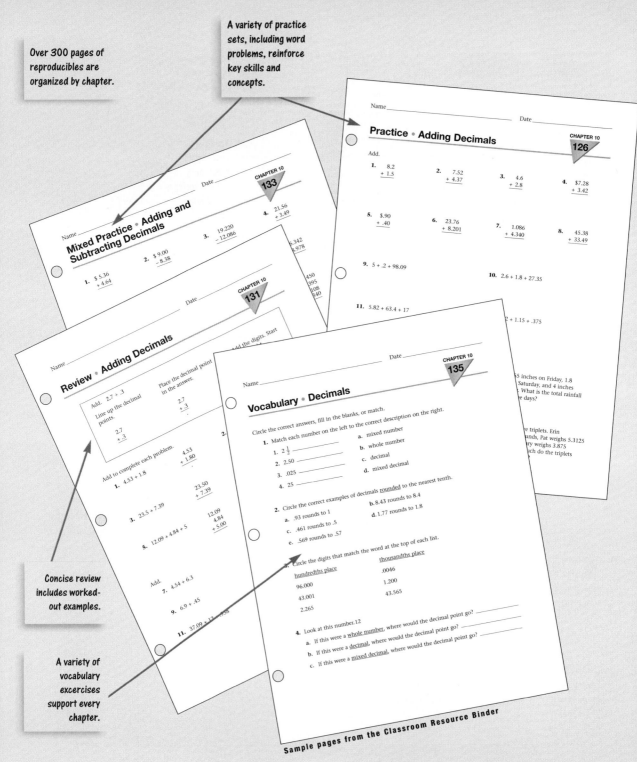

Name _____ Date _____

Practice • Adding Decimals

CHAPTER 10
126

Add.

1.   8.2
   + 1.5

2.   7.52
   + 4.37

3.   4.6
   + 2.8

4. $7.28
   + 3.42

5. $.90
   + .40

6.   23.76
   + 8.201

7.   1.086
   + 4.340

8.   45.38
   + 33.49

9. 5 + .2 + 98.09

10. 2.6 + 1.8 + 27.35

11. 5.82 + 63.4 + 17

Name _____ Date _____

CHAPTER 10
133

**Mixed Practice • Adding and
Subtracting Decimals**

2. $ 9.00
   – 8.38

3. 19.220
   – 12.086

4. 21.56
   + 3.49

1. $ 5.36
   + 4.64

Name _____ Date _____

CHAPTER 10
131

Review • Adding Decimals

Add. 2.7 + .3

Line up the decimal
points.

2.7
+ .3

Place the decimal point
in the answer.

2.7
+ .3

Add to complete each problem.

1. 4.53 + 1.8

4.53
+ 1.80

3. 23.5 + 7.39

23.50
+ 7.39

5. 12.09 + 4.84 + 5

12.09
4.84
+ 5.00

Add.

7. 4.54 + 6.3

9. 6.9 + .45

11. 37.09 + 12

Name _____ Date _____

CHAPTER 10
135

Vocabulary • Decimals

Circle the correct answers, fill in the blanks, or match.

1. Match each number on the left to the correct description on the right.

1. 2½ _____
2. 2.50 _____
3. .025 _____
4. 25 _____

a. mixed number
b. whole number
c. decimal
d. mixed decimal

2. Circle the correct examples of decimals rounded to the nearest tenth.

a. .93 rounds to 1
b. 8.43 rounds to 8.4
c. .461 rounds to .5
d. 1.77 rounds to 1.8
e. .569 rounds to .57

3. Circle the digits that match the word at the top of each list.

hundredths place

96.000
43.001
2.265

thousandths place

.0046
1.200
43.565

4. Look at this number. 12
a. If this were a whole number, where would the decimal point go? _____
b. If this were a decimal, where would the decimal point go? _____
c. If this were a mixed decimal, where would the decimal point go? _____

Concise review
includes worked-
out examples.

A variety of
vocabulary
excercises
support every
chapter.

Sample pages from the Classroom Resource Binder

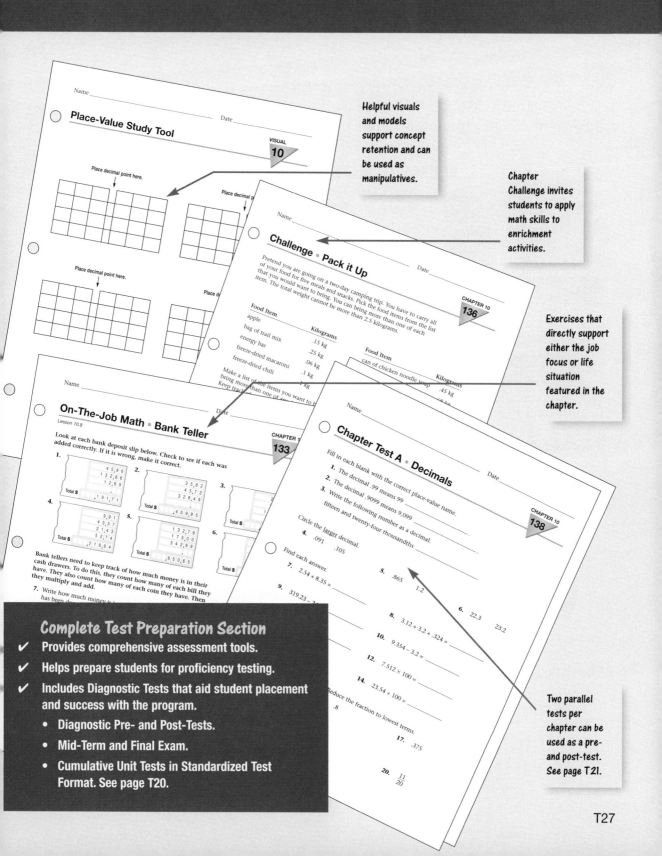

Name _____

Date _____

Place-Value Study Tool

VISUAL
10

Place decimal point here.

Place decimal point here.

Place decimal point here.

Place decimal point here.

Helpful visuals and models support concept retention and can be used as manipulatives.

Chapter Challenge invites students to apply math skills to enrichment activities.

Name _____

Date _____

Challenge • Pack it Up

CHAPTER 10
136

Pretend you are going on a two-day camping trip. You have to carry all of your food for five meals and snacks. Pick the food items from the list that you would want to bring. You can bring more than one of each item. The total weight cannot be more than 2.5 kilograms.

Food Item	Kilograms
apple	
bag of trail mix	.15 kg
energy bar	.25 kg
freeze-dried macaroni	.06 kg
freeze-dried chili	.1 kg

Food Item	Kilograms
can of chicken noodle soup	.45 kg

Make a list of the items you want to bring more than one of

Keep track

Exercises that directly support either the job focus or life situation featured in the chapter.

Name _____

Date _____

On-The-Job Math • Bank Teller

Lesson 10.8

CHAPTER 10
133

Look at each bank deposit slip below. Check to see if each was added correctly. If it is wrong, make it correct.

1.
	4 5,9 6
	1 3 2,8 6
	1 2,8 9
Total $	,1 9 1,7 1

2.
	3 5,8 2
	4 5,7 3
	3 2 8,4 9
Total $	,4 0 9,9 5

3.
| | |
| Total $ | |

4.
	9,9 1
	4 3,3 7
	2 1,4 3
	5 2,7 4
Total $	,2 1 6,0 6 4

5.
	1 3 2,7 6
	1 7 5,0 0
	3 4 2,8 9
Total $	,6 5 0,6 5

6.
| | |
| Total $ | |

Bank tellers need to keep track of how much money is in their cash drawers. To do this, they count how many of each bill they have. They also count how many of each coin they have. Then they multiply and add.

7. Write how much money is

has been do

Name _____

Date _____

Chapter Test A • Decimals

CHAPTER 10
138

Fill in each blank with the correct place-value name.

1. The decimal .99 means 99 _____

2. The decimal .9099 means 9,099 _____

3. Write the following number as a decimal.

fifteen and twenty-four thousandths _____

Circle the larger decimal.

4. .091   .105

5. .865   1.2

6. 22.3   23.2

Find each answer.

7. 2.54 + 8.35 = _____

8. 3.12 + 3.2 + .324 = _____

9. 319.23 − 2

10. 9.354 − 3.2 = _____

12. 7.512 × 100 = _____

14. 23.54 + 100 = _____

Reduce the fraction to lowest terms.

.8

17. .375

20. $\frac{11}{20}$

Two parallel tests per chapter can be used as a pre- and post-test. See page T21.

Complete Test Preparation Section

✔ Provides comprehensive assessment tools.

✔ Helps prepare students for proficiency testing.

✔ Includes Diagnostic Tests that aid student placement and success with the program.

• Diagnostic Pre- and Post-Tests.

• Mid-Term and Final Exam.

• Cumulative Unit Tests in Standardized Test Format. See page T20.

Many of these worktexts are correlated to *Pacemaker® Basic Mathematics* in the Teacher's Planning Guide. Use these worktexts for extra practice, reteaching, reinforcement, enrichment, and test preparation.

ACCESS TO MATH

A collection of 15 worktexts that target key math skills. Perfect for remediation or reteaching.

MATH IN ACTION

Eight worktexts designed to reinforce the basics and provide practice in a user-friendly format.

MATH FOR PROFICIENCY

Help your students develop the mastery and confidence they need to succeed on tests!

WRITING IN MATHEMATICS

Show your entire class how to communicate clearly in mathematics with this indispensable, practical worktext.

PASSAGE TO BASIC MATH

A parallel program to *Pacemaker Basic Mathematics* at a lower reading level. Teach the same content to all your students at just the right reading level.

PRACTICAL ARITHMETIC SERIES

This four-book series teaches students everyday math for everyday living with a focus on real-life applications of money skills.

Globe Fearon offers additional mathematics materials to help tailor instruction to meet the diverse needs of your students.

For more information on Globe Fearon worktexts call 1-800-848-9500.

The following chart shows the development and progression of math skills and concepts across the Pacemaker mathematics programs: *Basic Mathematics, Pre-Algebra,* and *Algebra 1.* The numbers following each entry indicate the chapter and lesson in which the skill or concept is first taught.

Basic Mathematics	Pre-Algebra	Algebra 1
NUMBER CONCEPTS		

Comparing and Ordering
  whole numbers; 1.1, 1.6, 1.7
  fractions; 7.6, 7.7, 7.10
  decimals; 10.3, 10.4
Divisibility
  by 2, 5, and 10; 6.1
  by 3, 6, and 9; 6.2
  by 4; 6.3
Exponents; 6.7
Factors; 6.4
Multiples; 6.5
Place Value
  whole numbers; 1.3, 1.4
  decimals; 10.2
Prime Factorization, Prime Numbers; 6.6
Properties, distributive; 18.2
Rounding
  whole numbers; 1.9
  decimals; 10.15
Square Roots; 6.8
	Comparing and Ordering
	  whole numbers; 1.2
	  fractions; 7.7
	  decimals; 5.1
	  integers; 11.1
	Divisibility; 6.1
	Exponents; 1.8
	Factors; 6.1, 6.2
	Multiples; 6.3
	Place Value
	  whole numbers; 1.1
	  decimals; 5.1
	Prime Numbers
	Prime Factorization; 6.4–6.5
	Properties; 2.6–2.8
	  addition; 2.6
	  multiplication; 2.7
	Rounding
	  whole numbers; 1.3
	  decimals; 5.2
	Scientific Notation; 5.8
		Comparing and Ordering
		  integers; 1.2
		Exponents; 1.8
		  multiplication; 10.3
		  division; 10.4
		  zero; 10.6
		  negative; 10.7
		Properties; 2.8–2.9
		  addition; 2.8
		  multiplication; 2.9
		  distributive; 2.10
		Scientific Notation; 10.8
		Square Roots; 11.5

WHOLE NUMBERS		

Addition; 2.1
  basic facts; 2.2–2.3
  no regrouping; 2.4
  regrouping; 2.6–2.8
Subtraction; 3.1
  basic facts; 3.2
  no regrouping; 3.3
  regrouping; 3.5–3.7
Multiplication; 4.1
  basic facts; 4.2
  no regrouping; 4.3
  regrouping; 4.4–4.5
  by 10, 100, 1,000; 4.7
  by numbers with zeros; 4.8
Division; 5.1
  basic facts; 5.2
  with remainders; 5.3
  1-digit divisors; 5.4, 5.5
  2-digit divisors; 5.7
  zeros in the quotient; 5.8
  estimating; 5.10
	Addition
	  basic facts and regrouping; 1.4
	  estimating; 1.6
	Subtraction
	  basic facts and regrouping; 1.5
	  estimating; 1.6
	Multiplication
	  basic facts and regouping; 1.7
	  estimating the product; 1.10
	Division
	  basic facts and with a remainder; 1.9
	  estimating a quotient; 1.10	

Basic Mathematics	Pre-Algebra	Algebra 1

FRACTIONS

Basic Mathematics	Pre-Algebra	Algebra 1

Fractions; 7.1
Equivalent Fractions; 7.2–7.4
Common Denominators; 7.5
Comparing; 7.6
Ordering; 7.7; 7.20
Writing
    fractions as mixed numbers; 7.8
    mixed numbers as fractions; 7.9
Multiplication; 8.1–8.3
    mixed numbers; 8.4
Division; 8.5
    by whole numbers; 8.6
    mixed numbers; 8.8, 8.9
Addition
    like fractions; 9.1
    like mixed numbers; 9.2
    unlike fractions; 9.5
    unlike mixed numbers; 9.7
Subtraction
    like fractions; 9.1
    like mixed numbers; 9.3
    from a whole number; 9.4
    unlike fractions; 9.6
    unlike mixed numbers; 9.8
	Fractions; 7.1
	Equivalent Fractions; 7.4–7.6
	Common Denominator; 8.2
	Comparing; 7.7
	Writing
	    fractions as mixed numbers; 7.3
	    mixed numbers as fractions; 7.3
	Multiplication; 9.1–9.2
	    mixed numbers 9.4
	Division; 9.3
	    mixed numbers; 9.4
	Addition
	    like fractions; 8.1
	    like mixed numbers; 8.5
	    unlike fractions; 8.3
	    unlike mixed numbers; 8.5
	Subtraction
	    like fractions; 8.1
	    like mixed numbers; 8.6
	    unlike fractions; 8.4
	    unlike mixed numbers; 8.6
		Rational Expressions
		    evaluate; 14.1
		    simplify; 14.3
		    addition and subtraction; 14.5–14.6
		    subtraction; 14.5–14.6
		    multiplication and division of; 14.7–14.8

DECIMALS

Basic Mathematics	Pre-Algebra	Algebra 1

Decimals; 10.1
Place Value; 10.2
Comparing; 10.3
Ordering; 10.4
Addition; 10.5
Subtraction; 10.6
Multiplication; 10.7
    by 10, 100, 1,000; 10.8
Division, by whole numbers; 10.9
    by decimals; 10.10
    by 10, 100, 1,000; 10.11
Writing
    decimals as fractions; 10.13
    fractions as decimals; 10.14
	Place Value; 5.1
	Comparing; 5.1
	Addition; 5.3
	Subtraction; 5.3
	Multiplication; 5.4
	    by 10, 100, 1,000; 5.5
	Division; 5.6
	    by 10, 100, 1,000; 5.7
	Writing
	    fractions as decimals; 7.9	

PERCENTS

Basic Mathematics	Pre-Algebra	Algebra 1

Percents; 11.1
Writing
    as decimals; 11.2
    decimals as percents; 11.7
    fractions as percents; 11.8
Finding the Part; 11.3
    sales tax; 11.4
    discounts; 11.5
    commissions; 11.6
Finding the Percent; 11.9
    increase/decrease; 11.10
Finding the Whole; 11.11
    finding the original price; 11.12
	Percents; 10.3
	Writing
	    as decimals; 10.4
	    decimals as percents; 10.4
	    fractions as percents; 10.5; 10.11
	Finding the Part; 10.7
	    discounts; 10.13
	Finding the Percent; 10.8
	    increase/decrease 10.10
	Finding the Whole; 10.9
		Writing equations; 3.13
		Finding the part
		    discounts; 3.14

RATIO AND PROPORTION

Basic Mathematics	Pre-Algebra	Algebra 1

Ratio; 12.1
Proportion; 12.2
Solving Proportions; 12.3
    multiple unit pricing; 12.4
    scale drawings; 12.5
	Ratio; 10.1
	Proportion; 10.2
	Solving Proportions; 10.2; 10.12
		Proportion
		    direct variation; 5.12
		Solving Proportions
		    in algebra; 14.10, 14.12

▶ Pacemaker® Mathematics Scope and Sequence

Basic Mathematics	Pre-Algebra	Algebra 1
STATISTICS AND PROBABILITY		

Graphs
    pictographs; 13.1
    bar graphs; 13.2–13.3
    graphs; 13.4–13.5
    circle graphs; 13.7
Mean; 13.8
Median and Mode; 13.9
Histograms; 13.10
Probability; 13.11
	Graphs
	    bar graphs; 6.8
	    line graphs; 13.6
	Mean; 7.11
	Median and Mode; 8.11
	Minimum, Maximum, and Range; 9.10
	Frequency Table; 5.14
	Counting; 11.9
	Probability; 12.9
		Graphs
		    bar graphs; 4.9
		    line graphs; 1.11
		    stem-and-leaf plots; 9.5
		    scatter plots; 9.6
		Mean; 9.1
		Median and Mode; 9.2
		Minimum, Maximum, and Range; 9.3
		Frequency Table; 9.4
		Counting; 15.2
		    permutations; 15.2, 15.8
		    combinations; 15.3, 15.8
		Probability; 15.4
		    complementary events; 15.5
		    compound events; 15.6
		    dependent events; 15.7
		    empirical; 15.9
		    predicting outcomes; 15.10

MEASUREMENT		

Customary Measurement; 14.1–14.3
    time; 14.4
    elapsed time; 14.6
    temperature; 14.7
Metric Measurement; 15.1–15.4
Comparing Measurements; 15.5		

GEOMETRY		

Points and Lines; 16.1
Angles
    measuring; 16.2
    drawing; 16.3
    in triangles; 16.4
Polygons; 16.5
    perimeter; 16.6
    area; 16.7–16.9
Circles
    circumference; 16.10
    area; 16.11
Space Figures
    volume; 16.13–16.14
	Polygons
	    perimeter; 1.13
	    area, squares, and rectangles; 2.11
	Prisms,
	    volume; 3.9
		Coordinate Geometry
		    ordered pairs; 4.1–4.3
		    linear equations; 5.2, 6.1, 8.1
		    inequalities; 7.5–7.6, 8.7–8.8
		    exponential functions; 10.10
		    quadratic functions; 11.2–11.4
		Formulas from Geometry; Appendix
		Right Triangles
		    Pythagorean Theorem; 13.7
		    special right triangles; 13.6, 13.9

INTEGERS		

Definition; 17.1
Addition
    with like signs; 17.2
    with unlike signs; 17.3
Subtraction; 17.4
Multiplication; 17.5
Division; 17.6
	Definition; 11.1
	Absolute Value; 11.2
	Addition;
	    on number line; 11.3
	    with absolute value; 11.4
	Subtraction; 11.5
	Multiplication; 11.6
	Division; 11.7
		Definition; 1.1
		Absolute Value; 1.2
		Addition; 1.3, 1.7
		Subtraction; 11.5
		Multiplication; 11.6
		Division; 11.7

Basic Mathematics	Pre-Algebra	Algebra 1
ALGEBRA		

Equation and Solution; 18.1
Order of Operations
    parentheses; 18.2
    operations; 18.3
Solving Equations
    addition and subtraction; 18.4
    multiplication and division; 18.5
    more than one operation; 18.7
	Number Expressions; 2.1–2.4
	Number Equations; 2.5
	Variable Expressions; Chapter 3
	    with decimals; 5.9, 5.10
	    with fractions; 9.5, 9.6
	Variable Equations; Chapter 4
	    with decimals; 5.11
	    with fractions; 9.7
	    with integers; Chapter 12
	Coordinate Plane; Chapter 13
		Expressions
		    number; 2.1, 2.2
		    variable; 2.3–2.6, 10.2–10.5
		Equations; 2.7
		Solving Equations; Chapter 3
		Functions; Chapter 4
		Linear Equations; Chapter 5
		Writing Equations; Chapter 6
		Inequalities; Chapter 7
		Systems; Chapter 8
		Quadratic Equations; Chapter 11
		Polynomials and Factoring;
		    Chapter 12
		Radicals; Chapter 13
		Rational Expressions and
		    Equations; Chapter 14

PROBLEM SOLVING		

Answers, do they make sense?; 8.10
Clue words; 2.5; 3.4; 4.6; 5.6
Extra Information; 6.9
Integers, using; 17.7
Multi-Part Decimal Problems; 10.12
Multi-Part Problems; 9.9
One-Step Equation, using; 18.16
Operation, Choosing the; 5.9
Part, Percent, or Whole, Finding the; 11.13
Patterns; 7.11
Proportions, using; 12.6
Reading Tables; 1.8
Scale, Choosing a; 13.6
Solve a Simpler Problem; 8.7
Subtracting to Find Area; 16.12
Two-Part Problems; 4.9; 15.6
Working with Units of Measure; 14.5
	Applications; 1.13, 2.11, 3.9, 4.12, 5.14, 6.8,
	    7.11, 8.11, 9.10, 10.13, 11.10, 12.9, 13.7
	Counting; 7.10
	Guess, Check, and Revise; 1.12
	Information, Too Much or Too Little; 8.10
	Line Graphs, using; 13.6
	Number Line, using; 12.8
	Number Patterns; 4.11
	Numbers for Words; 2.10
	Pattern, find a; 6.7
	Picture, Draw a; 3.8
	Proportions, using; 10.12
	Small Groups; 11.9
	Table, using; 9.9
	Working Backward; 5.13
		Applications; 1.11, 2.14, 3.14, 4.9, 5.12, 6.8, 7.9,
		    8.11, 9.9, 10.13, 11.10, 12.15, 13.12, 14.13,
		    15.10
		Counting Choices; 10.12
		Empirical Probability; 12.4
		Equations, writing; 2.13
		Functions, table or equation; 4.8
		Guess, Check, and Revise; 1.10
		Inequalities, using; 7.8
		Mean, Median, and Mode, choosing; 9.8
		Number Patterns, looking for; 6.7
		Percent Equations, writing; 3.13
		Proportions, using; 14.12
		Pythagorean Theorem; 13.11
		Quadratic Equations, using and writing; 11.9
		Slope, using; 5.11
		Systems, using; 8.10

LIFE SKILLS/LIFE CONNECTIONS		
Math In Your Life: Better Buy; Cooking; Determining Miles per Gallon; Making a Budget; Pay Day; Tipping; Understanding Computer Memory; Wind Chill Temperatures	**Math Connections: A piece of the Company;** **Earthquakes; Olympic Time; Perfect Numbers;** **Picture Perfect; The Great Pyramid**	**Math Connections: Comets; Currency;** **Elevation; Keeping Things in Balance;** **Muhammad Ibn Musa Al Khwarizmi**
VOCATIONAL SKILLS		
On-the-Job Math: Bank Teller; Car Rental Agent; Computer Programmer; Courier; Dietician; Meter Reader; Physical Therapist; Picture Framer	**Math Connections: Automobile Technician;** **Benjamin Banneker; Dr. Mae Jemison; Fashion** **Designer; Hurricane Warning; Pharmacy** **Assistant; What's Your Opinion?**	**Math Connections: Air Traffic Controller;** **Assembly Line; Building with Blueprints;** **Chlen Shlung-Wu; Evelyn Boyd Granville; Luis** **Alvarez; Making Maps; Physician's Assistant;** **Restaurant Managers; Weather Forecasting**
CALCULATOR SKILLS		
A Place-Value Game; Beat the Calculator; Checking Division; Checking Multiplication; Checking Solutions to Equations; Comparing Fractions; Finding Common Denominators; How Old Are You?; Keying in Integers; Measurements; Multiplying Fractions and Whole Numbers; Number Patterns; Perimeter and Area; Showing Probability as a Decimal or as a Percent; Solving Proportions; Test for Divisibility; The Percent Key	Adding and Subtracting Fractions; Checking Solutions; Checking the Prime Factorization; Decimals for Fractions; Estimating with Decimals; Evaluating Expressions; Finding Ordered Pairs; Multiplying and Dividing Fractions; Operations with Integers; Percents for Fractions; Performing Operations; Simplifying Expressions	Checking Possible Solutions; Checking Solutions; Finding Intercepts; Finding Ordered Pairs; Finding Square Roots; Finding the Mean; Finding the Value of Expressions; Finding Values of Powers; Is the Equation Correct?; Performing Operations; Permutations and Combinations

PACEMAKER®

Basic
Mathematics

Third Edition

GLOBE FEARON EDUCATIONAL PUBLISHER
Upper Saddle River, New Jersey
www.globefearon.com

REVIEWERS
We thank the following educators, who provided valuable comments
and suggestions during the development of this book:

Rosemarie Estok, Woodbridge Public Schools, Woodbridge, New Jersey
Audris Griffith, Glen Bard West High School, Glen, Illinois
Dorie Knaub, Downey Unified School District, Downey, California
Christine Sweat, Highland Middle School, Jacksonville, Florida

Subject Area Consultant: Kay McClain, Department of Teaching and Learning,
Vanderbilt University, Nashville, Tennessee
Pacemaker Curriculum Advisor: Stephen C. Larsen, formerly of The University of Texas at Austin

Supervising Editor: Stephanie Petron Cahill
Senior Editor: Phyllis Dunsay
Editor: Dena Pollak
Production Editors: Laura Benford-Sullivan, Andrew Roney
Designers: Evelyn Bauer, Jennifer Visco
Photo Coordinator: Jennifer Hixson
Editorial Assistants: Kathy Bentzen, Wanda Rockwell
Market Manager: Donna Frasco
Research Director: Angela Darchi
Cover Design: Evelyn Bauer
Electronic Composition: Burmar Technical Corp., Linda Bierniak, Mimi Raihl, Phyllis Rosinsky

About the Cover: Mathematics is a way to help people understand and deal with their
environment. The images on the cover of this book show how an understanding of basic
mathematics is relevant in everyday life. Runners need to calculate their speed over distances.
Architects use geometric structures and formulas to build cities. Newspapers and magazines
display data visually in graphs. Mechanics use gearing ratios to repair machines such as cars
and airplanes. How do you use mathematics in your everyday life?

ISBN 0-835-93583-3

Printed in the United States of America
4 5 6 7 8 9 10   03 02 01

GLOBE FEARON EDUCATIONAL PUBLISHER
Upper Saddle River, New Jersey
www.globefearon.com

Contents

A Note to the Student

Today, students often wonder why they *still* have to study math. After all, calculators and computers are everywhere. These wonderful machines can answer the most complex problems in seconds.

Certainly there is some truth to that. But a calculator or a computer can only do what you tell it to do. You have to ask the right question to get the right answer. If you don't know whether to multiply or divide to solve a problem, a calculator can't help you. A calculator can't tell you whether or not an answer makes sense. To make these decisions, you must know something about basic mathematics.

You already use some form of mathematics in your life every day. You tell time. You measure. You spend money and count your change. You figure out how long it will take to get from one place to another. In fact, you couldn't survive in our fast-paced world without using basic math skills.

The purpose of this book is to help you develop the math skills you need to succeed in today's world. You will learn about whole numbers and how to add, subtract, multiply, and divide them. You will also learn about fractions, decimals, percents, different systems of measurement, and other basics of mathematics. Some of this information may not seem very useful right now. But a solid understanding of basic math will help you make good decisions all your life—at school, at home, and on the job.

For example, perhaps you want to figure out the discount on a sale item in your favorite store. Perhaps you want to know what skills you need to work as a computer programmer or a physical therapist. *Basic Mathematics* can help you find the answers to your questions. In every chapter, there are special features that show you how math relates to your life. The **Math in Your Life** and **On-the-Job Math** features take math out of the classroom and into the real world.

You probably hear a lot about problem solving in your math class. Do you wonder what it has to do with you? As an adult, you'll need to solve problems often. This is true both on the job and in the home. *Basic Mathematics* has many activities that allow you to practice problem solving in real-world situations. You'll also find lessons just on problem solving to help you succeed at this skill.

What about those calculators that seem so helpful until you try to use one? The **Using Your Calculator** features take the mystery out of calculators. You'll learn how to use a calculator to solve math problems using whole numbers, fractions, decimals, and integers.

Throughout the book you'll find notes in the margins of the pages. These friendly **margin notes** are there to remind you of something you already know.

You will also find several study aids in the book. At the beginning of every chapter, you'll find **Learning Objectives.** They will help you focus on the important points covered in the chapter. You'll also find **Words to Know,** a look ahead at the vocabulary you may find difficult. The colorful photos, graphs, and drawings in the book bring math concepts to life. **Test Tips** in the Chapter Review will help you prepare for—and succeed on—tests.

Everyone who put this book together worked hard to make it useful, interesting, and enjoyable. The rest is up to you. We wish you well in your studies. Our success is in your accomplishment.

Unit 1 ▷ Whole Numbers

Opening the Unit
Have students look through newspapers and brochures for used cars to find a car from at least two of the countries listed below. Have the students compare the prices of the cars.

Every year, U.S. car dealers import, or bring in, millions of cars from other countries.

The chart shows about how many cars are imported into the United States in one year.

1. From which country does the United States import the greatest number of cars? Canada

2. From which country does the United States import the fewest number of cars? South Korea

3. How did you find your answer for **Questions 1** and **2**? Encourage students to explain how they compared numbers.

Imported Cars in a Year	
Country	**Number of Cars**
Japan	1,114,000
Germany	204,000
South Korea	132,000
Mexico	463,000
Canada	1,552,000

1

Nonprofit organizations often raise money at large concert events. They sold 8,000 tickets for this concert. Tickets cost $10 each. They raised $80,000. A second concert raised $150,000. Why might the second concert have raised more money?

Caption It may have raised more money because the organizations sold more tickets, or the tickets cost more money.

Chapter 1 Understanding Whole Numbers

ESL Note In many countries, a space is used to mark the thousands place instead of a comma.

Words to Know

whole numbers	0, 1, 2, 3, 4, 5, 6, 7, and so on
number line	numbers in order shown as points on a line
even numbers	numbers that end in 0, 2, 4, 6, or 8
odd numbers	numbers that end in 1, 3, 5, 7, or 9
digits	the symbols used to write numbers: 0, 1, 2, 3, 4, 5, 6, 7, 8, and 9
rename	to show a number another way; to show place value, 28 can be renamed as 2 *tens* + 8 *ones*
rounding	changing a number to the nearest ten, hundred, thousand, or so on

Words to Know Group words by function: words that describe a number; things you can do to a number.

Number Journal Project

Keep a daily journal of whole numbers you see. Look for them in different places. Read containers, signs, newspapers, and magazines. Write what each number is about and where you found it.

2001	year	newspaper
110	calories	milk carton
$1,000	money	"For Sale" sign

Project The project can be done individually or in groups. Have students keep math journals. Or have them contribute their entries to a bulletin board display.

Learning Objectives

- Identify whole numbers.
- Identify odd and even numbers.
- Recognize place value.
- Read and write whole numbers.
- Compare and order whole numbers.
- Round whole numbers.
- Solve problems by reading a table.
- Apply whole numbers to computer memory.

More Practice is provided in Exercise 1 of the *Workbook*.

1·1 What Is a Whole Number?

Number Sense
Have students make a list of the numbers they see every day and describe how the numbers are used.

The numbers 0, 1, 2, 3, 4, 5, and so on, are called **whole numbers.** Whole numbers are used to count. They tell how many or how much.

Look at the **number line** below. It shows numbers in order on a line. This number line shows the whole numbers from 0 to 16. A number line can begin or end with any number.

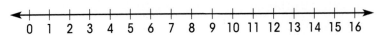

▶ **EXAMPLE**

Find the missing numbers on the number line below.

Avoiding Errors
Point out that a number line can start and end with any number. Students can practice counting up from any number. Thus, you can find numbers that are missing from a number line.

STEP 1 Copy the number line above.

STEP 2 Begin with 15 and count each point. Fill in the blanks as you count.

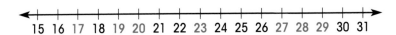

Practice

Common Error Students skip numbers. Have students count by ones from the first number in the sequence.

Find the missing numbers on each number line. Be sure to copy each number line onto your paper first.

1.

2.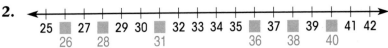

More Practice is provided in Exercise 2 of the *Workbook*.

1·2 ▶ Odd and Even Numbers

Number Sense
Point out that the numbers 34 and 92 are even numbers, although the leading digits 3 and 9 are odd digits. Use the numbers 45 and 87 as examples of odd numbers whose leading digits are even.

Look at the number line below. The numbers in blue are called **even numbers**. The numbers in black are called **odd numbers**. There is a pattern. Every even number is followed by an odd number.

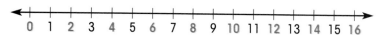

Notice that even numbers end in 0, 2, 4, 6, or 8. Odd numbers end in 1, 3, 5, 7, or 9. You can look at the last digit on the right in a number. This digit tells you if the number is even or odd.

▶ **EXAMPLE**

Avoiding Errors
Emphasize that every whole number is either even or odd, but cannot be both.

Write only the odd numbers from this set of numbers:

11   12   13   14   15   16   17   18   19   20
21   22   23   24   25   26   27   28   29   30

STEP 1   Look at the last digit in each number.
11   12   and so on...

STEP 2   Write the numbers that end in 1, 3, 5, 7, or 9.
11, 13, 15, 17, 19, 21, 23, 25, 27, 29

The odd numbers in the set above are:
11, 13, 15, 17, 19, 21, 23, 25, 27, and 29.

Common Error All the digits of a number must be even for the number to be even. Stress that only the last digit of a number determines if it is even or odd.

Practice

1. Write only the odd numbers from this set of numbers:

51   52   53   54   55   56   57   58   59   60
61   62   63   64   65   66   67   68   69   70
51, 53, 55, 57, 59, 61, 63, 65, 67, 69

2. Write only the even numbers from this set of numbers:

91   92   93   94   95   96   97   98   99   100
101   102   103   104   105   106   107   108   109   110
92, 94, 96, 98, 100, 102, 104, 106, 108, 110

More Practice is provided in Exercise 3 of the *Workbook*.

1·3 Place Value to Thousands

Number Sense
Use the numbers 4, 40, 400, and 4,000 to show the importance of correct placement of digits and the importance of zeros.

You can use the **digits** 0, 1, 2, 3, 4, 5, 6, 7, 8, and 9 to write any number. It is important to put each digit in the correct place.

thousands	hundreds	tens	ones
		2	4
		4	2

24 means 2 *tens* and 4 *ones*.

42 means 4 *tens* and 2 *ones*.

The numbers 24 and 42 are different numbers.

You can **rename** a number to show the place value of each digit.

Rename 3,724 to show the place value of each digit.

▶ **EXAMPLE**

STEP 1 Look at the place value of each digit.

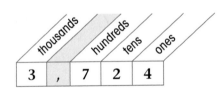

3 means **3** thousands.
7 means **7** hundreds.
2 means **2** tens.
4 means **4** ones.

Avoiding Errors
Point out that zeros in the middle of a number change the value of the number: for example, 13, 103, 1,003, 10,003.

STEP 2 Write the number this way:

3,724 = **3** *thousands* + **7** *hundreds* + **2** *tens* + **4** *ones*

To show the place value of each digit, rename 3,724 as 3 *thousands* + 7 *hundreds* + 2 *tens* + 4 *ones*.

Practice A

Common Error Incorrect place values are used. Have students start with the digit in the ones place to help them name each place correctly.

Rename each number to show the place value of each digit.

1. 17
1 ten + 7 ones

2. 69
6 tens + 9 ones

3. 46
4 tens + 6 ones

4. 81
8 tens + 1 one

5. 55
5 tens + 5 ones

6. 2,473

7. 7,502

8. 5,439

9. 8,037

10. 4,800

6. 2 thousands + 4 hundreds + 7 tens + 3 ones   8. 5 thousands + 4 hundreds + 3 tens + 9 ones

7. 7 thousands + 5 hundreds + 2 ones   9. 8 thousands + 3 tens + 7 ones

10. 4 thousands + 8 hundreds

Practice B

The place value of each digit in a number is shown below.
Write the number.

11. 3 tens + 2 ones   32

12. 9 tens + 5 ones   95

13. 7 tens + 4 ones   74

14. 6 tens + 6 ones   66

15. 8 tens   80

16. 8 ones   8

17. 3 thousands + 4 tens + 6 ones
3,046

18. 7 thousands + 5 hundreds
7,500

19. 4 hundreds + 3 tens
430

20. 5 thousands + 6 hundreds + 2 tens
5,620

Everyday Problem Solving

Ms. Polk's class is collecting soda can tabs for a charity. They want to collect 5,000. They group the tabs by thousands, hundreds, tens, and ones.

1. How many hundreds are in 1,000?   10 hundreds

2. The class has 3,421 tabs. How many thousands are there?   3 thousands

3. Eileen has 999 tabs. How many more tabs does she need to make 1,000?   1 tab

4. Is 3,421 an even number or an odd number? How do you know?
Odd number; It ends with the digit 1.

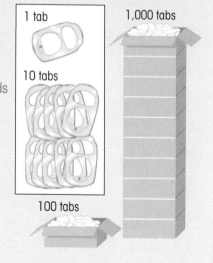

1 tab

10 tabs

100 tabs

1,000 tabs

1·4 ▶ **Place Value to Millions**

Number Sense
Have students tell the number of ones in 1 *ten*, tens in 1 *hundred*, hundreds in 1 *thousand*, and thousands in 1 *ten thousand*.

A place-value chart can help you to understand large numbers.

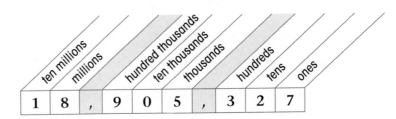

▶ **EXAMPLE**

Avoiding Errors
Point out the importance of the digit 0 in holding places within a number.

Find the value of the underlined digit in 18,9̲05,327.

STEP 1 Identify the place of the underlined digit. Look at the place-value chart above.

hundred thousands
↓
18,9̲05,327

STEP 2 Write the underlined digit. Then write the name of the place.

9 hundred thousands

The value of the digit 9 in the number 18,905,327 is 9 *hundred thousands*.

Practice

Common Error Incorrect places result in incorrect values. Have students use the commas as a way to identify correct values of digits.

Find the value of the underlined digit in each number.

1. 7,8̲32
8 hundreds

2. 56,5̲29,100
5 hundred thousands

3. 14̲,635,123
4 millions

4. 46̲,718
6 thousands

5. 90,7̲16
7 hundreds

6. 629̲,350
2 ten thousands

7. 90,31̲5
1 ten

8. 1,678,943̲
3 ones

9. 97̲,510
9 ten thousands

10. 3,456̲,789
5 ten thousands

11. 78̲,600
8 thousands

12. 17̲9,360,121
7 ten millions

13. 1,5̲78,469
5 hundred thousands

14. 563,3̲99
3 hundreds

15. 6̲7,013,269
6 ten millions

16. 20̲0,856
0 ten thousands

Extra Practice for this lesson is provided on page 415.

USING YOUR CALCULATOR
A Place-Value Game

You can use the calculator to play a game about place value. You will use the keys shown on the picture.

DISPLAY Shows the number you enter.

Player 1   Key a number into the calculator. Choose a digit in that number.

PRESS   `3` `4` `7` `2`   3472.

CHOOSE   four

CLEAR Use to erase.

NUMBER KEYS Use to enter numbers.

Player 2   Tell the place value of the digit.
SAY   4 *hundreds*

Key in one or more digits.
PRESS   `9` `1`   347291.

FUNCTION KEYS You will use these in later chapters.

Player 3   Tell the place value of the same digit in the new number.
SAY   4 *ten thousands*

All   Change roles and play again.
PRESS   `C`   0.

Play the place-value game. Player 1 begins with each number below.

  1. 237   **2.** 46   **3.** 2,428   **4.** 63,821

Answers will vary. Check that place names and values make sense for the number given.

  5. 125,325   **6.** 7,013,825   **7.** 10,025,362   **8.** 367,420

You may wish to have students keep a written record of the game as they play.

  9. 9,863,254   **10.** Now player 1 begins with any number.

1·5 ▶ Reading and Writing Whole Numbers

Number Sense
Have students make their own place-value chart by turning lined paper sideways. Have them copy the chart into their notebooks.

A place-value chart can help you to read and write numbers. Numbers are read from left to right.

ten millions	millions		hundred thousands	ten thousands	thousands		hundreds	tens	ones
4	9	,	1	0	8	,	5	0	0
2	8	,	0	0	0	,	1	3	2

Commas group every three places starting from the right. They can help you read and write numbers.

▶ **EXAMPLE 1**

Read the number 49,108,500 in the place-value chart above. Write it in words.

Avoiding Errors
Point out that commas separate the "periods" of numbers in a place-value chart. Explain that they show when to say *million*, *thousand*, or *hundred* (or just the number).

STEP 1 Find the place name to the left of each comma.
   49 million 108 thousand 500 hundred

STEP 2 Read the number before each comma and then the place name.
   forty-nine million, one hundred eight thousand, five hundred

The number 49,108,500 is read: forty-nine million, one hundred eight thousand, five hundred.

▶ **EXAMPLE 2**

Use digits to write twenty-eight million, one hundred thirty-two. Write zeros for missing places.

STEP 1 Write the number for each group named.
   28 million 132

STEP 2 Write a comma every three places from the right. Write zeros for any missing places.
   28,000,132

Twenty-eight million, one hundred thirty-two can be written as 28,000,132.

Practice A

Read each number. Write each number in words.

1. 32,584

2. 74,800,000

3. 6,002,070

4. 175,081

5. 837,000,495

6. 463,000

Common Error Zeros are skipped when determining places. Have students write the number, draw horizontal bars between the digits, and write the places above each digit.

Practice B

Use digits to write each number.

7. three million, six hundred thousand, forty-nine 3,600,049

8. nine hundred fifty-eight thousand, six hundred three 958,603

9. one hundred fifty-two million, seven hundred three 152,000,703

10. sixteen million, five hundred thousand 16,500,000

11. seven hundred million, twelve 700,000,012

12. six hundred sixteen thousand, ninety-five 616,095

13. twenty million, three thousand, sixty 20,003,060

14. forty-one million, forty-one thousand, forty-one 41,041,041

Everyday Problem Solving

A newspaper headline can have a whole number in it.

1. Write the number in Headline A in words.
   five thousand, three hundred

2. Write the number in Headline B using digits.
   1,000,000

3. Create your own headline involving at least one whole number. Write that number in words.
   Check placement of commas and use of place names.

Today's Sports

(A) 5,300 Fans at Game

Local News

One Million People Will Vote

(B)

More Practice is provided in Exercise 6 of the *Workbook*.

1·6 Comparing Whole Numbers

Number Sense
Have students look at a place-value chart. Recall that 10 is greater than 1, 100 is greater than 10, and so on. Point out that the greater number has more digits.

You can use symbols to show if a number is larger than, or smaller than, or the same as another number.

$10 > 4$	$2 < 13$	$5 = 5$
10 is greater than 4	2 is less than 13	5 is equal to 5

The symbol > means *is greater than*. The symbol < means *is less than*. The symbol = means *is equal to*.

▶ EXAMPLE 1

Compare. 6,325 and 978

STEP 1 Line up the digits by place and count the number of digits.

6,325 ← 4 digits
978 ← 3 digits

STEP 2 Compare the number of digits.

6,325 has more digits.

STEP 3 Use a symbol to show how the numbers compare.

6,325 > 978

The number 6,325 is greater than 978.

You can compare numbers with the same number of digits. You will need to compare each digit.

▶ EXAMPLE 2

Compare. 8,536 and 8,701

Avoiding Errors
Help students remember the meaning of < by explaining that it looks like a sideways letter L for less than. Or the arrow points to the smaller number.

STEP 1 Line up the digits by place and count the number of digits.

8,536 ← 4 digits
8,701 ← 4 digits

STEP 2 Compare the number of digits.

They have the same number of digits.

STEP 3 Compare the value of each digit, starting at the left. Skip digits that are the same.

8,536
8,701
└ 5 is less than 7

STEP 4 Use a symbol to show how the numbers compare.

8,536 < 8,701

The number 8,536 is less than 8,701.

Compare. 52,743 and 52,743

STEP 1	Line up the digits by place and count the number of digits.	52,743 ← 5 digits 52,743 ← 5 digits
STEP 2	Compare the number of digits.	They have the same number of digits.
STEP 3	Compare the value of each digit, starting at the left. Skip digits that are the same.	52,743 52,743 All digits are the same.
STEP 4	Use a symbol to show how the numbers compare.	52,743 = 52,743

Common Error Numbers with digits greater than 5 are larger than numbers with digits less than 5. Encourage students to write the numbers below each other to easily compare the number of digits and their values.

Practice A

Choose the greater number in each pair.

1. 2   10
10

2. 152   99
152

3. 5,628   10,000
10,000

4. 1,002   1,003
1,003

5. 25,000   2,500
25,000

6. 700   800
800

7. 68,431   68,331
68,431

8. 69,000   70,000
70,000

9. 12,158   12,185
12,185

10. 11,000   9,999
11,000

11. 4,195   4,099
4,195

12. 349,999   350,000
350,000

Practice B

Compare each pair of numbers from left to right. Use the symbol >, <, or =.

13. 2,007 ▨ 2,676
<

14. 567 ▨ 89
>

15. 312 ▨ 321
<

16. 5,876 ▨ 5,303
>

17. 709 ▨ 1,100
<

18. 4,567 ▨ 4,567
=

19. 5,601 ▨ 7,601
<

20. 62,514 ▨ 63,412
<

21. 50,982 ▨ 50,820
>

22. 72,999 ▨ 72,999
=

23. 31,008 ▨ 29,999
>

24. 17,230 ▨ 17,320
<

Extra Practice for this lesson is provided on page 415.

More Practice is provided in Exercise 7 of the *Workbook*.

 1·7 ▶ **Ordering Whole Numbers**

You can use what you know about comparing numbers to order numbers. You can order numbers from least to greatest.

▶ **EXAMPLE**

Order the numbers from least to greatest.
3,208   569   3,502

Number Sense
Give three numbers out of order. Tell students to use a number line to order them from smallest to largest.

STEP 1 Find the smallest number by counting the digits. Circle the smallest number.

3,208 ← 4 digits
⟨569⟩ ← 3 digits
3,502 ← 4 digits

Avoiding Errors
Tell students to look for the numbers with different numbers of digits first. These will often be the largest or smallest of the set.

STEP 2 Compare the other two numbers.

3,208
3,502
↑
└ 2 is less than 5.

STEP 3 Write the numbers in order from least to greatest.

569   3,208   3,502

The numbers from least to greatest are:
569   3,208   3,502

You can also order numbers from greatest to least. Begin by looking for the largest number.

Common Error Numbers with similar digits are confused. Tell students to write the numbers in a place-value chart to compare each digit one place at a time.

Practice A

Order the numbers from least to greatest.

1. 25 9
52 25
9 52

2. 573 564
564 573
580 580

3. 1,003 958
985 985
958 1,003

4. 8,060 860
860 8,060
80,006 80,006

5. 32,153 31,978
33,000 32,153
31,978 33,000

6. 9,100 9,090
9,090 9,091
9,091 9,100

7. 25,525 6,825
6,825 25,525
26,125 26,125

8. 97 97
968 968
978 978

Practice B

Order the numbers from least to greatest.

9. 46   87   3
3, 46, 87

10. 789   505   690
505, 690, 789

11. 712   478   203
203, 478, 712

12. 888   349   901
349, 888, 901

13. 2,309   1,781   890
890; 1,781; 2,309

14. 305   2,020   2,041
305; 2,020; 2,041

15. 23,560   19,709   24,001
19,709; 23,560; 24,001

16. 54,800   60,723   51,244
51,244; 54,800; 60,723

Practice C

Order the numbers from greatest to least.

17. 15   35   20
35; 20; 15

18. 23,152   32,182   33,132
33,132; 32,182; 23,152

19. 1,287   7,002   1,087
7,002; 1,287; 1,087

20. 62,961   69,001   65,452
69,001; 65,452; 62,961

Everyday Problem Solving

Sam found information on the U.S. population for his history report. He used the chart below to answer these questions.

1. Which state had the greatest population?
Massachusetts

2. Which state had the least population?
Rhode Island

3. Did New York have fewer people than Connecticut? Explain. No. There were more people in New York, because 340,000 > 238,000.

4. If 1,000 more people settle in Rhode Island, what would be the population? 70,000

Year 1790	
State	Population
Connecticut	238,000
Massachusetts	379,000
New York	340,000
Rhode Island	69,000

5. Make a new chart. List the states by population from least to greatest. Rhode Island, 69,000; Connecticut, 238,000; New York, 340,000; Massachusetts, 379,000

1·8 ▶ Problem Solving: Reading Tables

Some word problems can be solved by using numbers from a table.

▶ **EXAMPLE**

Number Sense
Review the parts of a table. Have students read across rows, making complete sentences. "Nori scored two hundred sixty million points."

Hector and Lucy both play the same video game. They both are on the high scores list. Who is the best player on the list?

Game High Scores	
Name	**Points Scored**
Hector	285,800,000
Lucy	357,100,000
Nori	260,000,000
Marcel	306,200,000
Jewel	399,800,000
Cliff	322,700,000

Avoiding Errors
Be sure students compare numbers by looking at the same places in each number. Have them put the numbers in a place-value chart.

STEP 1 **READ** What do you need to find out?
You need to find the best player.
Which player scored the most points?

STEP 2 **PLAN** What do you need to do?
Compare each number.
Find the greatest number.

STEP 3 **DO Follow the plan.**
399,800,000   Jewel
322,700,000   Cliff
357,100,000   Lucy
399,800,000 > 357,100,000

STEP 4 **CHECK** Does the answer make sense?
Look at the other numbers in the table. Are all the other numbers less than 399,800,000? ✓

The best player is Jewel.

Problem Solving

Common Error Wrong item in table is chosen. Have students use a ruler to follow across a row.

READ the problem. Use the table on page 16 to follow the steps under PLAN. DO the plan to solve each problem.

1. How many points did Marcel score?

PLAN
Find Marcel in the table.
Write the number next to him under "Points Scored." 306,200,000

2. Who scored 357,100,000?

PLAN
Find 357,100,000 in the table.
Write the name of the person next to it in the first column. Lucy

3. Which player scored more, Cliff or Hector?

PLAN
Compare the numbers next to Cliff and Hector.
Choose the person with the greater number of points. Cliff

4. Which player scored the least number of points?

PLAN
Compare each number in the table.
Choose the person with the least number of points. Nori

Problem Solving Strategy

Often, problems can be solved by making a table.

Dan and his friends scored the following on their favorite video game: Dan, 35,354; Bill, 34,352; Dave, 33,534; Marie, 34,354; and Jill, 35,254. Who scored the highest? Who scored the lowest? highest: Dan; lowest: Dave

Copy the table shown. Use it to solve the problem. The first row is done for you.

Video Game Scores	
Person	Score
Dan	35,354
Bill	34,352
Dave	33,534
Marie	34,354
Jill	35,254

1·9 ▶ Rounding Whole Numbers

Number Sense
Draw a number line showing 400 and 500. Plot 435 and 480 on the number line. Round these numbers to the nearest hundred, emphasizing how close they are in distance to 400 or 500.

Look at the numbers below. These are the hundreds numbers.

100, 200, 300, 400, 500, 600, 700, 800, 900

Changing numbers to the nearest ten, hundred, or thousand is called **rounding.**

▶ **EXAMPLE 1**

Round 352 to the nearest hundred.

STEP 1	Underline the digit in the rounding place. Look at the digit to the right.	3̲52
STEP 2	Compare this digit to 5.	5 is equal to 5.
STEP 3	If this digit is 5 or more, add 1 to the rounding place.	3̲52 ↓ Add 1. 4
STEP 4	Change the digits to the right to 0.	400

352 rounded to the nearest hundred is 400.

If the digit in the rounding place is a 9, you may need to round up to the next-higher place.

▶ **EXAMPLE 2**

Round 42,971 to the nearest hundred.

STEP 1	Underline the digit in the rounding place. Look at the digit to the right.	42,9̲71
STEP 2	Compare this digit to 5.	7 is greater than 5.
STEP 3	Since the digit in the rounding place is 9, change it to 0 and add 1 to the place to the left.	42,9̲71 ↓ Add 1. 43,0
STEP 4	Change the digits to the right to 0.	43,000

1 hundred + 9 hundreds
= 1 thousand

42,971 rounded to the nearest hundred is 43,000.

Do not change the digit in the rounding place, if the digit to the right is less than 5.

▶ **EXAMPLE 3**

Round 542,489 to the nearest thousand.

STEP 1	Underline the digit in the rounding place. Look at the digit to the right.	542,489
STEP 2	Compare this digit to 5.	4 is less than 5.
STEP 3	Since this digit is less than 5, do not change the digit in the rounding place.	542,489 ↓ Do not change. 542,
STEP 4	Change the digits to the right to 0.	542,000

Avoiding Errors
Stress the importance of underlining the rounding place. Numbers to the right will be zeros when finished.

542,489 rounded to the nearest thousand is 542,000.

Practice A

Common Error Digit in rounding place is compared to 5. Have students circle the digit to the right.

Round each number to the nearest ten.

1. 213
210

2. 467
470

3. 843
840

4. 961
960

5. 2,458
2,460

6. 1,661
1,660

7. 4,228
4,230

8. 32,702
32,700

Practice B

Round each number to the nearest hundred.

9. 88,027
88,000

10. 53,595
53,600

11. 50,514
50,500

12. 105,336
105,300

13. 29,947
29,900

14. 20,682
20,700

15. 69,817
69,800

16. 245,568
245,600

Practice C

Round each number to the nearest thousand.

17. 77,223
77,000

18. 43,567
44,000

19. 20,501
21,000

20. 109,736
110,000

21. 49,933
50,000

22. 20,682
21,000

23. 99,817
100,000

24. 425,508
426,000

Lesson continues on next page.

Practice D

Round each number to the nearest ten, to the nearest hundred, and to the nearest thousand. The first one is done.

	Tens	Hundreds	Thousands
25. 3,256	3,260	3,300	3,000
26. 4,641	? 4,640	? 4,600	? 5,000
27. 9,897	? 9,900	? 9,900	? 10,000
28. 12,560	? 12,560	? 12,600	? 13,000
29. 29,705	? 29,710	? 29,700	? 30,000
30. 129,999	? 130,000	? 130,000	? 130,000
31. 934,650	? 934,650	? 934,700	? 935,000
32. 350,549	? 350,550	? 350,500	? 351,000
33. 744,375	? 744,380	? 744,400	? 744,000

Everyday Problem Solving

Mr. Barnes is the manager of a sneaker store. Use the table to answer the following questions.

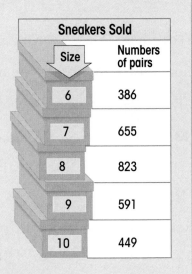

Sneakers Sold

Size	Numbers of pairs
6	386
7	655
8	823
9	591
10	449

1. Which size is sold most often? Write the number of sneakers sold in this size in words.
   size 8; eight hundred twenty-three
2. Mr. Barnes needs to order more sneakers. Orders are rounded to the nearest hundred. How many will he order in size 7? In size 9?
   size 7: 700; size 9: 600
3. Make a new chart of **Sneakers Sold**. List the **Number of Pairs** in order from least to greatest. Then write the correct sizes.
   sizes: 6, 10, 9, 7, 8
4. Which chart is easier to use, the chart on the right or the chart you made for **question 3**? Explain. Accept reasonable answers with explanations.

MATH IN YOUR LIFE
Understanding Computer Memory

Did you ever try to play a computer game but found out your computer did not have enough memory? To play games and use software, you need to know about memory.

Memory is the space something takes up on a computer or disk. Memory is measured in bytes. A *byte* is a unit of information. A *megabyte* is the same as 1,000,000 bytes. Megabyte is abbreviated as MB.

You can change megabytes to bytes by writing six zeros to the right. Then you can compare sizes of memory.

1 MB	is the same as	1,000,000 bytes
10 MB	is the same as	10,000,000 bytes
64 MB	is the same as	64,000,000 bytes

This tiny chip stores computer memory.

Look at the computers below. Decide if each computer has enough memory to fit the software.

1.
Memory: 68MB

 Software:
63,000,000 bytes

Memory: 68,000,000 bytes; yes

2.
Memory: 13MB

 Software:
30,000 bytes

Memory: 13,000,000 bytes; yes

3.
Memory: 7MB

 Software:
7,400,000 bytes

Memory: 7,000,000 bytes; no

Critical Thinking

If you are going to buy a computer, what do you need to know about memory size? What do you need to know about software size?

Critical Thinking
Students should discuss relationships between memory size and sizes of software and games they might want.

1 ▷ Review

digit

even number

number line

odd number

rename

round

whole numbers

Vocabulary Review

Complete each sentence with a word from the list.

1. Because 156 ends in a 6, it is a(n) __?__ but 157 is a(n) __?__. even number; odd number

2. The value of the __?__ 3 in 360 is 3 hundreds. digit

3. __?__ are the numbers we use to count. Whole numbers

4. You can __?__ a number to the nearest ten. round

5. You can show numbers as points on a __?__. number line

6. You can __?__ 32 as 3 tens + 2 ones. rename

7. Writing Write an example to explain each word.
Answers will vary. Check math for accuracy.

Chapter Quiz

LESSONS 1·1 and 1·2

Test Tip
To decide if a number is odd or even, just look at the last digit.

Identifying Whole, Odd, and Even Numbers
Copy the number line and answer the questions.

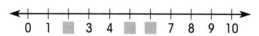

1. Find the missing numbers. 2, 5, 6

2. List only the even numbers shown above. 4, 8, 10

LESSONS 1·3 and 1·4

Test Tip
To find a place in a number, always start with the ones place.

Recognizing Place Value
Write the value of each underlined digit.

3. 3 millions
4. 5 thousands
5. 1 ten thousand

3. <u>3</u>,607,800   **4.** 1<u>5</u>,987   **5.** 2,0<u>1</u>3,000

6. 30,7<u>4</u>1 4 tens   **7.** 56,90<u>3</u> 3 ones   **8.** 2,805,<u>7</u>04
7 hundreds

LESSON 1·5

Test Tip
Commas help you group parts of a number.

Reading and Writing Whole Numbers
Write each number using digits or in words.

9. fifty-two thousand, nine hundred eleven 52,911

10. two hundred sixteen thousand, forty-five 216,045

11. 105,000,089 **12.** 34,320   **13.** 5,023
Answers on page 23.

11. one hundred five million, eighty-nine

12. thirty-four thousand, three hundred twenty

13. five thousand, twenty-three

LESSONS 1·6 and 1·7

Comparing and Ordering Whole Numbers

Compare the numbers. Use the symbol >, < , or =.

Test Tip
When comparing or ordering numbers with the same number of digits, start at the left side of each number.

14. 2,398 ▬ 2,399
 <

15. 18,007 ▬ 17,999
 >

16. 1,607,800 ▬ 1,607,800
 =

17. 7,611 ▬ 7,630
 <

Order the numbers from least to greatest.

18. 5,609 5,609
   6,905 6,905
   9,605 9,605

19. 12,386 12,386
   13,682 12,655
   12,655 13,682

20. 45,700 7,213
   7,213 38,924
   38,924 45,700

LESSON 1·8

Solving Problems By Reading a Table

Use the table to solve the problem.

Test Tip
Compare each number in the chart.

21. A hardware store sells types of nails in bins. Julie needs to refill bins that contain fewer than 1,500. Which nail types should she refill? roofing, tacking

Nail Bins	
Type	Amount
finishing	1,543
roofing	570
tacking	1,055

LESSON 1·9

Rounding Whole Numbers

Round each number to the nearest hundred.

Test Tip
Underline the rounding place, then circle the digit to the right of the rounding place.

22. 456 500

23. 1,231 1,200

24. 703,862 703,900

Round each number to the nearest thousand.

25. 456 0

26. 1,231 1,000

27. 703,862 704,000

Group Activity See the *Teacher Planning Guide* for a Scoring Rubric for this activity.

With your group, find five numbers in three different sections of a newspaper. Write the numbers and sections in a chart. How many numbers are less than 1,000? How many are greater than 1,000,000? Compare the sizes of the numbers in the different sections of the paper.

Some people fly thousands of miles each year. One Frequent Flier's club rewards you with a free ticket after flying 30,000 miles. How many miles do you need to fly to get two free tickets?

Caption You would need 60,000 miles.

Chapter 2

Adding Whole Numbers

ESL Note Have students use different forms of the same word in sample sentences.
For example: *That is a good _estimate_.* (noun form) *I can _estimate_ the answer.* (verb form)

Words to Know

add	put numbers together; find the total amount
sum	the amount obtained by adding; the total
plus	the symbol or word that means to add
horizontal	written across the page from left to right
vertical	written as one thing under the other
column	numbers placed one below the other
solve	to find the answer to a problem
regroup	to rename and then carry a tens digit to the place on the left when adding
estimate	to quickly find an answer that is close to an exact answer; to make a good guess

Words to Know Discuss possible words formed from roots in the list, such as *addition, estimation, solution*.

Logging Minutes Project

Keep a daily log of the minutes you spend doing two activities, such as homework and watching TV. One hour equals 60 minutes. Add the minutes for each activity.

DAY	HOMEWORK	TV
Monday	15	60
	20	+ 30
	+ 45	90
	80	

Learning Objectives

- Add whole numbers.
- Add larger numbers.
- Add with regrouping.
- Estimate sums.
- Solve problems using addition.
- Apply addition to counting calories.

Project Students could organize their log into a chart or add their minutes together with others in a small group. You may have them add the minutes for the entire class.

2·1 ▶ What Is Addition?

Number Sense
Compare the sum to each addend. Use manipulatives to show why the sum is always greater than any of the numbers that were added.

Addition is putting numbers together to get a total. When you **add**, the answer is called the **sum**.

5	+	3	=	8 ◀— Sum
Five	**plus**	three	equals	eight

Addition problems may be written across, or in **horizontal** form. Addition problems may also be written with one number under the other, or in **vertical** form.

▶ **EXAMPLE**

Avoiding Errors
Remind students to write numbers directly under each other in correct place-value columns.

Write three plus four equals seven, using numbers.

STEP 1 Write numbers and symbols in horizontal form. $3 + 4 = 7$

STEP 2 Write numbers and symbols in vertical form.

$$\begin{array}{r} 3 \\ + 4 \\ \hline 7 \end{array}$$

Practice A

Common Error Wrong numbers are written for words. Have students make a study chart of numbers from 0 to 20 and their word names.

Write each addition problem in horizontal form using numbers.

1. Four plus two equals six.
$4 + 2 = 6$

2. Eight plus three equals eleven.
$8 + 3 = 11$

3. Four plus five equals nine.
$4 + 5 = 9$

4. Six plus seven equals thirteen.
$6 + 7 = 13$

5. Two plus ten equals twelve.
$2 + 10 = 12$

6. Seven plus eight equals fifteen.
$7 + 8 = 15$

Practice B

7. $\begin{array}{r}6\\+4\\\hline10\end{array}$	**8.** $\begin{array}{r}5\\+8\\\hline13\end{array}$	**9.** $\begin{array}{r}6\\+2\\\hline8\end{array}$	**10.** $\begin{array}{r}1\\+5\\\hline6\end{array}$	**11.** $\begin{array}{r}7\\+8\\\hline15\end{array}$	**12.** $\begin{array}{r}9\\+9\\\hline18\end{array}$	**13.** $\begin{array}{r}8\\+4\\\hline12\end{array}$	**14.** $\begin{array}{r}1\\+9\\\hline10\end{array}$	**15.** $\begin{array}{r}8\\+1\\\hline9\end{array}$

Write each problem in words and in vertical form using numbers.

7. $6 + 4 = 10$
six plus four equals ten

8. $5 + 8 = 13$
five plus eight equals thirteen

9. $6 + 2 = 8$
six plus two equals eight

10. $1 + 5 = 6$
one plus five equals six

11. $7 + 8 = 15$
seven plus eight equals fifteen

12. $9 + 9 = 18$
nine plus nine equals eighteen

13. $8 + 4 = 12$
eight plus four equals twelve

14. $1 + 9 = 10$
one plus nine equals ten

15. $8 + 1 = 9$
eight plus one equals nine

More Practice is provided in Exercise 11 of the *Workbook*.

2·2 ▶ Basic Addition

A number line can help you add.

▶ **EXAMPLE**

Add.   5 + 3

Number Sense
Point out that on a number line, a number to the right is greater.

STEP 1 Find the first number on the number line.
Circle the number.

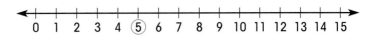

Avoiding Errors
Be sure students understand that movement to the right on a number line represents addition.

STEP 2 Move to the *right* as many spaces as the second number.
Where you stop is the sum.

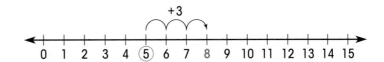

The number line shows that 5 + 3 = 8.

Practice A

Common Error Students move left on a number line to add. Point out that since the sum must be greater than either addend, the sum should be to the right of both addends.

Use a number line to add.

1. 9 + 1 10

2. 6 + 7 13

3. 4 + 9 13

4. 0 + 7 7

5. 8 + 6 14

6. 7 + 9 16

7. 9 + 8 17

8. 7 + 8 15

9. 7 + 5 12

10. 9 + 7 16

11. 3 + 0 3

12. 8 + 5 13

Practice B

Use a number line to add.

13. 6
     + 9
     ———
      15

14. 9
     + 3
     ———
      12

15. 7
     + 6
     ———
      13

16. 5
     + 0
     ———
      5

17. 4
     + 8
     ———
      12

18. 6
     + 5
     ———
      11

19. 6
     + 8
     ———
      14

20. 8
     + 8
     ———
      16

21. 9
     + 5
     ———
      14

22. 7
     + 9
     ———
      16

Extra Practice for Lesson 2.1 and 2.2 is provided on page 416.

USING YOUR CALCULATOR
Beat the Calculator

You can use a calculator to add. If you know your basic addition facts, you may be faster than a calculator.

Write one number from 0 to 9 on two sets of index cards.

Caller   Choose two index cards and call out the numbers as an addition problem.
SAY   seven plus three

Player 1   Use a calculator to find the sum.
PRESS   7 + 3 = | 10.

EQUALS KEY   PLUS KEY
Press to find   Press to add.
the sum.

Player 2   Use basic facts to find the sum.
THINK   7 + 3 = 10

Players 1 and 2   Call out the sum when you know it. The faster player gets one point.
SCORE   1 point

All   Change places and play again. When someone scores 8 points, he or she wins.

Play the Beat the Calculator game. The "caller" can choose any of these different versions of the game.

1. Choose and call out three numbers to add.

2. Write the addition problem instead of saying it aloud.

3. Give a sum and ask players to write an addition problem. Check to make sure it is correct.

2-3 ▶ Column Addition

Number Sense
Review addition strategies, such as making a five or ten, or skip counting.

Sometimes, you need to add more than two numbers. You can use **column** addition. Group the numbers two at a time. Then, find each sum.

▶ **EXAMPLE**

Add. $2 + 3 + 4 + 6$

Avoiding Errors
Have students memorize basic facts to 10. Have them quiz each other or use flash cards.

STEP 1
Write the numbers in a column.

$$\begin{array}{r} 2 \\ 3 \\ 4 \\ +\,6 \end{array}$$

STEP 2
Group the numbers two at a time. Find each sum.

$$\begin{array}{r} 2 \\ 3 \\ 4 \\ +\,6 \\ \hline 15 \end{array}$$

The sum of 2, 3, 4, and 6 is 15.

Practice

Common Error Addends are added more than once. Students can cross out addends as they find each partial sum.

Add.

1. $\begin{array}{r}3\\+\,1\\\hline 4\end{array}$	**2.** $\begin{array}{r}7\\+\,4\\\hline 11\end{array}$	**3.** $\begin{array}{r}5\\+\,3\\\hline 8\end{array}$	**4.** $\begin{array}{r}2\\+\,7\\\hline 9\end{array}$	**5.** $\begin{array}{r}8\\+\,7\\\hline 15\end{array}$
6. $\begin{array}{r}5\\+\,4\\\hline 9\end{array}$	**7.** $\begin{array}{r}4\\+\,3\\\hline 7\end{array}$	**8.** $\begin{array}{r}9\\+\,7\\\hline 16\end{array}$	**9.** $\begin{array}{r}6\\+\,6\\\hline 12\end{array}$	**10.** $\begin{array}{r}3\\+\,9\\\hline 12\end{array}$
11. $\begin{array}{r}3\\1\\+\,2\\\hline 6\end{array}$	**12.** $\begin{array}{r}6\\3\\+\,9\\\hline 18\end{array}$	**13.** $\begin{array}{r}5\\3\\+\,7\\\hline 15\end{array}$	**14.** $\begin{array}{r}2\\7\\+\,6\\\hline 15\end{array}$	**15.** $\begin{array}{r}4\\2\\+\,3\\\hline 9\end{array}$
16. $\begin{array}{r}2\\5\\2\\+\,8\\\hline 17\end{array}$	**17.** $\begin{array}{r}5\\1\\2\\+\,3\\\hline 11\end{array}$	**18.** $\begin{array}{r}4\\2\\3\\+\,2\\\hline 11\end{array}$	**19.** $\begin{array}{r}5\\3\\0\\+\,1\\\hline 9\end{array}$	**20.** $\begin{array}{r}7\\1\\9\\+\,0\\\hline 17\end{array}$

Extra Practice for this lesson is provided on page 416.

2·4 Adding Larger Numbers

Number Sense
Discuss why the sum will be greater than the greatest addend.

You can use basic facts to add larger numbers. The digits in each number need to be lined up by place value. Then, you can add the digits in each column.

▶ **EXAMPLE 1**

Add. 5,304 + 675

Avoiding Errors
Point out that zeros can be used to hold places:

        102
      + 035
        137

STEP 1 Line up the digits in each number by place value.

thousands		hundreds	tens	ones
5	,	3	0	4
		6	7	5

STEP 2 Add the digits in each column starting with the ones place.

        5,304
      +   675
        5,979

The sum of 5,304 and 675 is 5,979.

▶ **EXAMPLE 2**

Add. 5,302 + 11 + 675

STEP 1
Line up the digits in each number by place value.

        5,302
           11
      +   675

STEP 2
Add the digits in each column, starting with the ones place.

        5,302
           11
      +   675
        5,988

The sum of 5,302, 11, and 675 is 5,988.

Practice A

Common Error Digits are not lined up by place value. Have students turn lined paper sideways to help them line up the digits correctly.

Add.

1.	37 + 41 78	**2.**	95 + 3 98	**3.**	47 + 42 89	**4.**	64 + 23 87	**5.**	73 + 15 88
6.	67 + 32 99	**7.**	83 + 12 95	**8.**	120 32 + 35 187	**9.**	26 102 + 51 179	**10.**	13 43 + 102 158

Practice B

Add.

11.   200
        + 705
        905

12.   711
        + 234
        945

13.   403
        + 222
        625

14.   514
        + 123
        637

15.   3,562
        + 5,420
        8,982

16.   4,275
        + 1,022
        5,297

17.   2,318
        + 3,641
        5,959

18.   1,708
        + 7,191
        8,899

19.   1,502
          213
        +   13
        1,728

20.   7,134
           12
        + 233
        7,379

Practice C

Add. Remember to line up the digits in each number
by place value.

21. 245 + 53   298

22. 506 + 132   638

23. 173 + 22   195

24. 1,204 + 555   1,759

25. 2,381 + 5,213   7,594

26. 514 + 6,144   6,658

27. 2,053 + 123 + 321
    2,497

28. 303 + 1,002 + 4,102
    5,407

Everyday Problem Solving

Football is a popular sport. Receivers run down the field to
catch passes from the quarterback. As they run down the field
they gain yards.

1. How many yards did Cris Carter gain?
    8,367 yards

2. Which receiver gained 13,177 yards?
    Henry Ellard

3. How many total yards did Art Monk and
    Henry Ellard gain?   25,898 yards

4. Which receiver gained 3,200 more yards
    than Henry Ellard? How do you know?
    Jerry Rice; 13,177 plus 3,200 equals 16,377

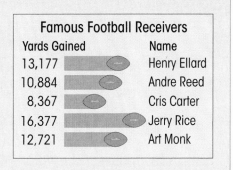

Famous Football Receivers

Yards Gained		Name
13,177		Henry Ellard
10,884		Andre Reed
8,367		Cris Carter
16,377		Jerry Rice
12,721		Art Monk

More Practice is provided in Exercise 14 of the *Workbook*.

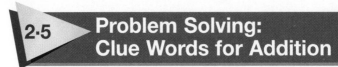

2·5   Problem Solving: Clue Words for Addition

Number Sense
Have students make up sentences using the clue words.

To find the answer to a word problem, you need to **solve** it. Clue words can help you find the answer to a word problem.

CLUE WORDS FOR ADDITION				
in all	*together*	*altogether*	*total*	*both*

► **EXAMPLE**

Jerry drove 322 miles on Monday. He drove 204 miles on Tuesday. On Wednesday, he drove 173 miles. How many miles did he drive in all?

STEP 1   **READ**   What do you need to find out?
You need to find the number of miles Jerry drove **in all**.

STEP 2   **PLAN**   What do you need to do?
The clue words **in all** tell you to **add** the miles.

Remember to line up the numbers by place value.

STEP 3   **DO**   Follow the plan.
Start adding with the number of miles Jerry drove on Monday.

Avoiding Errors
Be sure students include the mileage from each of the three days in their computation.

$$\begin{array}{r} 322 \text{ miles on Monday} \\ 204 \text{ miles on Tuesday} \\ + \ 173 \text{ miles on Wednesday} \\ \hline 699 \text{ miles in all} \end{array}$$

STEP 4   **CHECK**   Does the answer make sense?
Use a different order to add.

$$\begin{array}{r} 173 \text{ miles} \\ 204 \text{ miles} \\ + \ 322 \text{ miles} \\ \hline 699 \text{ miles} \checkmark \end{array}$$

Jerry drove 699 miles in all. Remember to write "miles" as part of your answer.

Problem Solving

READ the problem. Answer the questions under PLAN.
DO the plan to solve the problem.

1. Nick made 15 sales calls in the morning. Then he made 12 sales calls in the afternoon. How many sales calls did he make in all? 27 sales calls

   PLAN
   What are the clue words? in all
   What do the clue words tell you to do? add the calls for the morning and the afternoon

2. Dan typed 6 letters. Maria typed 12 letters. Together, how many letters did they type? 18 letters

   PLAN
   What are the clue words? together
   What do the clue words tell you to do? add the letters Dan and Maria typed

3. The first bus carried 40 students. The second bus carried 24 students. The third bus carried 33 students. How many students were carried altogether on all three buses? 97 students

   PLAN
   What are the clue words? altogether
   What do the clue words tell you to do? add the number of students on each of the 3 buses

Problem Solving Strategy

Often, problems can be solved by working backward.

Sean read 10 books during the summer. His sister Meg read some books. They read 28 books altogether. How many books did Meg read?

Fill in the blank to find how many books Meg read.

$$\begin{array}{r} 10 \\ +\ \blacksquare\ 18 \\ \hline 28 \text{ books} \end{array}$$

More Practice is provided in Exercise 15 of the *Workbook*.

2·6 Adding with One Regrouping

Sometimes when you add the digits in a column, the sum is 10 or greater than 10. You need to rename the number and **regroup**.

Add.   24 + 548

EXAMPLE

Number Sense Discuss when regrouping is needed.

No regrouping
$$
\begin{array}{r}
13 \\
+\ 16 \\
\hline
29
\end{array}
$$

Regrouping
$$
\begin{array}{r}
\overset{1}{} \\
13 \\
+\ 17 \\
\hline
30
\end{array}
$$

Avoiding Errors
Students may find it easier to add if the addend with the largest number of digits is listed first. They can reverse the addends since order does not matter.

STEP 1

Start in the ones place and add the digits.
Regroup 12 by writing a 1 over the tens place.

$$
\begin{array}{r}
\overset{1}{} \\
24 \\
+\ 548 \\
\hline
2
\end{array}
$$

STEP 2

Add all the digits in the tens place.
Add the other columns.

$$
\begin{array}{r}
\overset{1}{} \\
24 \\
+\ 548 \\
\hline
572
\end{array}
$$

The sum of 24 and 548 is 572.

Practice A

Common Error Sums are found without proper regrouping. Remind students that sums greater than 9 require regrouping.

Add.

1.
$$
\begin{array}{r}
28 \\
+\ 3 \\
\hline
31
\end{array}
$$

2.
$$
\begin{array}{r}
35 \\
+\ 57 \\
\hline
92
\end{array}
$$

3.
$$
\begin{array}{r}
67 \\
+\ 23 \\
\hline
90
\end{array}
$$

4.
$$
\begin{array}{r}
48 \\
+\ 23 \\
\hline
71
\end{array}
$$

5.
$$
\begin{array}{r}
64 \\
+\ 19 \\
\hline
83
\end{array}
$$

6.
$$
\begin{array}{r}
101 \\
+\ 359 \\
\hline
460
\end{array}
$$

7.
$$
\begin{array}{r}
19 \\
+\ 813 \\
\hline
832
\end{array}
$$

8.
$$
\begin{array}{r}
231 \\
+\ 174 \\
\hline
405
\end{array}
$$

9.
$$
\begin{array}{r}
3,814 \\
+\ 251 \\
\hline
4,065
\end{array}
$$

10.
$$
\begin{array}{r}
7,528 \\
+\ 412 \\
\hline
7,940
\end{array}
$$

11.
$$
\begin{array}{r}
3,027 \\
+\ 3,882 \\
\hline
6,909
\end{array}
$$

12.
$$
\begin{array}{r}
2,318 \\
+\ 4,931 \\
\hline
7,249
\end{array}
$$

13.
$$
\begin{array}{r}
7,902 \\
+\ 505 \\
\hline
8,407
\end{array}
$$

14.
$$
\begin{array}{r}
6,331 \\
+\ 2,559 \\
\hline
8,890
\end{array}
$$

15.
$$
\begin{array}{r}
5,448 \\
+\ 2,951 \\
\hline
8,399
\end{array}
$$

16.
$$
\begin{array}{r}
16 \\
+\ 70 \\
\hline
86
\end{array}
$$

Practice B

Add. In some problems, you will not need to regroup.

17. 48
     + 47
     95

18. 2,617
     +   782
     3,399

19.   302
     + 59
     361

20.   548
     + 245
     793

21.   237
     + 411
     648

22. 6,293
     + 2,704
     8,997

23.   567
     + 1,352
     1,919

24.   86
     + 1,422
     1,508

Practice C

Add. Remember to line up the digits in each number by place value.

25. 9,177 + 619 9,796

26. 345 + 1,723 2,068

27. 75 + 182 + 301 558

28. 536 + 202 + 141 879

29. 4,123 + 4,329 8,452

30. 11 + 362 + 215 588

31. 86 + 3,712
    3,798

32. 3,413 + 124 + 852
    4,389

33. 95 + 672 + 501
    1,268

Everyday Problem Solving

The school held elections for student government. The school newspaper printed the election results in a table.

1. How many students altogether voted in the election? Add the number of votes in the table. Tell how many *students* voted.
957 students

2. Suppose Marla had received 56 more votes. Would she win the election instead of Chris? How do you know? No; 324 + 56 = 380; 380 < 381

SCHOOL NEWS

Election Results

Candidate Names	Number of Votes
Ben James	252
Marla Carne	324
Chris Yencheck	381

More Practice is provided in Exercise 16 of the *Workbook*.

2·7 Adding with More Than One Regrouping

Sometimes when you add two numbers, you need to regroup more than once.

▶ **EXAMPLE 1**

Add. 9,548 + 837

Number Sense
Discuss what happens if regrouping is not done.

Incorrect	Correct
	¹¹
678	678
+ 155	+ 155
723	833

STEP 1 Write the numbers in vertical form.
STEP 2 Add. Regroup if needed.

```
  ¹ ¹
  9,548
+   837
 10,385
```

The sum of 9,548 and 837 is 10,385.

Sometimes, you need to regroup in every place.

▶ **EXAMPLE 2**

Add. 9,736 + 5,489

Avoiding Errors
Be sure students write the regrouped digit over the correct place-value column.

STEP 1 Write the numbers in vertical form.
STEP 2 Add. Regroup if needed.

```
  ¹ ¹¹
  9,736
+ 5,489
 15,225
```

The sum of 9,736 and 5,489 is 15,225.

Common Error Regrouping is done when it is not needed. Have students work on lined paper turned sideways to align the regrouping digits.

Practice A

Find each sum. Do not forget to regroup.

	1.	2.	3.	4.	5.
	347	618	739	389	761
	+ 173	+ 798	+ 167	+ 582	+ 839
	520	1,416	906	971	1,600

	6.	7.	8.	9.	10.
	1,243	9,595	5,744	389	4,507
	+ 4,069	+ 2,512	+ 2,856	+ 3,752	+ 1,696
	5,312	12,107	8,600	4,141	6,203

	11.	12.	13.	14.	15.
	135	7,392	5,327	821	290
	1,529	412	1,062	3,506	2,271
	+ 791	+ 1,295	+ 587	+ 181	+ 1,846
	2,455	9,099	6,976	4,508	4,407

Practice B

Add. Remember to line up the digits in each number by place value.

16. $312 + 408 + 596$ 1,316

17. $155 + 723 + 86 + 412$ 1,376

18. $96 + 816 + 540$ 1,452

19. $1,372 + 868 + 45$ 2,285

20. $92 + 107 + 253 + 34$ 486

21. $1,633 + 48 + 905 + 18$ 2,604

Practice C

Each sum below is wrong. Find the error and the correct sum.

22.
$$
\begin{array}{r}
5,628 \\
+ \ 392 \\
\hline
5,910 \\
\end{array}
$$
6,020

23.
$$
\begin{array}{r}
7,675 \\
+ \ 1,238 \\
\hline
8,803 \\
\end{array}
$$
8,913

24.
$$
\begin{array}{r}
561 \\
+ \ 899 \\
\hline
1,350 \\
\end{array}
$$
1,460

25.
$$
\begin{array}{r}
2,789 \\
+ \ 3,119 \\
\hline
5,898 \\
\end{array}
$$
5,908

26.
$$
\begin{array}{r}
3,866 \\
+ \ 342 \\
\hline
3,108 \\
\end{array}
$$
4,208

Everyday Problem Solving

Victor lives in Denver, Colorado. He plans to fly to several cities to visit relatives during the year. Use the chart to answer the questions.

1. Victor plans to travel from Denver to Indianapolis and then back home. How many miles will he travel? 2,116 miles

2. In May, Victor will travel from Denver to Dallas and back home. How many miles will he travel? 1,562 miles

Travel Miles	
Denver to:	**Distance in Miles**
New York, NY	1,771
Dallas, TX	781
San Francisco, CA	1,235
Indianapolis, IN	1,058

3. Victor travels from Denver to San Francisco and then back home in October. He makes the same trip again in December. How many miles does he travel during those two trips? 4,940 miles

2·8 Estimating Sums

You can **estimate** to quickly find an answer that is close to but not an exact answer to a problem.

▶ **EXAMPLE**

Use rounding to estimate $572 + 347 + 55$.

Number Sense
Point out to students that an estimated answer will be greater or less than the actual answer, depending on whether the numbers are rounded up or down.

STEP 1	Round each number to the nearest hundred.	$5$72 → 600
		$3$47 → 300
		$0$55 → 100

STEP 2	Add the rounded numbers.	600
		300
		+ 100
		1,000

Avoiding Errors
Remind students to round each addend to the same place. Review rounding rules from Chapter 1.

The estimated sum is 1,000.

You can use estimation to check an exact sum.
 The *exact* sum of 572 + 347 + 55 is 974.
 The *estimated* sum of 572 + 347 + 55 is 1,000.

974 is close to 1,000. The exact sum makes sense.

Practice A

Common Error Students round the exact sum for the estimate. Remind them that rounding the addends makes estimating easy.

Estimate each sum to the nearest hundred.

1.	126	2.	588	3.	291	4.	374	5.	835
	+ 452		+ 234		+ 763		+ 588		+ 656
	600		800		1,100		1,000		1,500

Practice B

Use estimation to check each exact sum. If an answer does not make sense, find the correct sum.

6.	238	7.	405	8.	782	9.	381	10.	629
	93		372		822		92		315
	+ 179		+ 267		+ 58		+ 75		+ 447
	310		1,044		1,962		448		1,391
	510		correct		1,662		548		correct

ON-THE-JOB MATH
Dietician

Selene Yang is a dietician. She works in a large health center in a city. Selene helps patients choose foods to meet requirements that their doctors have prescribed.

Selene likes her job because she enjoys talking with people and helping them develop good eating habits.

1. Selene planned the following diet for Ann. Estimate to the nearest hundred the number of calories she ate. Then, find the exact number.

BREAKFAST		LUNCH		DINNER	
	calories		calories		calories
scrambled egg	116	hot dog	160	chicken breast	155
muffin	139	apple	76	corn	164
oatmeal	130	tomato juice	38	skim milk	90
skim milk	90	cake	136	baked potato	93
				tomato salad	50

Estimate: 1,500 calories; exactly 1,437 calories

2. Ann's doctor now feels that Ann should be eating between 1,100 and 1,400 calories a day. How might Selene change the diet to meet the doctor's new requirements? Explain your thinking.

2. Answers may vary. One possible answer: She could leave out the cake for lunch to be within the doctor's limit.

Critical Thinking

Selene can show the patient a list of alternative foods that still meet the doctor's requirements. She needs to be sure that the foods will add up to the correct number of calories.

Critical Thinking

What do you think Selene should do when a patient does not like the foods she has selected? Work with a partner to decide what she should do. Share your answer with the class.

adding

column

estimate

horizontal

plus

regroup

solve

sum

vertical

Vocabulary Review

Complete each sentence with a word from the list.

1. When the sum of the digits in a column is 10 or more, you can __?__ to add. regroup

2. You can __?__ to find an answer that is close to the exact answer. estimate

3. An answer to an addition problem is the __?__. sum

4. Putting numbers together to get a total is called __?__. adding

5. You can __?__ a problem by finding the answer. solve

6. Forming a __?__ is when you place numbers below one another to make a __?__ problem. column, vertical

7. Symbols or words that tell you to add are called __?__ signs. plus

8. You can write a __?__ problem across the page. horizontal

9. **Writing** Create a crossword puzzle using the words in the list above. Be sure to give ACROSS and DOWN clues for the words.

Chapter Quiz

LESSONS 2·1 and 2·2

Test Tip
Check that the sum is greater than each addend.

Adding Whole Numbers

Use a number line to add.

1. $\begin{array}{r} 6 \\ + 7 \\ \hline 13 \end{array}$

2. $\begin{array}{r} 8 \\ + 2 \\ \hline 10 \end{array}$

3. $\begin{array}{r} 3 \\ + 4 \\ \hline 7 \end{array}$

4. $\begin{array}{r} 7 \\ + 7 \\ \hline 14 \end{array}$

5. $\begin{array}{r} 9 \\ + 6 \\ \hline 15 \end{array}$

6. $\begin{array}{r} 5 \\ + 4 \\ \hline 9 \end{array}$

7. $9 + 8$ 17

8. $6 + 5$ 11

9. $3 + 9$ 12

Test Tip
Remember to line up the digits
in each number by place value.

Adding Larger Numbers
Add.

10. 7
8
+ 1
16

11. 8
5
+ 2
15

12. 34
12
+ 13
59

13. 78
10
+ 11
99

Solving Problems by Using Addition
Solve each problem.

14. One computer file uses 12,460 bytes. Another file uses 34,500 bytes. How many bytes do they use altogether?   46,960 bytes

Test Tip
Line up the place values when
adding whole numbers. Be sure
to regroup if needed.

Adding with Regrouping
Add.

15. 67
153
+   8
228

16. 109
357
+ 1,084
1,550

17. 2,405
6,893
+   562
9,860

18. 1,834 + 755   2,589

19. 176 + 439 + 921   1,536

Test Tip
Compare the estimated sum
with the exact sum to check
your work.

Estimating Sums
Estimate each sum to the nearest hundred. Then, find the exact sum.

20. 467
+ 344
800, 811

21. 567
+ 827
1,400; 1,394

22. 1,378
+ 2,482
3,900; 3,860

Group Activity   Students' total budget should not exceed $1,950. See the *Teacher Planning Guide* for a Scoring Rubric for this activity.

With your group, make a vacation plan. Your budget includes $650 for travel, $850 for lodging, and $450 spending money. Look in brochures to decide where to go and how to manage your money. Explain.

Musical artists need to sell 500,000 copies of their album to call it a Gold Album. If your favorite tape or CD had sold 450,000 copies, how many more would need to be sold for it to reach Gold?

Caption Subtract 450,000 from 500,000; 50,000 more copies must be sold to reach Gold.

Chapter 3 Subtracting Whole Numbers

ESL Note Point out that the word *difference* may be a famliar term with another definition. Model the word in context. For example: When I subtract, I find the <u>difference</u> (between two numbers).

Words to Know

subtract	to take away one number from another; to find the amount that remains
difference	the amount obtained by subtracting; the amount by which one number is larger or smaller than another
minus	the symbol or word that means to subtract
regroup	to rename and then carry a tens digit to the place on the right when subtracting

Words to Know Compare the words *subtract*, *difference*, and *minus* with the addition words *add*, *sum*, and *plus*.

Years Ago Timeline Project

Research events that interest you. Include events in history, art, music, or science. Include events that are important to you and your family. Find out the date on which each event occurred. Make a timeline. Then find out how many "years ago" each event occurred. Subtract the year of the event from *this* year.

Learning Objectives

- Subtract whole numbers.
- Subtract larger numbers.
- Subtract with regrouping.
- Subtract from zeros.
- Solve word problems using subtraction.
- Apply subtraction to monthly expenses.

U.S. independence 224 years ago			My birth 15 years ago		This year 0 years ago
1776	**1955**		**1985**	**1990**	**2000**
	Mom was born 45 years ago			Won first place 10 years ago	

Project Have students organize the years and events they find on index cards before making a timeline. You might have students contribute to a class timeline.

More Practice is provided in Exercise 18 of the *Workbook*.

3·1 ▶ What Is Subtraction?

Number Sense
Compare the *difference* to the numbers in the problem. Use manipulatives to show why the difference is always less than the number you start with.

Subtraction is taking one number away from another number. When you **subtract**, you **minus** one number from another. The answer is called the **difference**.

$$8 \quad - \quad 3 \quad = \quad 5 \longleftarrow \text{Difference}$$
Eight minus three equals five

Horizontal means written across. Vertical means written one under the other.

Subtraction problems may be written in horizontal or vertical form, using numbers.

▶ **EXAMPLE**

Avoiding Errors
Stress that order in subtraction is very important. Point out that $9 - 5 = 4$ but $5 - 9 \neq 4$.

Write seven minus four equals three, using numbers.

STEP 1 Write numbers and symbols in horizontal form. $7 - 4 = 3$

STEP 2 Write numbers and symbols in vertical form.
$$\begin{array}{r} 7 \\ -\ 4 \\ \hline 3 \end{array}$$

Practice A

Common Error Problems are not written in correct order. Have students say the problem aloud as they write each number and symbol.

Write each subtraction problem in horizontal form using numbers.

1. Nine minus three equals six.
$9 - 3 = 6$

2. Twelve minus four equals eight.
$12 - 4 = 8$

3. Fifteen minus six equals nine.
$15 - 6 = 9$

4. Fourteen minus nine equals five.
$14 - 9 = 5$

5. Eleven minus seven equals four.
$11 - 7 = 4$

6. Twelve minus zero equals twelve.
$12 - 0 = 12$

Practice B

7. $\begin{array}{r} 9 \\ -\ 4 \\ \hline 5 \end{array}$ **8.** $\begin{array}{r} 12 \\ -\ 6 \\ \hline 6 \end{array}$ **9.** $\begin{array}{r} 17 \\ -\ 8 \\ \hline 9 \end{array}$ **10.** $\begin{array}{r} 13 \\ -\ 9 \\ \hline 4 \end{array}$ **11.** $\begin{array}{r} 11 \\ -\ 11 \\ \hline 0 \end{array}$ **12.** $\begin{array}{r} 18 \\ -\ 9 \\ \hline 9 \end{array}$ **13.** $\begin{array}{r} 10 \\ -\ 9 \\ \hline 1 \end{array}$ **14.** $\begin{array}{r} 7 \\ -\ 4 \\ \hline 3 \end{array}$ **15.** $\begin{array}{r} 16 \\ -\ 7 \\ \hline 9 \end{array}$

Write each problem in words and in vertical form using numbers.

7. $9 - 4 = 5$
nine minus four equals five

8. $12 - 6 = 6$
twelve minus six equals six

9. $17 - 8 = 9$
seventeen minus eight equals nine

10. $13 - 9 = 4$
thirteen minus nine equals four

11. $11 - 11 = 0$
eleven minus eleven equals zero

12. $18 - 9 = 9$
eighteen minus nine equals nine

13. $10 - 9 = 1$
ten minus nine equals one

14. $7 - 4 = 3$
seven minus four equals three

15. $16 - 7 = 9$
sixteen minus seven equals nine

More Practice is provided in Exercise 19 of the *Workbook*.

3·2 ▶ Basic Subtraction

A number line can help you subtract.

▶ **EXAMPLE**

Subtract.   9 − 3

Number Sense
Point out that on a number line, the number to the left is less than the number to the right.

STEP 1   Find the first number on the number line.
Circle the number.

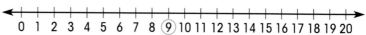

STEP 2   Move to the *left* as many spaces as the second number.
Where you stop is the difference.

Avoiding Errors
Be sure students understand that moving to the left on the number line means to subtract.

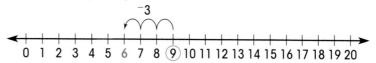

The number line shows that 9 − 3 = 6.

Practice A

Common Error   Students miscounted or moved in the wrong direction on the number line. Have students check their answers using addition.

Use a number line to subtract.

1. 8 − 2 6

2. 12 − 3 9

3. 15 − 7 8

4. 9 − 9 0

5. 14 − 9 5

6. 11 − 5 6

7. 13 − 6 7

8. 17 − 9 8

9. 7 − 4 3

10. 15 − 15 0

11. 12 − 8 4

12. 16 − 7 9

Practice B

Use a number line to subtract.

13.   7
        − 3
        ―――
          4

14.   14
        − 5
        ―――
          9

15.   12
        − 12
        ―――
          0

16.   14
        − 8
        ―――
          6

17.   11
        − 6
        ―――
          5

18.   15
        − 8
        ―――
          7

19.   13
        − 4
        ―――
          9

20.   16
        − 0
        ―――
         16

21.   18
        − 9
        ―――
          9

22.   17
        − 8
        ―――
          9

Extra Practice for Lesson 3.1 and 3.2 is provided on page 417.

Materials per group: set of index cards numbered 0–9, set of index cards numbered 0–18, calculator, pencil and paper, stopwatch (optional)

USING YOUR CALCULATOR
Beat the Calculator

You can use a calculator to subtract. If you know your basic subtraction facts, you may be faster than a calculator.

Write one number from 0 to 9 on one set of index cards and 0 to 18 on another set of index cards.

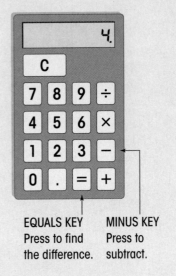

EQUALS KEY
Press to find the difference.

MINUS KEY
Press to subtract.

Caller   Choose two index cards. Put the larger number first. Call out the numbers as a subtraction problem.

            SAY   seven minus three

Player 1   Use a calculator to find the difference.

            PRESS   7 − 3 =   4

Player 2   Use basic facts to find the difference.

            THINK $7 - 3 = 4$

Players 1 and 2   Call out the difference when you know it. The faster player gets 1 point.

            SCORE   1 point

All   Change roles and play again. When someone scores 8 points, he or she wins.

Play the Beat the Calculator game. The "caller" can choose any of these different versions of the game.

1. Choose and call out two numbers to subtract. Then choose and call a third number to add.

2. Write the subtraction problem instead of saying it aloud.

3. Give a difference and ask players to write a subtraction problem. Check to make sure it is correct.

More Practice is provided in Exercise 20 of the *Workbook*.

3·3 Subtracting Larger Numbers

You can use basic facts to subtract larger numbers. Line up the digits in each number by place value.

▶ **EXAMPLE**

Subtract. 968 − 625

Number Sense
Show the importance of place value.

$$
\begin{array}{r} 777 \\ -\ 7 \\ \hline 077 \end{array}
\qquad
\begin{array}{r} 777 \\ -\ 7 \\ \hline 770 \end{array}
$$

Incorrect   Correct

STEP 1 Line up the digits in each number by place value.

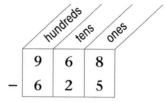

STEP 2 Subtract the numbers in each column. Always start with the ones.

$$
\begin{array}{r} 968 \\ -\ 625 \\ \hline 343 \end{array}
$$

The difference between 968 and 625 is 343.

Practice A

Avoiding Errors Have students review subtraction facts, if needed.

Subtract.

1. $\begin{array}{r} 67 \\ -41 \\ \hline 26 \end{array}$	**2.** $\begin{array}{r} 98 \\ -\ 5 \\ \hline 93 \end{array}$	**3.** $\begin{array}{r} 47 \\ -12 \\ \hline 35 \end{array}$	**4.** $\begin{array}{r} 69 \\ -24 \\ \hline 45 \end{array}$	**5.** $\begin{array}{r} 73 \\ -52 \\ \hline 21 \end{array}$
6. $\begin{array}{r} 819 \\ -705 \\ \hline 114 \end{array}$	**7.** $\begin{array}{r} 689 \\ -\ 78 \\ \hline 611 \end{array}$	**8.** $\begin{array}{r} 9{,}568 \\ -5{,}420 \\ \hline 4{,}148 \end{array}$	**9.** $\begin{array}{r} 7{,}868 \\ -3{,}641 \\ \hline 4{,}227 \end{array}$	**10.** $\begin{array}{r} 5{,}376 \\ -\ \ 26 \\ \hline 5{,}350 \end{array}$
11. $\begin{array}{r} 597 \\ -\ 44 \\ \hline 553 \end{array}$	**12.** $\begin{array}{r} 957 \\ -\ 56 \\ \hline 901 \end{array}$	**13.** $\begin{array}{r} 8{,}469 \\ -7{,}128 \\ \hline 1{,}341 \end{array}$	**14.** $\begin{array}{r} 6{,}998 \\ -\ 547 \\ \hline 6{,}451 \end{array}$	**15.** $\begin{array}{r} 9{,}557 \\ -3{,}446 \\ \hline 6{,}111 \end{array}$

Practice B

Common Error Numbers are not aligned properly by place values. Have students use lined paper turned sideways to align numbers.

Subtract. Remember to line up each digit by place value.

16. 588 − 65 523   **17.** 609 − 106 503   **18.** 673 − 51 622

19. 9,762 − 550 9,212   **20.** 5,394 − 344 5,050   **21.** 6,739 − 28 6,711

Extra Practice for this lesson is provided on page 417.

More Practice is provided in Exercise 21 of the *Workbook*.

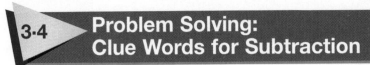

3.4 ▶ Problem Solving: Clue Words for Subtraction

 EXAMPLE

There are words in a word problem that mean subtraction.

CLUE WORDS		
how much more	*how much less*	*how many more*
left	*remain*	*difference*

Kim and Paul hiked 9 miles on Tuesday. They hiked 12 miles on Wednesday. How many more miles did they hike on Wednesday than on Tuesday?

STEP 1   READ   What do you need to find out?
You need to find how many more miles Kim and Paul hiked on Wednesday than on Tuesday.

STEP 2   PLAN   What do you need to do?
The clue words how many more tell you to subtract. Begin with the 12 miles hiked on Wednesday.

STEP 3   DO   Follow the plan.
Subtract.

$$
\begin{array}{r}
12 \text{ miles} \leftarrow \text{Wednesday} \\
- \quad 9 \text{ miles} \leftarrow \text{Tuesday} \\
\hline
3 \text{ miles} \quad more
\end{array}
$$

STEP 4   CHECK   Does the answer make sense?
Add to check.

$$
\begin{array}{r}
9 \\
+ \quad 3 \\
\hline
12 \checkmark
\end{array}
$$

Kim and Paul hiked 3 more miles on Wednesday than on Tuesday.

Problem Solving

Common Error Digits are not aligned by place value. Have students draw horizontal lines between place values.

READ the problem. Answer the questions under PLAN. Do the plan to solve the problem.

1. Nat's new car cost $8,769. Lori's car cost $6,152. How much more did Nat's car cost than Lori's? $2,617

   PLAN
   What are the clue words? how much more
   What do the clue words tell you to do? subtract to compare the cost of each car

2. Kay saved $287. Meg saved $155. How much less did Meg save than Kay? $132

   PLAN
   What are the clue words? how much less
   What do the clue words tell you to do? subtract to compare savings

3. The monthly rent for Apartment 1B is $575. The monthly rent for Apartment 1A is $561. What is the difference between the rents in Apartment 1A and 1B? $14

   PLAN
   What are the clue words? difference
   What do the clue words tell you to do? subtract to find the difference

---

Problem Solving Strategy

You can solve a problem by working backward.

> Jim had some videotapes. He sold 15 at a garage sale. He had 20 left. How many videotapes did he start with?

Add the given numbers to fill in the blank and find how many videotapes he had to start with.

$$\begin{array}{r} \blacksquare\ 35 \\ -\ 15 \\ \hline 20 \text{ videotapes} \end{array}$$

Chapter 3 • Subtracting Whole Numbers

3·5 ▶ Subtracting with One Regrouping

Number Sense
Emphasize that the bottom number is being subtracted from the top number. You regroup when a digit in the top number is smaller than the digit below it.

Avoiding Errors
Be sure that students rename the digit to the left when regrouping is needed.

Incorrect
$$\begin{array}{r} 54 \\ -\ 39 \\ \hline 25 \end{array}$$

Correct
$$\begin{array}{r} {}^{4\,14} \\ \cancel{54} \\ -\ 39 \\ \hline 15 \end{array}$$

▶ **EXAMPLE 1**

Sometimes you need to **regroup** before you can subtract the digits in a column. Look at the problem below.

$$\begin{array}{r} 34 \\ -\ 19 \end{array}$$

You cannot subtract the digits in the ones column. You need to regroup a ten for more ones.

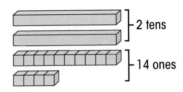

$$34 = 2\ tens + 14\ ones = 20 + 14$$

Follow the steps below to do the subtraction.

Subtract. $34 - 19$

STEP 1
Regroup to show more ones.

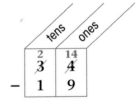

STEP 2
Subtract the digits in each place.

$$\begin{array}{r} {}^{2\ 14} \\ \cancel{34} \\ -\ 19 \\ \hline 15 \end{array}$$

The difference between 34 and 19 is 15.

You can regroup in any place. Subtract the digits in each column. If you cannot subtract in a column, then regroup.

▶ **EXAMPLE 2**

Subtract.   8,574 − 6,831

Remember to lineup the digits vertically by place value.

STEP 1
Subtract the
digits in the
ones and tens
places.

$$\begin{array}{r} 8,574 \\ -\ 6,831 \\ \hline 43 \end{array}$$

STEP 2
Regroup for more
hundreds. Subtract
the hundreds and
thousands.

$$\begin{array}{r} {\scriptstyle 7\ 15} \\ 8,\!\cancel{5}74 \\ -\ 6,831 \\ \hline 1,743 \end{array}$$

The difference between 8,574 and 6,831 is 1,743.

The answer to a subtraction problem can be checked by addition. The top number in the subtraction should be the same as the sum.

$$\begin{array}{r} 8,574 \\ -\ 6,831 \\ \hline 1,743 \end{array} \qquad \begin{array}{r} 6,831 \\ +\ 1,743 \\ \hline 8,574\ \checkmark \end{array}$$

Practice A

Common Error Regrouping is not done correctly. Have students practice regrouping 1 hundred as 10 tens, 1 ten as 10 ones.

Subtract. Remember to regroup for more ones.

1. $\begin{array}{r} 83 \\ -\ 16 \\ \hline 67 \end{array}$
2. $\begin{array}{r} 92 \\ -\ 37 \\ \hline 55 \end{array}$
3. $\begin{array}{r} 61 \\ -\ 39 \\ \hline 22 \end{array}$
4. $\begin{array}{r} 87 \\ -\ 19 \\ \hline 68 \end{array}$
5. $\begin{array}{r} 32 \\ -\ 23 \\ \hline 9 \end{array}$

6. $\begin{array}{r} 74 \\ -\ 45 \\ \hline 29 \end{array}$
7. $\begin{array}{r} 51 \\ -\ 32 \\ \hline 19 \end{array}$
8. $\begin{array}{r} 95 \\ -\ 7 \\ \hline 88 \end{array}$
9. $\begin{array}{r} 57 \\ -\ 18 \\ \hline 39 \end{array}$
10. $\begin{array}{r} 93 \\ -\ 57 \\ \hline 36 \end{array}$

Practice B

Subtract. Remember to regroup for more ones or more tens.

11. $\begin{array}{r} 315 \\ -\ 192 \\ \hline 123 \end{array}$
12. $\begin{array}{r} 325 \\ -\ 134 \\ \hline 191 \end{array}$
13. $\begin{array}{r} 634 \\ -\ 551 \\ \hline 83 \end{array}$
14. $\begin{array}{r} 611 \\ -\ 409 \\ \hline 202 \end{array}$
15. $\begin{array}{r} 823 \\ -\ 715 \\ \hline 108 \end{array}$

16. $\begin{array}{r} 531 \\ -\ 161 \\ \hline 370 \end{array}$
17. $\begin{array}{r} 655 \\ -\ 417 \\ \hline 238 \end{array}$
18. $\begin{array}{r} 438 \\ -\ 293 \\ \hline 145 \end{array}$
19. $\begin{array}{r} 492 \\ -\ 137 \\ \hline 355 \end{array}$
20. $\begin{array}{r} 856 \\ -\ 475 \\ \hline 381 \end{array}$

Practice C

Subtract. Remember to regroup whenever you need.

21. 419
− 295
___
124

22. 836
− 545
___
291

23. 5,724
− 2,800
___
2,924

24. 867
− 359
___
508

25. 518
− 247
___
271

26. 8,362
− 5,450
___
2,912

27. 9,856
− 3,009
___
6,847

28. 3,622
− 1,715
___
1,907

29. 622
− 371
___
251

30. 8,458
− 7,195
___
1,263

31. 685
− 392
___
293

32. 8,533
− 6,604
___
1,929

Practice D

Subtract. Remember to line up digits by place value.

33. 45,899 − 12,985
32,914

34. 7,538 − 4,216
3,322

35. 41,745 − 22,624
19,121

36. 35,729 − 13,563
22,166

37. 29,472 − 14,391
15,081

38. 5,529 − 2,317
3,212

Everyday Problem Solving

The Manasquan High School took a survey to find out the heights of their students. The table shows the survey results.

Manasquan High School Survey		
Heights	Number of Female Students	Number of Male Students
5 ft 1 in. to 5 ft 3 in.	165	80
5 ft 4 in. to 5 ft 6 in.	152	130
5 ft 7 in. and taller	56	180

1. How many more females than males are there between 5 ft 1 in. and 5 ft 3 in.? Subtract 165 and 80. 165 − 80 = 85

2. How many more males than females are 5 ft 7 in. or taller? 124

3. How many fewer females than males were part of the entire survey? First add all the females. Then add all the males and subtract. 17

MATH IN YOUR LIFE
Monthly Expenses

Donna earns $1,100 a month at her job. Each month, she needs to pay rent, the phone bill, and the gas and electric bill and to buy groceries. After paying her expenses, how much will Donna have left for spending money?

For Donna to find out how much she has left, she needs to follow two steps. Step 1: Add all her expenses. Step 2: Subtract the total from her monthly earnings.

JANUARY EXPENSES:

Rent	$600	Monthly earning	$1,100
Phone	$43	Total expenses	– $880
Gas and electric	$52	Spending money	$220
Groceries	+ $185		
Total	$880		

Donna has $220 left over for spending money after her expenses are paid.

Donna earns the same amount every month. Find out Donna's spending money after her expenses are paid for each month below. Follow the steps above.

Critical Thinking
Answers will vary. A few examples of answers are: entertainment, dry cleaning, laundry.

	1. February Bills:	**2.** March Bills:	**3.** April Bills:	**4.** May Bills:
Rent	$600	$600	$600	$600
Phone	$40	$58	$45	$40
Gas and electric	$50	$50	$47	$45
Groceries	$180	$193	$175	$183

Critical Thinking
What other items would you include in your monthly expenses?

1. $1,100 - 870 = 230$ 2. $1,100 - 901 = 199$
3. $1,100 - 867 = 233$ 4. $1,100 - 868 = 232$

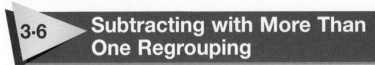

3·6 Subtracting with More Than One Regrouping

Sometimes, you will need to regroup more than once, so you can subtract.

▶ EXAMPLE 1

Number Sense
Discuss ways to check if an answer is reasonable.

$$\begin{array}{r} 312 \\ -\ 192 \\ \hline 280 \end{array} \qquad \begin{array}{r} 300 \\ -\ 200 \\ \hline 100 \end{array}$$

The difference of 280 is not close to 100 and thus unreasonable.

Subtract.   721 − 298

STEP 1
Regroup for more ones.
Subtract.

$$\begin{array}{r} {\scriptstyle 1\ 11} \\ 7\cancel{2}\cancel{1} \\ -\ 298 \\ \hline 3 \end{array}$$

STEP 2
Regroup for more tens.
Subtract.

$$\begin{array}{r} {\scriptstyle 6\ 11} \\ {\scriptstyle \cancel{7}\ 11} \\ \cancel{7}\cancel{2}\cancel{1} \\ -\ 298 \\ \hline 423 \end{array}$$

The difference between 731 and 298 is 423.

In some problems, you do not need to regroup in every place.

▶ EXAMPLE 2

Avoiding Errors
Stress the importance of crossing out the digit when it is regrouped so that it is not used to find the difference.

Subtract.   34,681 − 9,253

STEP 1
Regroup for more ones.
Subtract.

$$\begin{array}{r} {\scriptstyle 7\ 11} \\ 34,6\cancel{8}\cancel{1} \\ -\ 9,253 \\ \hline 428 \end{array}$$

STEP 2
Regroup for more thousands.
Subtract.

$$\begin{array}{r} {\scriptstyle 2\ 14\ \ \ 7\ 11} \\ \cancel{3}\cancel{4},\cancel{6}\cancel{8}\cancel{1} \\ -\ \ 9,253 \\ \hline 25,428 \end{array}$$

The difference between 34,681 and 9,253 is 25,428.

The answer to a subtraction problem can be checked by addition. The top number in the subtraction problem should be the same as the sum.

$$\begin{array}{r} 34,681 \\ -\ 9,253 \\ \hline 25,428 \end{array} \qquad \begin{array}{r} 9,253 \\ +\ 25,428 \\ \hline 34,681 \ \checkmark \end{array}$$

Practice

Common Error Incorrect regrouping is done. Encourage students to add their answer to the number above it. If the sum is not the top number, then their difference is incorrect.

Subtract. Regroup when you need to. Show all your work.

1.	523	2.	714	3.	395	4.	821	5.	871
	− 165		− 358		− 207		− 473		− 281
	358		356		188		348		590

6.	927	7.	652	8.	739	9.	9,532	10.	6,423
	− 247		− 462		− 545		− 5,860		− 3,186
	680		190		194		3,672		3,237

11.	4,726	12.	8,614	13.	5,239	14.	9,268	15.	8,451
	− 2,853		− 6,796		− 3,655		− 1,749		− 5,953
	1,873		1,818		1,584		7,519		2,498

16.	7,378	17.	7,753	18.	7,582	19.	6,492	20.	9,673
	− 4,889		− 4,846		− 5,619		− 1,657		− 5,794
	2,489		2,907		1,963		4,835		3,879

21.	23,858	22.	11,723	23.	39,535	24.	36,225	25.	73,325
	− 11,299		− 10,446		− 28,287		− 24,877		− 47,717
	35,157		1,277		11,248		11,348		25,608

Everyday Problem Solving

Aaron keeps track of his savings account in a *passbook* from the bank. The *balance* is the amount of money in the account on that date. A *withdrawal* means that money has been taken out of the account. A *deposit* means that money has been added to it. Some of the amounts are missing in his passbook.

1. What was Aaron's balance on October 20?
Subtract $40 from $632. $592

2. What was Aaron's balance on October 21? $464

3. Aaron withdrew money on October 25. He forgot the amount withdrawn. He knows that the balance is $400. How much did he take out? $64

Savings Account Passbook

DATE	WITHDRAWAL	DEPOSIT	BALANCE
10/11		$ 682	$ 682
10/15	$ 50		$ 632
10/20	$ 40		? $592
10/21	$ 128		? $464
10/25	? $64		$ 400

More Practice is provided in Exercise 24 of the *Workbook*.

3·7 ▶ Regrouping with Zeros

When you subtract from zeros, regroup more than once.

▶ EXAMPLE 1

Subtract. $8,000 - 5,624$

Number Sense
Place 7 hundreds on an overhead. Ask students to regroup to show 10 tens. Then ask them to regroup to show 10 ones.

STEP 1 Regroup for more hundreds.

$$
\begin{array}{r}
\overset{7\ \ 10}{8{,}\cancel{0}00} \\
-\ 5{,}624 \\
\end{array}
$$

STEP 2 Regroup for more tens.

$$
\begin{array}{r}
\overset{\ \ \ 9}{\overset{7\ \cancel{10}\ 10}{8{,}\cancel{0}\cancel{0}0}} \\
-\ 5{,}624 \\
\end{array}
$$

Remember:
1 thousand = 10 hundreds
1 hundred = 10 tens
1 ten = 10 ones

STEP 3 Regroup for more ones. Subtract beginning with the ones place.

$$
\begin{array}{r}
\overset{\ \ 9\ 9}{\overset{7\ \cancel{10}\cancel{10}\ 10}{8{,}\cancel{0}\cancel{0}\cancel{0}}} \\
-\ 5{,}624 \\
\hline
2{,}376 \\
\end{array}
$$

The difference between 8,000 and 5,624 is 2,376.

▶ EXAMPLE 2

Subtract. $200 - 109$

Avoiding Errors
Point out that each regrouping involves 10 of the next place.

STEP 1 Regroup in every place.

STEP 2 Subtract, beginning with the ones place.

$$
\begin{array}{r}
\overset{\ \ 9}{\overset{1\ \cancel{10}\ 10}{\cancel{2}\cancel{0}\cancel{0}}} \\
-\ 109 \\
\hline
91 \\
\end{array}
$$

The difference between 200 and 109 is 91.

Practice A

Common Error Students miscopy numbers or transpose digits. Have students read the problems out loud to each other.

Subtract. Remember to regroup for more ones, tens, and hundreds as needed.

1. $\begin{array}{r} 600 \\ -\ 276 \\ \hline 324 \end{array}$	**2.** $\begin{array}{r} 800 \\ -\ 629 \\ \hline 171 \end{array}$	**3.** $\begin{array}{r} 400 \\ -\ 103 \\ \hline 297 \end{array}$	**4.** $\begin{array}{r} 9{,}000 \\ -\ 5{,}920 \\ \hline 3{,}080 \end{array}$	**5.** $\begin{array}{r} 7{,}000 \\ -\ 2{,}045 \\ \hline 4{,}955 \end{array}$
6. $\begin{array}{r} 5{,}000 \\ -\ 2{,}974 \\ \hline 2{,}026 \end{array}$	**7.** $\begin{array}{r} 6{,}000 \\ -\ 3{,}621 \\ \hline 2{,}379 \end{array}$	**8.** $\begin{array}{r} 50{,}000 \\ -\ 39{,}764 \\ \hline 10{,}236 \end{array}$	**9.** $\begin{array}{r} 40{,}000 \\ -\ 31{,}769 \\ \hline 8{,}231 \end{array}$	**10.** $\begin{array}{r} 20{,}000 \\ -\ 12{,}584 \\ \hline 7{,}416 \end{array}$

Practice B

Subtract. Remember to regroup whenever you need to.

11. 7,040
  −   67
  6,973

12. 8,100
  − 5,089
  3,011

13. 32,007
  −   635
  31,372

14. 20,020
  − 4,883
  15,137

15. 31,005
  − 10,648
  20,357

16. 3,002
  − 1,229
  1,773

17. 17,006
  − 5,845
  11,161

18. 54,080
  − 32,320
  21,760

19. 20,060
  − 8,397
  11,663

20. 80,800
  −   937
  79,863

21. 8,090
  − 6,797
  1,293

22. 5,000
  − 234
  4,766

23. 36,700
  − 14,855
  21,845

24. 47,020
  − 9,263
  37,757

25. 30,500
  − 26,456
  4,044

Practice C

Subtract. Remember to line up the digits by place value.

26. 580 − 354 226

27. 7,000 − 4,892 2,108

28. 1,500 − 783 717

29. 43,030 − 21,724 21,306

30. 34,008 − 567 33,441

31. 2,001 − 38 1,963

32. 47,900 − 5,963 41,937

33. 7,000 − 5,555 1,445

34. 2,700 − 1,584 1,116

Everyday Problem Solving

The number of seats at baseball stadiums are not the same. Use the table to answer the questions.

1. How many fewer seats are available in Wrigley Field than in the Astrodome? 15,056 fewer

2. How many more seats are available in 3 Com Park than in Shea Stadium?
7,399 more seats

3. Suppose that an extra 20,000 seats were added to Wrigley Field. Would the stadium then have more seats than 3 Com Park?
no, 58,765 < 63,000

National League Baseball Stadiums	
Stadium	Seating Capacity
Wrigley Field	38,765
The Astrodome	53,821
Dodger Stadium	56,000
3 Com Park	63,000
Shea Stadium	55,601

3·8 ▶ Problem Solving: Add or Subtract?

Sometimes, you must decide whether to add or subtract in order to solve a word problem. The clue words can help you to decide.

▶ **EXAMPLE**

Number Sense
Tell students to think about the answer to a word problem after reading it. If a larger number is needed, then add. If a smaller number is needed, then subtract.

Avoiding Errors
Review the clue words for addition as well as for subtraction.

Marla drives to work. Driving costs her $532 a year. Joel takes the bus to work. Bus fare costs Joel $366 a year. How much less does Joel spend than Marla?

STEP 1   READ   What do you need to find?
You need to find **how much less** Joel spends.

STEP 2   PLAN   What do you need to do?
The clue words **how much less** tell you to **subtract**. Begin with $532.

STEP 3   DO   Follow the Plan.
Subtract.

$$
\begin{array}{r}
{\scriptstyle 12} \\
{\scriptstyle 4\ \not{2}\,12} \\
\$\not{5}\not{3}\not{2} \\
-\ \ 366 \\
\hline
\$166
\end{array}
$$

STEP 4   CHECK   Does your answer make sense?
Add to check.

$$
\begin{array}{r}
{\scriptstyle 1\ 1} \\
\$366 \\
+\ \ 166 \\
\hline
\$532\ \checkmark
\end{array}
$$

Joel spends $166 less than Marla.

Problem Solving

READ each problem. Answer the questions under PLAN.
DO the plan to solve the problem.

1. Diane spent $320 last week. She spent $247 this week.
How much less did she spend this week than last week? $73

PLAN

What are the clue words? how much less
What do they mean? subtract

DO

$320 − $247 = $73

2. Ramon bought 600 boxes of cards. He sold
439 boxes. How many does he have left to sell? 161 boxes

PLAN

What is the clue word? left
What do the clue words tell you to do? subtract

DO

$600 − $439 = $161

3. Barbara bought a new computer for $1,500.
She also bought a printer for $479. How much
did she pay in all? $1,979

PLAN

What are the clue words? in all
What do they mean? add

DO

$1,500 + $479 = $1,979

Problem Solving Strategy

Drawing a diagram can help you solve a problem.

Anna and Sam work at different places. They drive together.
Anna drives 35 miles to Sam's office. Then she drives on to
her office. Anna drives a total of 60 miles. How much
farther does Anna drive to get to her office? 25 miles

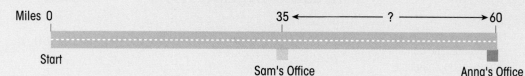

Miles 0   35 ←——— ? ———→ 60

Start   Sam's Office   Anna's Office

Look at the diagram. What operation should you use? subtraction

difference
minus
regroup
subtract

Vocabulary Review

True or false? If the statement is false, change the underlined word to make the statement true.

1. When you <u>subtract</u>, you take one number away from another number. true

2. The answer in a subtraction problem is called the <u>sum</u>. false; difference

3. Naming 1 thousand as 10 hundreds or 1 hundred as 10 tens is called <u>regrouping</u>. true

4. This is a subtraction problem: Five <u>plus</u> two equals three. false; minus

5. **Writing** Create flash cards for these words: subtraction, difference, regrouping, and minus. Write the word on one side and its definition and an example on the back.

Chapter Quiz

LESSONS 3·1 and 3·2

Test Tip
Practicing your basic facts will help you to remember them.

Subtracting Whole Numbers
Subtract.

1. 12 − 4 8
2. 9 − 5 4
3. 16 − 9 7
4. 15 − 7 8
5. 13 − 6 7
6. 13 − 7 6
7. 11 − 8 3
8. 17 − 8 9
9. 17 − 9 8
10. 12 − 7 5
11. 13 − 5 8
12. 15 − 9 6

LESSON 3·3

Test Tip
Be sure to subtract the bottom number from the top number.

Subtracting Larger Numbers
Subtract.

13.
```
   56
 − 33
   23
```

14.
```
  778
− 251
  527
```

15.
```
  160
− 140
   20
```

16.
```
  3,457
− 1,442
  2,015
```

17.
```
  8,705
− 3,402
  5,303
```

18.
```
  8,584
− 4,122
  4,462
```

Test Tip
Look for clue words to help you
to solve word problems.

Solving Problems Using Subtraction

Solve each problem. Write the clue words. Show your work.

19. The history book has 1,759 pages. Cory read 632 pages. How many pages are left to be read?
left: $1,759 - 632 = 1,127$ pages

20. Jan bought a used car. He drove the car 925 miles the first year. He drove the car 1,200 miles the second year. How many more miles did he drive the second year than the first year? how many more; $1,200 - 925 = 275$; 275 miles

21. The school bought 452 reams of paper last month. This month, 296 reams were bought. How many reams were bought in all? in all; $452 + 296 = 748$; 748 reams

Test Tip
Line up the digits in vertical
form by place value. Then
subtract.

Subtracting with Regrouping

Subtract. Show your work in vertical form.

22.
$$\begin{array}{r} 859 \\ -\ 74 \\ \hline 785 \end{array}$$

23.
$$\begin{array}{r} 856 \\ -\ 177 \\ \hline 679 \end{array}$$

24.
$$\begin{array}{r} 600 \\ -\ 361 \\ \hline 239 \end{array}$$

25. $5,000 - 205$ 4,795

26. $7,006 - 3,674$ 3,332

27. $695 - 547$ 148

28. $25,080 - 6,757$ 18,323

29. $8,706 - 983$ 7,723

30. $20,000 - 18,394$ 1,606

Group Activity
See the *Teacher Planning Guide* for a Scoring Rubric for this activity.

With your group, use the newspaper to find the price of the same model car from different places. Compare the price of each car. Then compare the options that come with each car. Discuss with your group which car you would buy and why. Record your decision and reasons on paper.

A flash of lightning is often followed by a rumble of thunder. Suppose the time between the lightning and the thunder is 2 seconds. How far away did the lightning strike? Multiply the time by the speed of sound, 1,100 feet per second.

Caption Multiply 1,100 feet per second × 2 seconds = 2,200 feet.

Chapter 4 Multiplying Whole Numbers

ESL Note Point out that the word *product* may be a famliar term with another definition. Model the word in context. For example: When I multiply, I find the <u>product</u> (between two numbers).

Words to Know

multiplication	a quick way to add; repeated addition
multiply	to add a number to itself one or more times; $2 + 2 + 2 + 2 = 8$ or $4 \times 2 = 8$
factors	the numbers that are multiplied to obtain a product
product	the final answer to a multiplication problem
partial product	number obtained by multiplying a number by only one digit of a two or more digit number

Words to Know Compare the words *multiply, multiplication*, and *product* with the words *addition, subtraction, sum*, and *difference*.

Nutrition Label Project

Collect nutrition labels from your favorite foods. These labels give the number of servings per package. They also give nutritional information for one serving. Find out how many Calories there are in an entire package. Multiply the number of servings by the Calories. Share your information with the class.

Project Have students calculate amounts of other nutrients in a package, such as total fat grams, carbohydrates, etc. Students could draw new labels that show nutritional information for entire packages of food. Save labels for use in the project in Chapter 11.

Learning Objectives

- Multiply whole numbers.
- Multiply larger numbers.
- Multiply with regrouping.
- Multiply numbers by 10, 100, 1,000.
- Multiply by numbers that contain zero.
- Solve word problems using multiplication.
- Solve two-part word problems.
- Apply multiplication to counting items for inventory.

More Practice is provided in Exercise 26 of the *Workbook*.

4-1 **What Is Multiplication?**

Number Sense
Show that repeated addition is multiplication.

▶ **EXAMPLE 1**

For whole numbers, the product is greater than either factor unless 1 is a factor. Use this fact to check your product.

▶ **EXAMPLE 2**

Avoiding Errors
Explain how *horizon* can be used to help remember horizontal.

Multiplication is the process of adding the same number one or more times.

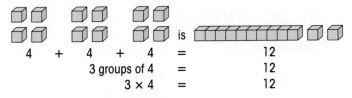

4	+ 4	+ 4	=	12
	3 groups of 4		=	12
	3×4		=	12

The numbers you **multiply** are called **factors**. The answer is called the **product**.

Horizontal			or	Vertical
3 × 4 = 12				3 ← Factor
↑ ↑ ↑				× 4 ← Factor
Factor × Factor = Product				12 ← Product

The order in multiplication does not matter.

$$3 \times 4 = 4 \times 3 = 12$$

Common Error Factors and products are transposed. Have students read problems aloud. As they read the numbers, they should write them down.

Practice A

Write each addition problem as a multiplication problem.

1. $8 + 8 = 16$
$2 \times 8 = 16$

2. $9 + 9 + 9 = 27$
$3 \times 9 = 27$

3. $3 + 3 + 3 + 3 + 3 = 15$
$5 \times 3 = 15$

4. $6 + 6 + 6 + 6 = 24$
$4 \times 6 = 24$

5. $8 + 8 + 8 + 8 + 8 + 8 + 8 = 56$
$7 \times 8 = 56$

6. $3 + 3 + 3 + 3 = 12$
$4 \times 3 = 12$

Practice B

7. 6	**8.** 9	**9.** 8	**10.** 4
× 7	× 2	× 3	× 5
42	18	24	20

Write each problem in vertical form using numbers.

7. $6 \times 7 = 42$ **8.** $9 \times 2 = 18$ **9.** $8 \times 3 = 24$ **10.** $4 \times 5 = 20$

Extra Practice for this lesson is provided on page 418.

More Practice is provided in Exercise 27 of the *Workbook*.

4·2 ▶ Basic Multiplication

You can use the multiplication table below to learn the basic multiplication facts.

▶ **EXAMPLE**

Number Sense
Review rows and columns on a table. Have students point to numbers as their positions in the table are read aloud.

Avoiding Errors
Sometimes, students do not find the right box for the product. Have them use their fingers to find where the row and column meet.

Use the table to multiply. 5×6

STEP 1 Find the row that begins with the number 5.

STEP 2 Find the column that begins with the number 6.

STEP 3 The product is where the row meets the column.

x	0	1	2	3	4	5	6	7	8	9
0	0	0	0	0	0	0	0	0	0	0
1	0	1	2	3	4	5	6	7	8	9
2	0	2	4	6	8	10	12	14	16	18
3	0	3	6	9	12	15	18	21	24	27
4	0	4	8	12	16	20	24	28	32	36
5	0	5	10	15	20	25	30	35	40	45
6	0	6	12	18	24	30	36	42	48	54
7	0	7	14	21	28	35	42	49	56	63
8	0	8	16	24	32	40	48	56	64	72
9	0	9	18	27	36	45	54	63	72	81

Factor

Factor → 5

Product

The multiplication table shows that $5 \times 6 = 30$.

Common Error If students get the wrong answer, they may not know it. Have them double check their answers by switching the factors in the rows and columns.

Practice

Use the multiplication table to multiply.

1. 6×5 30

2. 8×7 56

3. 3×9 27

4. 6×7 42

5. 4×3 12

6. 7×7 49

7. 8×9 72

8. 5×4 20

9. 7×3 21

10. 4×7 28

11. 2×9 18

12. 8×8 64

13. 4×5 20

14. 3×6 18

15. 7×8 56

16. 9×4 36

Extra Practice for this lesson is provided on page 418.

4-3 ▶ Multiplying Larger Numbers

You will use basic multiplication facts to multiply larger numbers. When you multiply larger numbers, multiply each place.

▶ **EXAMPLE 1**

Remember: $3 \times 2 = 6$
$3 \times 7 = 21$

Number Sense
Write on the board:

$$\begin{array}{r} 243 \\ \times\ \ 2 \\ \hline 486 \end{array} \qquad \begin{array}{r} 243 \\ \times\ \ 20 \\ \hline 4{,}860 \end{array}$$

Discuss the relationship between the factors 2 and 20 and the products 486 and 4,860.

Multiply. 3×72

STEP 1 Multiply the digit in the *ones* place by 3.

$$\begin{array}{r} 72 \\ \times\ \ 3 \\ \hline 6 \end{array} \ (3 \times 2)$$

STEP 2 Multiply the digit in the *tens* place by 3.

$$\begin{array}{r} 72 \\ \times\ \ 3 \\ \hline 216 \end{array} \ (3 \times 7)$$

The product of 3 and 72 is 216.

When you multiply by a two-digit number, there will be two **partial products**. Add the partial products to get the product.

▶ **EXAMPLE 2**

Remember: $3 \times 2 = 6$
$3 \times 7 = 21$
$2 \times 2 = 4$
$2 \times 7 = 14$

Multiply. 72×23

STEP 1 Multiply 72 by the *ones* place in the bottom number.

$$\begin{array}{r} 72 \\ \times\ \ 23 \\ \hline 216 \end{array} \ \text{First partial product}$$

STEP 2 Multiply 72 by the *tens* place in the bottom number. Write a zero in the *ones* place. Write the second partial product to the left of the zero.

$$\begin{array}{r} 72 \\ \times\ \ 23 \\ \hline 216 \\ 1\ 440 \end{array} \ \text{Second partial product}$$

Avoiding Errors
Have students use zeros as placeholders so that the partial products are aligned properly.

STEP 3 Add the partial products.

$$\begin{array}{r} 72 \\ \times\ \ 23 \\ \hline 216 \\ +\ 1\ 440 \\ \hline 1{,}656 \end{array} \ \text{Product}$$

The product of 72 and 23 is 1,656.

You can use the same steps to multiply by larger numbers.

▶ **EXAMPLE 3**

Multiply. 512×431

STEP 1 Multiply 512 by the *ones* place in the bottom number.

$$
\begin{array}{r}
512 \\
\times\ 431 \\
\hline
512
\end{array}
$$
512 First partial product

STEP 2 Multiply 512 by the *tens* place in the bottom number. Write a zero in the *ones* place. Write the second partial product to the left of the zero.

$$
\begin{array}{r}
512 \\
\times\ 431 \\
\hline
512 \\
15\ 360
\end{array}
$$
15 360 Second partial product

STEP 3 Multiply 512 by the *hundreds* place in the bottom number. Write zeros in the *tens* and *ones* places. Write the third partial product to the left of the zeros.

$$
\begin{array}{r}
512 \\
\times\ 431 \\
\hline
512 \\
15\ 360 \\
204\ 800
\end{array}
$$
204 800 Third partial product

STEP 4 Add the partial products.

$$
\begin{array}{r}
512 \\
\times\ 431 \\
\hline
512 \\
15\ 360 \\
+\ 204\ 800 \\
\hline
220{,}672
\end{array}
$$
220,672 Product

The product of 512 and 431 is 220,672.

Practice A

Common Error Partial products are not aligned properly. Have students take lined paper and turn it sideways.

Multiply.

1.
$$
\begin{array}{r}
43 \\
\times\ 3 \\
\hline
129
\end{array}
$$

2.
$$
\begin{array}{r}
81 \\
\times\ 8 \\
\hline
648
\end{array}
$$

3.
$$
\begin{array}{r}
52 \\
\times\ 4 \\
\hline
208
\end{array}
$$

4.
$$
\begin{array}{r}
64 \\
\times\ 2 \\
\hline
128
\end{array}
$$

5.
$$
\begin{array}{r}
93 \\
\times\ 3 \\
\hline
279
\end{array}
$$

6.
$$
\begin{array}{r}
124 \\
\times\ 2 \\
\hline
248
\end{array}
$$

7.
$$
\begin{array}{r}
532 \\
\times\ 3 \\
\hline
1{,}596
\end{array}
$$

8.
$$
\begin{array}{r}
312 \\
\times\ 4 \\
\hline
1{,}248
\end{array}
$$

9.
$$
\begin{array}{r}
644 \\
\times\ 2 \\
\hline
1{,}288
\end{array}
$$

10.
$$
\begin{array}{r}
421 \\
\times\ 4 \\
\hline
1{,}684
\end{array}
$$

Practice B

Multiply.

11. $\begin{array}{r} 63 \\ \times\ 23 \\ \hline 1{,}449 \end{array}$	**12.** $\begin{array}{r} 87 \\ \times\ 11 \\ \hline 957 \end{array}$	**13.** $\begin{array}{r} 71 \\ \times\ 24 \\ \hline 1{,}704 \end{array}$	**14.** $\begin{array}{r} 52 \\ \times\ 42 \\ \hline 2{,}184 \end{array}$	**15.** $\begin{array}{r} 93 \\ \times\ 31 \\ \hline 2{,}883 \end{array}$
16. $\begin{array}{r} 811 \\ \times\ 22 \\ \hline 17{,}842 \end{array}$	**17.** $\begin{array}{r} 812 \\ \times\ 34 \\ \hline 27{,}608 \end{array}$	**18.** $\begin{array}{r} 623 \\ \times\ 31 \\ \hline 19{,}313 \end{array}$	**19.** $\begin{array}{r} 833 \\ \times\ 32 \\ \hline 26{,}656 \end{array}$	**20.** $\begin{array}{r} 231 \\ \times\ 12 \\ \hline 2{,}772 \end{array}$
21. $\begin{array}{r} 943 \\ \times\ 121 \\ \hline 114{,}103 \end{array}$	**22.** $\begin{array}{r} 731 \\ \times\ 332 \\ \hline 242{,}692 \end{array}$	**23.** $\begin{array}{r} 711 \\ \times\ 421 \\ \hline 299{,}331 \end{array}$	**24.** $\begin{array}{r} 523 \\ \times\ 123 \\ \hline 64{,}329 \end{array}$	**25.** $\begin{array}{r} 431 \\ \times\ 213 \\ \hline 91{,}803 \end{array}$

Practice C

Multiply. Remember to line up the digits in each number by place value.

26. 82×4 328

27. 63×3 189

28. 73×23 1,679

29. 97×11 1,067

30. 413×22 9,086

31. 623×313 194,999

32. 523×32 16,736

33. 712×431 306,872

34. 432×123 53,136

Everyday Problem Solving

This sign shows the ticket prices at Wild Rides park.

1. How much does it cost for 5 rides on the Corkscrew? Multiply 5 by the cost of the Corkscrew. $20

2. How much does it cost for 3 rides on the Starclimber? $9

3. Ayanna plans to take 5 rides on the Corkscrew. She plans to take 3 rides on the Water Slide. Why should Ayanna buy an all-day pass? $5 \times \$4 = \$20$; $3 \times \$2 = \$6$; Ayanna should buy an all-day pass because $21 is less than $20 plus $6.

Wild Rides Ticket Prices	
All Day Pass (unlimited rides)	$21
Corkscrew (each ride)	$ 4
Starclimber (each ride)	$ 3
Water Slide (each ride)	$ 2

Extra Practice for this lesson is provided on page 418.

You can use a calculator to check your multiplication.

Ann wrote this multiplication on the board. Is it correct?

$$\begin{array}{r} 321 \\ \times\ \ 34 \\ \hline 1\ 284 \\ 9\ 530 \\ \hline 10{,}814 \end{array}$$

1 284 ← Partial product
9 530 ← Partial product
10,814 ← Product

To find an error, first check the partial products.

PRESS [3] [2] [1] [×] [4] [=] | 1284. |

PRESS [3] [2] [1] [×] [3] [0] [=] | 9630. |

> **Calculator Tip**
> Remember that the 3 in 34 means 3 tens. Multiply 321 by 30 for the second partial product.

Ann made a mistake in the second partial product. Now, add the correct partial products found on the calculator.

PRESS [1] [2] [8] [4] [+] [9] [6] [3] [0] [=] | 10914. |

Is 10,914 the correct product? Multiply 321 × 34 on the calculator to check.

PRESS [3] [2] [1] [×] [3] [4] [=] | 10914. |

10,914 is the correct product!

Use your calculator to check each problem. If there is an error, write the problem correctly. There may be an error in the addition.

1.	2.	3.	4.
$\begin{array}{r} 502 \\ \times\ \ 41 \\ \hline 502 \\ +\ 2\ 008 \\ \hline 2{,}510 \end{array}$	$\begin{array}{r} 423 \\ \times\ \ 32 \\ \hline 846 \\ +\ 12\ 590 \\ \hline 13{,}036 \end{array}$	$\begin{array}{r} 1312 \\ \times\ \ 33 \\ \hline 3\ 936 \\ +\ 39\ 360 \\ \hline 43{,}296 \\ \text{correct} \end{array}$	$\begin{array}{r} 611 \\ \times\ \ 78 \\ \hline 4\ 888 \\ +\ 42\ 770 \\ \hline 46{,}558 \end{array}$

1. 502
× 41
502
√20 080
20,582

2. 423
× 32
846
√12 690
13,536

3. 611
× 78
4 888
42 770
√47,658

More Practice is provided in Exercise 29 of the *Workbook*.

4-4 ▶ Multiplying with One Regrouping

Number Sense
Have students quickly review the basic multiplication facts for 5, 6, 7, 8, and 9.

Sometimes, a multiplication fact has a product greater than 9. For example,

$$6 \times 8 = 48$$

You can rename 48 as 4 tens + 8 ones.

▶ **EXAMPLE**

Multiply. 576×8

Remember:
$8 \times 6 = 48$
$8 \times 7 = 56$
$8 \times 5 = 40$

STEP 1 Multiply the digit in the *ones* place by 8. Rename 48: 4 *tens* + 8 *ones*. Regroup. Put the 8 in the *ones* place. Put the 4 above the *tens* place.

$$\begin{array}{r} {}^{4} \\ 576 \\ \times8 \\ \hline 8 \end{array}$$

Avoiding Errors
Encourage students to write the number they are carrying directly over the digit they will add it to.

STEP 2 Multiply the digit in the *tens* place by 8. Add 56 + 4. Put the 0 in the *tens* place. Put a 6 above the *hundreds* place.

$$\begin{array}{r} {}^{6\,4} \\ 576 \\ \times8 \\ \hline 08 \end{array}$$

STEP 3 Multiply the digit in the *hundreds* place by 8. Add 40 + 6. Put the sum in the *hundreds* and *thousands* places.

$$\begin{array}{r} {}^{6\,4} \\ 576 \\ \times8 \\ \hline 4{,}608 \end{array}$$

The product of 576 and 8 is 4,608.

Common Error Students forget where to put the digit they are regrouping. It goes above the factor *to the left of* the one they just multiplied by.

Practice A

Multiply. Be sure to show your work as done above.

1. $\begin{array}{r} 79 \\ \times\ 4 \\ \hline 316 \end{array}$	**2.** $\begin{array}{r} 83 \\ \times\ 6 \\ \hline 498 \end{array}$	**3.** $\begin{array}{r} 16 \\ \times\ 9 \\ \hline 144 \end{array}$	**4.** $\begin{array}{r} 283 \\ \times\ \ 2 \\ \hline 566 \end{array}$	**5.** $\begin{array}{r} 154 \\ \times\ \ 8 \\ \hline 1{,}232 \end{array}$
6. $\begin{array}{r} 673 \\ \times\ \ 5 \\ \hline 3{,}365 \end{array}$	**7.** $\begin{array}{r} 88 \\ \times\ 6 \\ \hline 528 \end{array}$	**8.** $\begin{array}{r} 538 \\ \times\ \ 4 \\ \hline 2{,}152 \end{array}$	**9.** $\begin{array}{r} 47 \\ \times\ 7 \\ \hline 329 \end{array}$	**10.** $\begin{array}{r} 148 \\ \times\ \ 9 \\ \hline 1{,}332 \end{array}$

Practice B

Multiply. Regroup if you need to.

11.   794
    × 6
    4,764

12.   521
    × 4
    2,084

13.   681
    × 7
    4,767

14.   345
    × 5
    1,725

15.   411
    × 8
    3,288

16.   26
    × 15
    390

17.   38
    × 41
    1,558

18.   73
    × 12
    876

19.   42
    × 28
    1,176

20.   63
    × 53
    3,339

21.   531
    × 24
    12,744

22.   812
    × 42
    34,104

23.   189
    × 17
    3,213

24.   926
    × 51
    47,226

25.   423
    × 232
    98,136

Practice C

Multiply. Remember to line up the digits in each number by place value.

26. 56×8 448

27. 538×4 2,152

28. $4,508 \times 4$ 18,032

29. 681×17 11,577

30. 862×81 69,822

31. $7,641 \times 9$ 68,769

32. 775×11 8,525

33. 321×34 10,914

34. 423×215 90,945

Everyday Problem Solving

Joe has $500 to spend on a camping vacation. He saw this ad in a magazine.

1. How much will 4 days of fishing cost? $100

2. How much will 4 nights at a cabin cost? $260

3. How much spending money will Joe have left over if he chooses the package deal? $201

Camping and Fishing
Adventures

1-Day Fishing $25
1-Night Cabin Stay $65

4-Day Package Deal includes
Fishing and
Cabin Stay $299

Extra Practice for this lesson is provided on page 418.

4·5 ▶ Multiplying with More Than One Regrouping

Sometimes, there will be regrouping in more than one partial product. Then, there will be more than one row of regrouping digits.

▶ **EXAMPLE**

Number Sense
Place the following examples on the board.

```
   326          326
×    4       ×   20
 1,304        6,520
```

Explain how these two problems can help us understand that
$326 \times 24 = 7,824$.

Avoiding Errors
Be sure students understand that they must carry the tens digit or hundreds digit or both when regrouping is required.

Multiply. 536×96

STEP 1 Multiply 536 by the ones digit in the bottom number. Regroup as needed.

```
    2 3
   536
×   96
  3216  (536 × 6 ones)
```

STEP 2 Cross out the regrouping digits 23. Then, multiply 536 by the *tens* digit in the bottom number. Regroup as needed.

```
   3 5
   2̶3̶
   536
×   96
  3216
 48240  (536 × 9 tens)
```

STEP 3 Add the partial products.

```
   3 5
   2̶3̶
   536
×   96
  3 216
+ 48 240
 51,456
```

The product of 536 and 96 is 51,456.

Common Error Students fail to place the zero in the second partial product. Remind students why the zero is needed by reviewing the example given in the Number Sense above.

Practice A

Multiply. Remember to show the regrouping digits.

1.	**2.**	**3.**	**4.**
374	598	676	485
× 42	× 63	× 28	× 56
15,708	37,674	18,928	27,160

Practice B

Multiply. Regroup if you need to.

5. 38
    × 41
    1,558

6. 74
    × 36
    2,664

7. 87
    × 54
    4,698

8. 45
    × 28
    1,260

9. 412
    × 39
    16,068

10. 943
    × 12
    11,316

11. 593
    × 76
    45,068

12. 925
    × 88
    81,400

Practice C

Multiply. Remember to line up the digits in each number by place value.

13. $6,934 × 46$ 318,964

14. $67 × 1,345$ 90,115

15. $2,985 × 72$ 214,920

16. $196 × 519$ 101,724

17. $397 × 436$ 173,092

18. $3,278 × 125$ 409,750

Everyday Problem Solving

This table shows last month's driving records for four of Ace Trucking's drivers.

1. Complete the table by finding the distance each driver traveled. To find the distance, multiply speed by hours driven. (distance = speed × hours)

Ace Trucking			
Driver	Average Speed	Hours Driven	Total Distance
Ann	58 mph	75 hrs	?
Don	61 mph	58 hrs	?
Carlos	65 mph	97 hrs	?
Bianco	55 mph	83 hrs	?

2. Which driver traveled the greatest distance? Carlos

3. Which driver traveled the least distance? Don

Distance traveled: Ann – 4,350 miles; Don – 3,538 miles; Carlos – 6,305 miles; Bianco – 4,565 miles

4. What is the total number of miles the drivers traveled altogether? 18,758 miles

More Practice is provided in Exercise 31 of the *Workbook*.

4·6 Problem Solving: Clue Words for Multiplication

Clue words can help you find the answer to a word problem.

CLUE WORDS FOR MULTIPLICATION			
of	*for 6 hours*	*in 5 months*	*at $13 each*

▶ EXAMPLE

Number Sense
Relate the clue words to repeated addition, then to multiplication. 3 meals a day *for* 5 days means
1 day = 3 meals
2 days = 3 + 3 meals
3 days = 3 + 3 + 3 meals, etc. So 3 meals for 5 days = 15 meals.

Avoiding Errors
If some numbers in a problem are written using numerals and some are written in words, students may overlook those written as words. Stress the importance of reading the entire problem before deciding on a plan.

Norm packs 16 boxes in 1 hour. How many boxes does Norm pack in 7 hours?

STEP 1 READ   What do you need to find out?
You need to find how many boxes Norm can pack in 7 hours.

STEP 2 PLAN   What do you need to do?
The clue words **in 7 hours** tell you to multiply the number of boxes by the number of hours.

STEP 3 DO   Follow the plan.
Multiply 16 boxes by 7 hours.

$$\begin{array}{r} 16 \\ \times\ \ 7 \\ \hline 112 \text{ boxes} \end{array}$$

STEP 4 CHECK   Does your answer make sense?
Draw a picture.

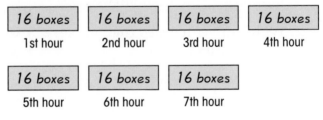

Add to find the total number of boxes.

$$16 + 16 + 16 + 16 + 16 + 16 + 16 = 112 \checkmark$$

Norm packs 112 boxes in 7 hours.

Problem Solving

READ the problem. Answer the questions under PLAN.
DO the plan to solve the problem.

1. Mr. Ryan ordered 23 computers at $1,295 each. How much did he spend for computers? $29,785

   PLAN
   What are the clue words? at $1,295 each
   What do the clue words tell you to do?
   Multiply the number of computers by the price of each computer.

2. The drama club put on a play. A total of 1,246 tickets were sold. Tickets were sold for $8. How much money did the drama club make from ticket sales? $9,968

   PLAN
   What are the clue words? for $8
   What do the clue words tell you to do?
   Multiply the number of tickets by the price of each ticket.

3. A program was on sale at the play. The program cost $2. They sold 987 programs. How much money was made from selling programs? $1,974

   PLAN
   There are no clue words. Each program costs the same, so you can multiply the cost of the program by the number of programs sold.

Problem Solving Strategy

Often, problems can be solved by working backward.

Diane packs 9 boxes in 1 hour. She packs 63 boxes. How many hours does she work?

Fill in the blank to find the number of hours.

$$\begin{array}{r} 9 \\ \times \ \blacksquare \ 7 \\ \hline 63 \end{array}$$

More Practice is provided in Exercise 32 of the *Workbook*.

4·7 Multiplying Whole Numbers by 10, 100, 1,000

Number Sense

Verify the shortcut method introduced in the lesson. Have students do the math the long way for the following:

```
    45        45          45
  × 10     × 100     × 1,000
    00        00          00
  450       000         000
  450      4 500        000
         4,500         0000
                     4 500
                    45,000
```

You can use what you know to learn a shortcut for multiplying whole numbers by 10, by 100, or by 1,000.

$$45 \times 10 \quad = \quad 450$$
1 zero   1 zero

$$45 \times 100 \quad = \quad 4,500$$
2 zeros   2 zeros

$$45 \times 1,000 \quad = \quad 45,000$$
3 zeros   3 zeros

To multiply by 10, by 100, or by 1,000, place as many zeros as you need to the right of the number.

▶ EXAMPLE

Avoiding Errors
Make sure students count the zeros on the factor that is a power of 10. For example, in 400×10, be sure they count the zeros in 10, not 400.

Multiply. 617×100

2 zeros
617×100

STEP 1 Count the zeros in 100.

STEP 2 Write 617. Then place two zeros to the right of the number.

$617 \times 100 = 61,700$

The product of 617 and 100 is 61,700.

Practice A

Multiply.

Common Error Students put commas in the wrong places. Make sure they know to count three places to the left for every comma.

1. 37×10
370

2. 86×100
8,600

3. $59 \times 1,000$
59,000

4. 29×100
2,900

5. $5,279 \times 100$
527,900

6. 305×10
3,050

7. 596×100
59,600

8. $421 \times 1,000$
421,000

9. $1,401 \times 1,000$
1,401,000

10. $152 \times 1,000$
152,000

11. $3,715 \times 1,000$
3,715,000

12. $700 \times 1,000$
700,000

ON-THE-JOB MATH
Inventory Clerk

Inventory is the number of goods a store has on the shelves and in the warehouse. Bob is an inventory clerk. He counts the items in a store.

Bob travels to different stores everyday. He likes his job, because he meets new people and travels.

Bob uses multiplication to make his job easier.

Bob has to fill in the table below. To begin, he has to find out how many Tasty Oats boxes there are in the store. He counts 16 cartons on the shelves. He knows there are 12 boxes in each carton. So, Bob multiplies.

Bob takes inventory on all kinds of food. Here, Bob is taking an inventory of avocados.

$$
\begin{array}{r}
16 \text{ cartons} \\
\times\ 12 \text{ boxes per carton} \\
\hline
32 \\
+\ 160 \\
\hline
192 \text{ total boxes of cereal}
\end{array}
$$

Copy the table below. Multiply to find the total number of boxes of each cereal. The first is done for you.

Name of Cereal	Number of Cartons	Boxes per Carton	Total Boxes of Cereal
Tasty Oats	16	12	192
Sweet Puffs	72	24	?
Healthy Grains	126	16	?
Berry Bran	35	48	?

Sweet Puffs – 1,728; Healthy Grains – 2,016; Berry Bran – 1,680

Critical Thinking

While taking inventory of pasta, Bob found 5 cartons of spaghetti. They do not say how many boxes are in one carton. What should he do to finish the inventory?

Critical Thinking

Students should suggest that Bob find out how many boxes are in a carton. He could open a carton and count, or find a shipping receipt. Bob should not "make up" numbers.

More Practice is provided in Exercise 33 of the *Workbook*.

4·8 Multiplying by Numbers That Contain Zero

Number Sense
Estimate to determine the size of the product.

$$
\begin{array}{r}
927 \rightarrow \quad 900 \\
\times\, 305 \rightarrow \times \quad 300 \\
\hline
270{,}000
\end{array}
$$

When you multiply any number by zero, the product is zero.

$$3 \times 0 = 0 \quad 978 \times 0 = 0 \quad 1{,}349{,}576 \times 0 = 0$$

You can multiply by a number that contains a zero. The partial product for the zero digit is zero.

▶ **EXAMPLE**

Multiply. 927×305

Avoiding Errors
Be sure to have students put zeros down for the partial product of the zero digit so that the other partial products will line up correctly.

STEP 1 Multiply by the digit in the *ones* place.

$$
\begin{array}{r}
{\scriptstyle 1\ 3} \\
927 \\
\times\ 305 \\
\hline
4635
\end{array}
$$

STEP 2 Multiply by the digit in the *tens* place. Place a zero in the *ones* place as a placeholder. Then, write a zero for each digit in 927.

$$
\begin{array}{r}
{\scriptstyle 1\ 3} \\
927 \\
\times\ 305 \\
\hline
4635 \\
0000
\end{array}
$$

STEP 3 Multiply by digit in the *hundreds* place. Add the partial products.

$$
\begin{array}{r}
{\scriptstyle 2} \\
{\scriptstyle \not{1}\,\not{3}} \\
927 \\
\times\quad 305 \\
\hline
4\ 635 \\
0\ 000 \\
+\ 278\ 100 \\
\hline
282{,}735
\end{array}
$$

The product of 927 and 305 is 282,735.

Practice A

Multiply. Remember to write all the partial products.

1.	498	**2.**	926	**3.**	793	**4.**	387	**5.**	580
	$\times\ 70$		$\times\ 306$		$\times\ 50$		$\times\ 942$		$\times\ 409$
	34,860		283,356		39,650		364,554		237,220
6.	635	**7.**	829	**8.**	625	**9.**	360	**10.**	290
	$\times\ 804$		$\times\ 470$		$\times\ 709$		$\times\ 549$		$\times\ 378$
	510,540		389,630		443,125		197,640		109,620
11.	537	**12.**	805	**13.**	970	**14.**	761	**15.**	807
	$\times\ 420$		$\times\ 609$		$\times\ 260$		$\times\ 801$		$\times\ 903$
	225,540		490,245		252,200		609,561		728,721

Practice B

Multiply. Remember to line up the digits in each number by place value.

16. 623×506 315,238   **17.** 535×402 215,070   **18.** 645×204 131,580

19. 29×609 17,661   **20.** 753×250 188,250   **21.** 850×503 427,550

Everyday Problem Solving

Jon wants to buy a car. He compares the distance each car can travel on a full tank of gas.

1. Find the distance Car A can travel on a full tank of gas. Multiply 35 mpg by 20 gallons. 700 miles

Car	Miles per Gallon	Size of Tank
Car A	35 mpg	20 gallons
Car B	23 mpg	25 gallons
Car C	28 mpg	22 gallons

2. Which car can travel 616 miles on a full tank of gas? Car C

3. Which car can travel the farthest on a full tank of gas? Car A

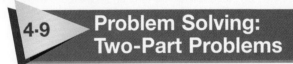

4-9 Problem Solving: Two-Part Problems

EXAMPLE

Number Sense
Review the four-step plan for problem solving. Have students write the answers to each step so that they can refer to them as they go along.

Avoiding Errors
Have students underline the key phrases in a word problem.

Matt bought <u>6 basketballs</u> for his team. <u>Each basketball costs $15.</u> He bought <u>a basketball hoop for $32.</u> How much did Matt spend altogether?

Some problems have a hidden question. You need to answer this question before you can solve the problem.

Matt bought 6 basketballs for his team. Each basketball costs $15. He bought a basketball hoop for $32. How much did Matt spend altogether?

STEP 1   READ   What do you need to find out?
You need to find how much Matt spent altogether. But first, you need to find how much 6 basketballs cost.

STEP 2   PLAN   What do you need to do?
How much do 6 basketballs cost?
Multiply to find out.
How much did Matt spend altogether?
Add to find out.

STEP 3   DO   Follow the plan.

Multiply

$$\begin{array}{r} \overset{3}{\$15} \\ \times\ 6 \\ \hline \$90 \text{ for basketballs} \end{array}$$

Add

$$\begin{array}{r} \$90 \text{ basketballs} \\ +\ \$32 \text{ basketball hoop} \\ \hline \$122 \text{ altogether} \end{array}$$

STEP 4   CHECK   Does your answer make sense?
Use a calculator to check.

PRESS [1] [5] [×] [6] [=] | 90.

Do not clear the display.

PRESS [+] [3] [2] [=] | 122. ✓

Matt spent $122 for the 6 basketballs and a basketball hoop.

Common Error Students answer in the wrong units. Have students
check to make sure their answer fits the question in Step 1, "What do
you need to find out?"

Problem Solving

READ the problem. Answer the questions under PLAN.
DO the plan to solve the problem.

1. Zachary saves $25 a week. There are 52 weeks in a
    year. How much will he save in 5 years?

    PLAN   DO
    How much will Zachary save in 1 year? $1,300 $52 × 25 = $1,300
    How much will he save in 5 years? $6,500 $1,300 × 5 = $6,500

2. A round-trip plane ticket to Jamaica costs $529. Four
    people can stay for 1 week in a hotel room for $1,248.
    How much will a Jamaican vacation for 4 people cost?

    PLAN   DO
    What is the cost of 4 plane tickets? $2,116 $529 × 4 = $2,116
    What is the cost for 4 people to stay in a hotel $2,116 + $1, 248 = $3,364
    for a week? $1,248
    What is the cost of the whole trip? $3,364

3. A new theater opened in town. The first night it
    sold 1,245 season tickets at $125 each. It also
    sold $2,452 worth of snacks. How much money did
    the theater make its first night?

    PLAN $155,625   DO
    How much money was made from ticket sales?   1,245 × $125 = $155,625
    How much was made from snack sales? $2,452 $155,625 + $2,452 =
    How much money was made altogether? $158,077 $158,077

Problem Solving Strategy

Sometimes, you need to make a table to
solve a word problem.

Cashier Name	AL		
BILLS	COUNT		AMOUNT

Al counts the money in a cash register.
There are 56 ten-dollar bills, 78 five-dollar
bills, and 123 one-dollar bills. How much
money is there altogether? $1,073

BILLS		COUNT		AMOUNT
$10	X	56	=	$560
$ 5	X	78	=	$390
$ 1	X	123	=	$123

factor

multiplication

multiply

partial product

product

Vocabulary Review

Tell whether *true* or *false*. If it is false, replace the underlined word to make it true.

1. Two numbers that are multiplied together are called <u>factors</u>. true

2. Multiplication is a faster way to do repeated <u>addition</u>. true

3. The answer to a multiplication problem is called the <u>product</u>. true

4. Some <u>addition</u> problems have a partial product.
   false; multiplication

5. **Writing** Explain partial products to a classmate. Draw a sample problem and label it.

Chapter Quiz

LESSONS 4·1 to 4·3

Test Tip
When multiplying larger numbers, remember to move the second partial product over one place value to the left.

Multiplying Numbers

Multiply.

1. 6×7 42

2. 9×2 18

3. 8×5 40

4. 3×5 15

5. 3×8 24

6. 7×8 56

7. 4×9 36

8. 9×8 72

9. 6×4 24

10.
$$\begin{array}{r} 22 \\ \times\ 13 \\ \hline 286 \end{array}$$

11.
$$\begin{array}{r} 35 \\ \times\ 11 \\ \hline 385 \end{array}$$

12.
$$\begin{array}{r} 31 \\ \times\ 15 \\ \hline 465 \end{array}$$

13.
$$\begin{array}{r} 423 \\ \times\ \ 22 \\ \hline 9,306 \end{array}$$

14.
$$\begin{array}{r} 123 \\ \times\ \ 12 \\ \hline 1,476 \end{array}$$

15.
$$\begin{array}{r} 3,112 \\ \times\ \ \ \ 21 \\ \hline 65,352 \end{array}$$

LESSONS 4·4 and 4·5

Test Tip
When the product of digits in a column is 10 or more, you must regroup.

Multiplying with Regrouping
Multiply.

16.   65
     $\times$ 3
      195

17.   78
     $\times$ 5
      390

18.   87
     $\times$ 32
     2,784

19.   87
     $\times$ 64
     5,568

20.   345
     $\times$ 21
     7,245

21.   3,463
     $\times$ 164
     567,932

LESSONS 4·6 and 4·9

Test Tip
Read problems carefully and look for clue words that tell you what to do.

Solving Problems Using Multiplication
Solve each problem.

22. Suni bought 4 pairs of shoes on sale for $28 each. How much did Suni spend on shoes? $112

23. Chester earned $345 dollars a month for 3 months during the summer delivering papers. During the rest of the year, he earns $1,350 on his paper route. How much does he earn in 1 year delivering newspapers? $2,385

LESSONS 4·7 and 4·8

Test Tip
When multiplying by multiples of 10, add the number of zeros in the multiple of 10 factor to the other factor to find the product.

Multiplying with Zeros

24.   40
     $\times$ 3
      120

25.   102
     $\times$ 6
      612

26.   307
     $\times$ 46
     14,122

27. 231×10 2,310

28. $4,060 \times 100$ 406,000

29. $6,023 \times 1,000$ 6,023,000

30. 500×20 10,000

Group Activity See the *Teacher Planning Guide* for a Scoring Rubric for this activity.
Work with your group to plan a four-city concert tour for a musical group. You must decide how much to charge for tickets. Use an almanac to find the number of seats in four stadiums. Estimate how much money will be made if all the tickets are sold for each performance.

Students should multiply ticket prices by number of seats in stadium.

The rain forest is a place where many types of trees and plants grow. People are cutting trees down without replanting so animals are losing their homes. Right now, 20 acres of trees are being cut down every 5 minutes. How many acres are being cut every 1 minute? Divide.

Caption 4 acres per minute

Chapter 5 / Dividing Whole Numbers

ESL Note Ask students to show the class how division is written and displayed in the country of origin.

Words to Know

division	the process of finding out how many times one number contains another
dividend	the number to be divided
divisor	the number to divide by
quotient	the number obtained by dividing one number into another; the answer in a division problem
remainder	the number left over in a division problem

Words to Know Give the students the division problem $9 \div 5 = 1$ R4. Then, have them label each number using a term from the Words to Know.

Life Journal Project

In your journal, list all the ways you think that you use division in your life. Check the list each day and see if you can add more ideas. For each idea, write a word problem that shows how division is used in your life. Go through the chapter for ideas.

Project Answers will vary. An example is one whole amount of money set aside for 4 weeks of food. You want to spend equal amounts of money for each week. How much can you spend for each of the 4 weeks? Other topics include: split the miles to drive for a trip between days or people; split bills equally among people who ate the meal; equally sharing food; gym teams; and mpg for cars. Key word for word problems is *equal amounts*.

Learning Objectives

- Divide whole numbers.
- Divide larger numbers.
- Divide and get remainders.
- Check division problems.
- Use estimating to choose the best answer.
- Solve word problems using division.
- Solve word problems using any operation
- Apply division to find miles per gallon.

More Practice is provided in Exercise 35 of the *Workbook*.

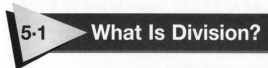

5·1   What Is Division?

Division is the process of finding how many times one number contains another.

► EXAMPLE 1

Number Sense
Place 6 chips on the overhead projector. Arrange the chips to make 2 groups with 3 to show
$2 \times 3 = 6$ and $6 \div 3 = 2$.

What is 12 divided by 3?

12

3   3   3   3   ]— 4 groups of 3
$12 \div 3 = 4$

The number to be divided is the **dividend**. The number to divide by is the **divisor**. The answer is the **quotient**. Division problems can be written in two different forms.

► EXAMPLE 2

Avoiding Errors
Point out that in Example 2 the quotient is 4 ones. You place the 4 over the ones place in the dividend.

$$ 12 \quad \div \quad 3 \quad = 4 \quad \text{or} \quad 3\overline{)12} $$

4 ← Quotient

Dividend   Divisor   Quotient   Divisor   Dividend

Common Error Divisors and dividends are exchanged in writing division problems: $12\overline{)3}$ is written instead of $3\overline{)12}$. Stress the difference between the dividend and divisor in a division problem.

Practice A

Use numbers to write each division problem in both forms.

1. Eight divided by two equals four.

$8 \div 2 = 4$ or $2\overline{)8}^{\,4}$

2. Sixteen divided by eight equals two.

$16 \div 8 = 2$ or $8\overline{)16}^{\,2}$

3. Six divided by three equals two.

$6 \div 3 = 2$ or $3\overline{)6}^{\,2}$

4. Thirty-two divided by four equals eight.

$32 \div 4 = 8$ or $4\overline{)32}^{\,8}$

Practice B

Use numbers to write each problem in the other form.

5. $8 \div 2 = 4$

$2\overline{)8}^{\,4}$

6. $28 \div 4 = 7$

$4\overline{)28}^{\,7}$

7. $18 \div 6 = 3$

$6\overline{)18}^{\,3}$

8. $48 \div 6 = 8$

$6\overline{)48}^{\,8}$

Extra Practice for this lesson is provided on pages 419–420.

More Practice is provided in Exercise 36 of the *Workbook*.

5·2 Basic Division

You can use the multiplication table below to learn the basic division facts.

EXAMPLE

Number Sense
Review use of the multiplication table. Have students find factors and products in the table. Explain that division is the opposite operation of multiplication.

Avoiding Errors
To avoid incorrrect quotients, show students how to check their answers on the multiplication table. For $12 \div 3 = 4$, show that $4 \times 3 = 12$.

What is $12 \div 3$?

STEP 1 Find the row that begins with the number 3.

STEP 2 Move across that row until you find the number 12.

STEP 3 Move up that column until you come to the top. The number in that box is the quotient.

$12 \div 3 = 4$

x	0	1	2	3	4	5	6	7	8	9
0	0	0	0	0	0	0	0	0	0	0
1	0	1	2	3	4	5	6	7	8	9
2	0	2	4	6	8	10	12	14	16	18
3	0	3	6	9	12	15	18	21	24	27
4	0	4	8	12	16	20	24	28	32	36
5	0	5	10	15	20	25	30	35	40	45
6	0	6	12	18	24	30	36	42	48	54
7	0	7	14	21	28	35	42	49	56	63
8	0	8	16	24	32	40	48	56	64	72
9	0	9	18	27	36	45	54	63	72	81

The multiplication table shows that $12 \div 3 = 4$.

Practice

Common Error Students lose their place in the table. Have students use a small ruler to help them read across the row and up the column.

Use the multiplication table to find the quotient.

1. $6 \div 2$
3

2. $9 \div 3$
3

3. $15 \div 5$
3

4. $32 \div 4$
8

5. $49 \div 7$
7

6. $3\overline{)6}$
2

7. $9\overline{)18}$
2

8. $7\overline{)21}$
3

9. $6\overline{)30}$
5

10. $8\overline{)40}$
5

11. $27 \div 3$
9

12. $36 \div 9$
4

13. $9\overline{)81}$
9

14. $7\overline{)63}$
9

15. $4\overline{)16}$
4

Extra Practice for this lesson is provided on pages 419–420.

5-3 ▶ Dividing with Remainders

The **remainder** is the number left over in division. What happens when you divide 7 by 2?

3 groups of 2 ⎡   2   2   2   1 ← Remainder 1

$$7 \div 2 = 3\,R1$$

There are 3 equal groups with 1 left over. The remainder is 1. You can write:

$$7 \div 2 = 3\ R\ 1$$

Remainder 1

You can do division in another way.

▶ **EXAMPLE**

dividend ÷ divisor
↓
divisor)dividend

What is $17 \div 3$?

STEP 1 Rewrite the division problem.   3)17

STEP 2 Think:
"What times 3 is closest to 17 without going over?"

$3 \times 4 = 12$
$3 \times 5 = 15$
$3 \times 6 = 18$

Write 5 above the *ones* place.

5 ← Five 3s in 17
3)17

STEP 3 Multiply 5×3. Write the product underneath 17.

5
3)17
15

STEP 4 Subtract.
The remainder is 2.
Check that the remainder is less than the divisor. $2 < 3$ ✓
Stop dividing.

5
3)17
-15
2 ← Remainder

STEP 5 Write the quotient with the remainder in the answer.

$5\ R2$
3)17

17 divided by 3 is 5 R 2.

Common Error The remainder is greater than the divisor. Explain that the quotient should be made a larger number so that the remainder becomes less than the divisor.

Divide. If the remainder is 0, do not write it.

1. $7 \div 3$ 2 R1

2. $6\overline{)9}$ 1 R3

3. $5 \div 2$ 2 R1

4. $3\overline{)9}$ 3

5. $9 \div 4$ 2 R1

6. $5\overline{)8}$ 1 R3

7. $5\overline{)7}$ 1 R2

8. $4\overline{)5}$ 1 R1

9. $8 \div 3$ 2 R2

10. $2\overline{)9}$ 4 R1

11. $5 \div 3$ 1 R2

12. $5\overline{)9}$ 1 R4

13. $7 \div 4$ 1 R3

14. $5\overline{)6}$ 1 R1

15. $9 \div 8$ 1 R1

16. $8 \div 2$ 4

Practice B

Divide. Remember to write the quotient above the ones place.

17. $11 \div 5$ 2 R1

18. $3\overline{)10}$ 3 R1

19. $20 \div 4$ 5

20. $6\overline{)25}$ 4 R1

21. $27 \div 8$ 3 R3

22. $8\overline{)50}$ 6 R2

23. $51 \div 6$ 8 R3

24. $4\overline{)36}$ 9

25. $37 \div 5$ 7 R2

26. $9\overline{)30}$ 3 R3

27. $3\overline{)25}$ 8 R1

28. $8\overline{)20}$ 2 R4

29. $42 \div 8$ 5 R2

30. $5\overline{)18}$ 3 R3

31. $8\overline{)18}$ 2 R2

32. $7\overline{)57}$ 8 R1

33. $48 \div 9$ 5 R3

34. $7\overline{)55}$ 7 R6

35. $4\overline{)39}$ 9 R3

36. $6\overline{)52}$ 8 R4

Everyday Problem Solving

Grant School has a small lunchroom. Six students can sit at each table. Find out how many tables you need for each group of students.

1. There are 30 students. How many tables do they need? Divide 30 by 6.
5 tables

2. There are 28 students. Will they need 4 tables or 5 tables. Why?
5 tables; so every student can sit at a table

3. There are 38 students. How many tables do they need? 7 tables

4. Are 9 tables enough for 53 students? Why? Yes; 9 tables can seat 54 people.

Extra Practice for this lesson is provided on pages 419–420.

Chapter 5 • Dividing Whole Numbers   89

5·4 Dividing Larger Numbers

You can divide larger numbers one step at a time. To begin, you need to decide where to place the first digit in the quotient.

▶ **EXAMPLE**

Remember:
$4 \times 1 = 4$
$4 \times 2 = 8$
$4 \times 3 = 12$
$4 \times 4 = 16$

Number Sense
Placement of the first digit in the quotient is important.

$$\frac{3}{5)15} \qquad \frac{30}{5)150}$$

Avoiding Errors
Have students write $\times$ as the first digit of a quotient when the division cannot be done in that place.

$$\frac{\times 30}{5)150}$$

This will help align the remaining digits.

Divide. $137 \div 4$

STEP 1 Rewrite the division problem. $4)\overline{137}$

STEP 2 Does 4 divide into 1? No.
Does 4 divide into 13? Yes.
Think: "What times 4 is
closest to 13 without
going over?" $3 \times 4 = 12$

$$\frac{3}{4)\overline{137}}$$

Write 3 above the *tens* place.

STEP 3 Multiply 3×4. Write the product
underneath 13. Then, subtract.

Bring down the next digit.

$$\begin{array}{r} 3 \\ 4)\overline{137} \\ -12\downarrow \\ \hline 17 \end{array}$$

STEP 4 Does 4 divide into 17? Yes.
Think: "What times 4 is
closest to 17 without going
over?" $4 \times 4 = 16$

$$\begin{array}{r} 34 \\ 4)\overline{137} \\ -12\downarrow \\ \hline 17 \end{array}$$

Write 4 above the *ones* place.

STEP 5 Multiply 4×4.
Write the product underneath 17.
Then, subtract.

Check that the remainder is less
than the divisor. $1 < 4$ ✓
Stop dividing.

$$\begin{array}{r} 34 \\ 4)\overline{137} \\ -12\downarrow \\ \hline 17 \\ -16 \\ \hline 1 \end{array} \leftarrow \text{Remainder}$$

STEP 6 Write the quotient with the
remainder in the answer.

$$\frac{34 \text{ R}1}{4)\overline{137}}$$

The quotient of $137 \div 4$ is 34 R1.

Practice A

Common Error Quotients stop after the first digit. Focus student attention on the steps involved in dividing. Remind students to bring down the next digit of the dividend and continue dividing until *all* digits of the dividend have been brought down.

Divide.

1. $4\overline{)84}$ 21

2. $2\overline{)86}$ 43

3. $3\overline{)39}$ 13

4. $2\overline{)27}$ 13 R1

5. $3\overline{)68}$ 22 R2

6. $4\overline{)96}$ 24

7. $8\overline{)96}$ 12

8. $3\overline{)84}$ 28

9. $6\overline{)89}$ 14 R5

10. $5\overline{)90}$ 18

11. $7\overline{)84}$ 12

12. $6\overline{)96}$ 16

Practice B

Divide.

13. $4\overline{)848}$ 212

14. $5\overline{)560}$ 112

15. $4\overline{)328}$ 82

16. $3\overline{)278}$ 92 R2

17. $3\overline{)282}$ 94

18. $3\overline{)298}$ 99 R1

19. $3\overline{)685}$ 228 R1

20. $6\overline{)869}$ 144 R5

21. $7\overline{)364}$ 52

22. $6\overline{)438}$ 73

23. $5\overline{)675}$ 135

24. $8\overline{)369}$ 46 R1

Everyday Problem Solving

The Food Co-op helps people in need. Henry is dividing the available food among 9 families. Each family will receive the same amount of food.

1. How many cans of tomato soup will each family receive? Divide 46 by 9. How many cans are left over? 5 cans; 1 can left over

2. How many muffins will each family receive? How many are left over?
6 muffins; 6 muffins left over

3. Can Henry give 4 boxes of pasta to each family? Why or why not? No. He can give 3 boxes to each family. There will be 7 boxes left over.

4. Henry wants to give each family 3 jars of spaghetti sauce. How many more jars of sauce does he need? 9 jars of sauce

Available Food
46 cans of tomato soup
100 eggs
60 muffins
34 boxes of pasta
18 jars of spaghetti sauce

5·5 ▶ Checking Division

Number Sense
Review fact families.

$7 \times 6 = 42 \qquad 42 \div 6 = 7$
$6 \times 7 = 42 \qquad 42 \div 7 = 6$

You can check the answer to a division problem. Multiply the quotient by the divisor. If this product equals the dividend, your answer is correct.

▶ **EXAMPLE 1**

Check the division problem.
$$\begin{array}{r}143\\2\overline{)286}\end{array}$$

143 ← Quotient
2)286 ← Dividend
↑
Divisor

STEP 1 Multiply the quotient by the divisor.

STEP 2 Does the product equal the dividend?

$$\begin{array}{r}143 \leftarrow \text{Quotient}\\\times\quad 2 \leftarrow \text{Divisor}\\\hline 286 \leftarrow \text{Product} \checkmark\end{array}$$

The division is correct.

You can also check a division problem that has a remainder.

▶ **EXAMPLE 2**

Check the division problem.
$$\begin{array}{r}143 \text{ R1}\\2\overline{)287}\end{array}$$

Remainder
↓
143 R1
2)287 ← Dividend

STEP 1 Multiply the quotient by the divisor.

STEP 2 Add the remainder.

STEP 3 Does the sum equal the dividend?

$$\begin{array}{r}143 \leftarrow \text{Quotient}\\\times\quad 2 \leftarrow \text{Divisor}\\\hline 286\\+\quad 1 \leftarrow \text{Remainder}\\\hline 287 \leftarrow \text{Sum} \checkmark\end{array}$$

Avoiding Errors
Remind students to add the remainder to the product of the divisor and quotient.

The division is correct.

Common Error Remainders are not added to the product of the divisor and quotient. Stress the importance of not ignoring the remainder in a division problem.

Practice

Check each answer. If the answer is incorrect, show the correct division.

1. $\begin{array}{r}104\\5\overline{)520}\end{array}$
$5 \times 104 = 520$
correct

2. $\begin{array}{r}430\\2\overline{)862}\end{array}$
$2 \times 430 = 860$
incorrect; 431

3. $\begin{array}{r}112 \text{ R3}\\4\overline{)450}\end{array}$
$4 \times 112 + 3 = 451$
incorrect; 112 R 2

4. $\begin{array}{r}21 \text{ R4}\\6\overline{)130}\end{array}$
$6 \times 21 + 4 = 130$
correct

5. $\begin{array}{r}53 \text{ R5}\\7\overline{)376}\end{array}$
$7 \times 53 + 5 = 376$
correct

6. $\begin{array}{r}127\\3\overline{)372}\end{array}$
$3 \times 127 = 381$
incorrect; 124

7. $\begin{array}{r}241\\4\overline{)964}\end{array}$
$4 \times 241 = 964$
correct

8. $\begin{array}{r}32 \text{ R1}\\7\overline{)225}\end{array}$
$7 \times 32 + 1 = 225$
correct

Extra Practice for this lesson is provided on page 420.

USING YOUR CALCULATOR
Checking Division

Remember the two ways to write division problems.

$$\begin{array}{r} 12 \\ 3\overline{)36} \end{array} \leftarrow \text{Quotient}$$

Divisor   Dividend

$$36 \div 3 = 12$$

Dividend Divisor Quotient

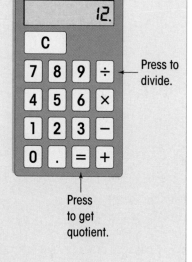

Press to divide.

Press to get quotient.

You can use a calculator to check your division. It does not matter the way the division is written.

Enter the dividend into the calculator.

PRESS 3 6 ÷ | 36.

Enter the divisor into the calculator.

PRESS 3 | 3.

Press the equal sign to get the quotient. See if the quotient on the calculator is the same as the one that was given to you.

PRESS = | 12.

The quotients are the same. So your division is correct.

Calculator Tip
Remember to enter the dividend into the calculator first.

Use a calculator to check each quotient. Tell if the quotient is correct or incorrect.

1. $\begin{array}{r} 10 \\ 7\overline{)77} \end{array}$
incorrect

2. $\begin{array}{r} 13 \\ 6\overline{)78} \end{array}$
correct

3. $\begin{array}{r} 899 \\ 11\overline{)8,899} \end{array}$
incorrect

4. $\begin{array}{r} 208 \\ 31\overline{)6,448} \end{array}$
correct

5. $\begin{array}{r} 501 \\ 50\overline{)25,050} \end{array}$
correct

6. $\begin{array}{r} 12 \\ 50\overline{)550} \end{array}$
incorrect

7. $\begin{array}{r} 28 \\ 15\overline{)430} \end{array}$
incorrect

8. $\begin{array}{r} 18 \\ 20\overline{)375} \end{array}$
incorrect

9. $612 \div 18 = 34$
correct

10. $200 \div 12 = 17$
incorrect

11. $165 \div 11 = 15$
correct

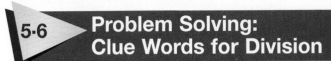

5·6 Problem Solving: Clue Words for Division

Clue words can help you find the answer to a word problem.

CLUE WORDS FOR DIVISION
how much did each
how many times
into how many

> **EXAMPLE**

Number Sense
Review the meaning of division. Emphasize that when you divide, you break up a set into equal parts. When you divide, you find how many parts you have or how many there are in each part.

Avoiding Errors
Be sure students bring down the digit 2 in 192 for the division. They can draw an arrow or an X under the 2 to show that it was brought down.

Marilyn sold 8 identical sets of dishes. Her sales totaled $192. How much did each set of dishes cost?

STEP 1   READ   What do you need to find out?
You need to find how much each set cost.

STEP 2   PLAN   What do you need to do?
The clue words, how much did each, tell you to divide. Divide the total sales by the number of sets Marilyn sold.

STEP 3   DO   Follow the plan.
Divide the total sales of $192 by the 8 sets.

$$
\begin{array}{r}
\$24 \\
8)\overline{\$192} \\
-16\!\downarrow \\
\hline
32 \\
-32 \\
\hline
0
\end{array}
$$

STEP 4   CHECK   Does the answer make sense?
Multiply to check the division.

$$
\begin{array}{r}
\$24 \\
\times\quad 8 \\
\hline
\$192 \checkmark
\end{array}
$$

Each set of dishes costs $24.

Common Error Incorrect clue words are chosen. Review with students the meaning of division as forming equal groups. To form equal groups, words like *each* are frequently used.

READ the problem. Answer the questions under PLAN.
DO the plan to solve the problem.

1. Juanita ran 1,600 yards. This was 4 laps around the track. How many yards is each lap? 400 yards

   PLAN   **DO** 1600 ÷ 4 = 400
   What are the clue words? How many yards is each
   What do the clue words tell you to do? Divide total yards by the number of laps.

2. On Stan's last sales trip, he drove 2,464 miles. The trip lasted 14 days. How many miles did Stan drive each day? 176 miles

   PLAN   **DO** 2464 ÷ 14 = 176
   What are the clue words? How many miles each day
   What do the clue words tell you to do? Divide total miles by the number of days.

3. Kim paid $153 for 9 books. Each book costs the same amount. How much did each book cost? $17

   PLAN   **DO** 153 ÷ 9 = 17
   What are the clue words? How much did each
   What do the clue words tell you to do? Divide total cost by the number of books.

Problem Solving Strategy

Sometimes, a formula can help you solve a problem. These formulas tell you to divide to find time or rate.

1. Bruce drove 165 miles at 55 miles per hour. How long did the trip take? Divide the 165-mile distance by the rate of 55 miles per hour. 3 hours

$$Time = \frac{Distance}{Rate}$$

$$Rate = \frac{Distance}{Time}$$

2. Cathy drove 96 miles in 2 hours. How fast was she driving? Divide the distance by the time. 48 miles per hour

5·7 Dividing by Numbers with More Than One Digit

Number Sense
Review the steps for dividing.

$$6\overline{)588}$$ 98

You can use what you know about dividing by a small number to divide by a larger number. Use the steps below to divide by a two-digit number.

▶ **EXAMPLE**

Divide. $26\overline{)598}$

STEP 1 Does 26 divide into 5? No.
Does 26 divide into 59? Yes.
Estimate:"About how many times does 25 go into 60?"
2×25 is close to 60.

Write 2 over the *tens* place.

$$26\overline{)598}$$ 2

STEP 2 Multiply 2×26.
Check that the product is not larger than the number above.
$52 < 59$ ✓

$$26\overline{)598}$$ 2
52

STEP 3 Subtract.
Bring down the next digit.

$$26\overline{)598}$$ 2
$- 52↓$
78

Avoiding Errors
Be sure students follow the order of divide, multiply, subtract, and bring down.

STEP 4 Does 26 divide into 78? Yes.
Estimate:"About how many times does 25 go into 78?"
3×25 is close to 78.

Write 3 over the *ones* place.

$$26\overline{)598}$$ 23
$- 52↓$
78

STEP 5 Multiply 3×26.
Then, subtract.

Check that the remainder is less than the divisor.
Stop dividing.

$$26\overline{)598}$$ 23
$- 52↓$
78
$- 78$
0 ✓

The quotient of $598 \div 26$ is 23.

Practice

Divide.

1. 22)594   27   **2.** 17)829   48 R13   **3.** 32)992   31   **4.** 40)487   12 R7

5. 52)578   11 R6   **6.** 32)585   18 R9   **7.** 15)960   64   **8.** 41)697   17

9. 92)828   9   **10.** 37)899   24 R11   **11.** 55)605   11   **12.** 64)870   13 R38

13. 67)938   14   **14.** 42)882   21   **15.** 23)851   37   **16.** 25)355   14 R5

17. 70)840   12   **18.** 35)705   20 R5   **19.** 11)475   43 R2   **20.** 19)589   31

21. 42)890   21 R8   **22.** 28)589   21 R1   **23.** 51)919   18 R1   **24.** 15)497   33 R2

Everyday Problem Solving

As a salesperson, Mr. Roberts travels each week to visit clients. His last four trips are shown on the map to the right.

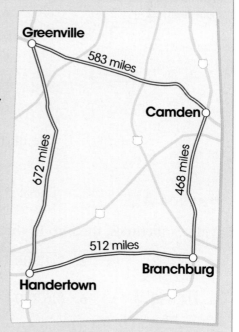

1. Mr. Roberts averaged a speed of 48 miles per hour from Handertown to Greenville. How many hours did the trip take? Divide the distance by the average speed.
14 hours

2. The trip from Greenville to Camden took 11 hours. What was Mr. Roberts' average speed? Divide the distance by the number of hours.   53 miles per hour

3. Mr. Roberts averaged 55 miles per hour for the trips from Camden to Branchburg and from Branchburg to Handertown. Without dividing, tell which trip took more time. Explain your answer.   trip from Branchburg to Handertown, because 512 miles is farther than 468 miles

5-8 ▶ Zeros in the Quotient

Sometimes, you will need to place a zero in the quotient.

▶ **EXAMPLE**

Divide. $6\overline{)4,836}$

Number Sense
Introduce zero as a placeholder in the quotient.

$$\frac{101}{2\overline{)202}} \qquad \frac{202}{3\overline{)606}}$$

Avoiding Errors
Point out that the zero is a placeholder. Without the zero, the quotient would be too small.

Do not stop dividing until each digit in the dividend has been brought down.

STEP 1 Does 6 divide into 4? No.
Does 6 divide into 48? Yes.
Think: ? × 6 = 48. Write 8
above the *hundreds* place.

Multiply 6 × 8.
Then subtract. Bring down the 3.

$$\begin{array}{r} 8 \\ 6\overline{)4,836} \\ -\ 4\ 8\downarrow \\ \hline 03 \end{array}$$

STEP 2 Does 6 divide into 3? No.
Write 0 above the *tens* place.
Bring down the 6.

$$\begin{array}{r} 80 \\ 6\overline{)4,836} \\ -\ 4\ 8\downarrow\downarrow \\ \hline 036 \end{array}$$

STEP 3 Does 6 divide into 36? Yes.
Think: ? × 6 = 36.
Write 6 above the ones place.

Multiply 6 × 6.
Then, subtract.

$$\begin{array}{r} 806 \\ 6\overline{)4,836} \\ -\ 4\ 8\downarrow\downarrow \\ \hline 036 \\ -\ 36 \\ \hline 0\ \checkmark \end{array}$$

Check that the remainder is less than the divisor.
Stop dividing.

The quotient of 4,836 ÷ 6 is 806.

Practice A

Common Error Zeros in the last place of the quotient are forgotten. Have students check that their quotients are reasonable.

Divide. Sometimes, the zero in the quotient is in the ones place.

1. $8\overline{)6,472}$
809

2. $2\overline{)1,808}$
904

3. $5\overline{)3,025}$
605

4. $4\overline{)1,800}$
450

5. $7\overline{)4,830}$
690

6. $8\overline{)6,720}$
840

7. $11\overline{)6,644}$
604

8. $27\overline{)8,316}$
308

9. $32\overline{)7,680}$
240

10. $25\overline{)7,700}$
308

11. $19\overline{)9,538}$
502

12. $43\overline{)8,901}$
207

Practice B

Divide. Be sure to write the remainder as part of your answer.

13. $35\overline{)7,080}$
202 R10

14. $26\overline{)2,357}$
90 R17

15. $50\overline{)5,032}$
100 R32

16. $14\overline{)4,225}$
301 R11

17. $5\overline{)3,029}$
605 R4

18. $7\overline{)3,540}$
505 R5

19. $9\overline{)8,015}$
890 R5

20. $8\overline{)7,217}$
902 R1

21. $10\overline{)4,907}$
490 R7

22. $26\overline{)2,800}$
107 R18

23. $34\overline{)2,901}$
85 R11

24. $17\overline{)5,108}$
300 R8

Practice C

Divide.

25. $9\overline{)8,640}$
960

26. $19\overline{)1,059}$
55 R14

27. $6\overline{)2,004}$
334

28. $25\overline{)10,200}$
408

29. $7\overline{)3,740}$
534 R2

30. $9\overline{)8,902}$
989 R1

Everyday Problem Solving

You can buy some items on an installment plan. You give the store a down payment. Then, you pay the remaining amount in equal payments.

CONSUMER FURNITURE
Installment plan

ITEM	COST	DOWN PAYMENT	NUMBER OF PAYMENTS
Television	$460	$100	6
Living room set	$2,708	$200	12

1. Neal bought a television set on the installment plan. How much was the down payment? $100

2. Neal paid the down payment for the television set. How much does he now owe? Subtract the down payment from the cost. $360

3. How much will each payment be for the television set? Divide the remaining amount of $360 by the 6 equal payments. $60

4. Pat bought a living room set on the installment plan. How much is each payment? $209

Extra Practice for this lesson is provided on page 420.

More Practice is provided in Exercise 43 of the *Workbook*.

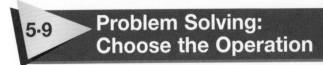

5·9 ▶ Problem Solving: Choose the Operation

Number Sense
Discuss the relationships between different operations. For example, you can use addition or multiplication to find the total number. Use multiplication when you have many sets that contain the same number of items.

Clue words help you decide how to solve a problem. You can add, subtract, multiply, or divide.

CLUE WORDS			
Add	**Subtract**	**Multiply**	**Divide**
in all	*how many more*	*total*	*how many times*
total	*difference*	*of*	*into how many*
altogether	*how many fewer*	*at*	*how much did each*
		for	
		in each	

▶ **EXAMPLE**

The florist ordered 18 flats of plants. There were 24 plants in each flat. How many plants were ordered?

Avoiding Errors
Students can also draw a picture to help them "see" the operation. Draw 18 squares and write *24 plants* in each square. This visually shows the need for multiplication.

STEP 1   READ   What do you need to find out?
You need to find the number of plants.

STEP 2   PLAN   What do you need to do?
The clue words **in each** tell you to **multiply**. Multiply the number of flats by the number of plants in each flat.

STEP 3   DO   Follow the plan.
Multiply 18 flats by the 24 plants in each flat.

$$\begin{array}{r} 18 \text{ flats} \\ \times\ 24 \text{ plants} \\ \hline 72 \\ +\ 360 \\ \hline 432 \text{ total plants} \end{array}$$

STEP 4   CHECK   Does the answer make sense?
Divide to check the multiplication.
$432 \div 18 = 24$ plants in each flat. ✓

The florist ordered 432 plants.

Problem Solving Practice

READ the problem. Decide what operation to use for the PLAN. Then, DO the plan to solve the problem.

1. Sara sold 36 begonias, 11 geraniums, and 25 lilies. How many plants did she sell in all? 72 plants

   PLAN
   What are the clue words? in all
   What do the clue words tell you to do? Add all plants together.

   DO
   $36 + 11 + 25 = 72$

2. Walter displayed 8 rows of roses. Each row had 19 roses. How many roses were on display? 152 roses

   PLAN
   What are the clue words? each
   What do the clue words tell you to do? Multiply the number of rows by the number of roses in each row.

   DO
   $8 \times 19 = 152$

3. Mike fills each empty flowerpot with 2 pounds of potting soil. How many pots can he fill with 150 pounds of potting soil? 75 flowerpots

   PLAN
   What are the clue words? each
   What do the clue words tell you to do? Divide the total amount of potting soil by the amount of potting soil in each pot.

   DO
   $150 \div 2 = 75$

4. The florist arranged a shipment of 600 mums into 20 groups. How many mums were in each group? 30 mums

   PLAN
   What are the clue words? each group
   What do the clue words tell you to do? Divide the number of mums in the shipment by the number of groups.

   DO
   $600 \div 20 = 30$

5. Six flower arrangements were delivered. Each arrangement cost $35. What was the total cost? $210

   PLAN
   What are the clue words? total cost
   What do the clue words tell you to do? Multiply the price of each arrangement by the number of arrangements delivered.

   DO
   $6 \times 35 = 210$

Extra Practice for this lesson is provided on page 420.

MATH IN YOUR LIFE
Determining Miles per Gallon (mpg)

Armando drove his car 352 miles. He used 16 gallons of gas. He wants to find the number of miles he can drive on 1 gallon of gas. This is the number of miles his car gets per gallon of gas. It is the miles per gallon or mpg for his car.

Armando can find the mpg. He divides the total miles driven by the number of gallons of gas used.

$$\begin{array}{r} 22 \leftarrow \text{Number of miles per gallon} \\ \text{Gallons of gas} \rightarrow 16\overline{)352} \leftarrow \text{Miles driven} \\ -32 \\ \hline 32 \\ -32 \\ \hline 0 \end{array}$$

Armando's car gets 22 mpg.

Find the mpg for each vehicle.

1. Compact car
377 miles
13 gallons
29 mpg

2. Luxury car
238 miles
17 gallons
14 mpg

3. Small truck
360 miles
20 gallons
18 mpg

4. Van
680 miles
34 gallons
20 mpg

Solve.

5. The new car sticker for Marsha's car shows that her car should get about 26 mpg. Marsha drove 784 miles on 28 gallons of gas. How did her car compare with its sticker information? Marsha's car got 28 mpg, which is more than 26 mpg.

Critical Thinking

Cars will get more miles per gallon of gasoline on the highway than on city streets. Why do you think this is true?

Critical Thinking
The stop-and-go driving that occurs in city traffic uses up more gasoline.

More Practice is provided in Exercise 44 of the *Workbook*.

5·10 ▶ Estimating and Thinking

Estimating an answer allows you to choose an answer that seems sensible. An answer that "makes sense" is neither too big nor too small to be possible.

▶ **EXAMPLE**

Number Sense
Discuss how many miles different cars can travel on 1 gallon of gasoline.

Avoiding Errors
Be sure students consider each choice before deciding on the *best* estimate.

Shelly drove a total of 354 miles. She used 20 gallons of gas. Estimate how many miles she traveled on each gallon.   (a) 50   (b) 6   (c) 18

Look at each answer to see if it makes sense.

(a) 50   This answer is too big. She would have traveled more miles if she could travel 50 miles per gallon.

(b) 6   This answer is too small. She would have traveled fewer miles if she could only travel 6 miles per gallon.

(c) 18   This answer makes sense and is close to the exact answer.

Shelly travels about 18 miles per gallon of gas.

Common Error Larger estimates are chosen incorrecty. Stress the need for students to state the answer in a sentence. This will help them hear and see if the answer makes sense.

Practice

Choose the estimate that is close to the exact answer.

1. Shelly made 7 trips between Union City and Jefferson last month. She traveled a total of 476 miles. Estimate how many miles each trip was. c

   (a) 9   **(b)** 100   **(c)** 70

2. For her job, Shelly visited 396 clients in her state. She saw these clients in 12 months. Estimate how many clients she visited each month. a

   (a) 30   **(b)** 300   **(c)** 3,000

3. From her records, Shelly found that she spent $308 for gas during the last 14 weeks. Estimate how much money she spent on gas each week. c

   (a) $50   **(b)** $100   **(c)** $20

dividend
division
divisor
quotient
remainder

Vocabulary Review

Fill in the blanks.

Complete each sentence with a word from the list.

1. __?__ is the process of finding how many times one number contains another. Division

2. In $42 \div 6 = 7$, the 6 is called the __?__. divisor

3. The problem $7 \div 3$ has a __?__ of 1. remainder

4. The __?__ of $42 \div 6 = 7$ is 42. dividend

5. In $42 \div 6 = 7$, the 7 is called the __?__. quotient

6. **Writing** A division problem has a divisor of 8 and a quotient of 10 R 7. Find the dividend and write the problem in two ways.

    $87 \div 8 = 10$ R7 or $8\overline{)87}$ with 10 R7

Chapter Quiz

LESSONS 5·1 and 5·2

Test Tip
You can use a multiplication table to find quotients.

Dividing Whole Numbers

Find each quotient.

1. $49 \div 7$ 7
2. $56 \div 7$ 8
3. $7\overline{)28}$ 4
4. $5\overline{)45}$ 9
5. $48 \div 8$ 6
6. $27 \div 3$ 9
7. What is eighteen divided by nine? 2
8. What is fifty-four divided by six? 9

LESSONS 5·3 and 5·4

Test Tip
Be sure to locate the correct place for the first digit of the quotient.

Dividing with Remainders

Divide.

9. $8\overline{)50}$ 6 R2
10. $14 \div 3$ 4 R2
11. $7\overline{)21}$ 3
12. $30 \div 8$ 3 R6
13. $5\overline{)70}$ 14
14. $600 \div 7$ 85 R5

Checking Division
Check each answer.

15.
$$7 \text{ R1}$$
$$9\overline{)64}$$

15. correct: $9 \times 7 + 1 = 64$

16.
$$31 \text{ R1}$$
$$7\overline{)220}$$

16. incorrect: $7 \times 31 + 1 = 218$

Problem Solving
Solve.

17. There are 12 boxes. Each box has 50 notebooks. How many notebooks are there in all? 600 notebooks

18. There are 32 stamps on each roll. Mark has 288 stamps. How many rolls does he have? 9 rolls

Dividing Larger Numbers
Divide.

19. $345 \div 12$ 28 R9

20. $191 \div 18$ 10 R11

21. $815 \div 4$ 203 R3

22. $546 \div 27$ 20 R6

23. $2,175 \div 7$ 310 R5

24. $1,985 \div 38$ 52 R9

Estimating Answers
Choose the best estimate.

25. Marta is rolling nickels for the bank. Each roll holds 40 nickels. How many rolls are needed for 760 nickels? (a) 20
(a) 20 **(b)** 200 **(c)** 2,000

Group Activity
See the *Teacher Planning Guide* for a Scoring Rubric for this activity.

In your group, research the term *unit price*. Write down its meaning. Visit a supermarket and record 10 examples of how unit pricing is used in the store. Then, create a word problem, with the answer, that asks the reader to find the unit price of an item.

This sports photographer takes photographs of other mountain climbers. He always tries to get the best photographs. To be sure, he always takes three photos of the same scene. Rolls of film come in sizes that make 24 or 36 photos. How many "different" scenes will he photograph from a roll of 24? from a roll of 36?

Caption With the roll of 24, the photographer will be able to photograph 8 different scenes. With the roll of 36, he can photograph 12 different scenes.

Chapter 6 ▷ More About Numbers

ESL Note Discuss words in related groupings: Factors and multiples are related to GCF and LCM; prime and composite are related.

Words to Know

divisible	can be divided without a remainder
factors	numbers multiplied to get a product
greatest common factor (GCF)	the largest factor that two or more numbers share
multiples	possible products of a given number
least common multiple (LCM)	the smallest multiple that two or more numbers share
prime number	number with only itself and 1 as factors
composite number	number with more than two factors
exponent	tells how many times to use a number as a factor
square	product of multiplying a number by itself
square root	number that was squared

Words to Know Have students create numerical examples for each Word to Know as they learn them.

Class Team Project

Find out how many students are in each of your classes. Your teachers want to divide each class into equal-sized teams. List all the different-sized teams that could be made for each class. The smallest team can be one person. The largest team can be the entire class. How many different teams can you make?

Project Students can stop after numbers repeat. For example: there are 6 students in the class: 6 teams of 1, 1 team of 6, 2 teams of 3, and 3 teams of 2.

Learning Objectives

- Use divisibility tests.
- Find the factors of a number.
- Find the multiples of a number.
- Write prime factorizations.
- Find squares and square roots.
- Solve problems with extra information.
- Apply number sense to reading electrical meters.

More Practice is provided in Exercise 45 of the *Workbook*.

6·1 Divisibility Tests for 2, 5, and 10

Sometimes, when you divide one number by another number, the remainder is zero. When this happens, the first number is **divisible** by the second number.

$18 \div 3 = 6$ R0 $18 \div 4 = 4$ R2
18 is divisible by 3.   18 is not divisible by 4.

You can use divisibility tests to quickly see if numbers are divisible by 2, 5, or 10.

Number Sense
Review the definition of even numbers. Tell students that any number that ends with an even digit is even.

Remember:
A number is even if it ends in 0, 2, 4, 6, or 8.

Divisible by 2   A number is divisible by 2 if it is an even number.
$126 \div 2 = 63$ R0

Divisible by 5   A number is divisible by 5 if the last digit is 0 or 5.
$6{,}840 \div 5 = 1{,}368$ R0

Divisible by 10   A number is divisible by 10 if the last digit is 0.
$80 \div 10 = 8$ R0

▶ **EXAMPLE**

Avoiding Errors
Have students circle the last digit of the number they are testing.

Tell if the number 5,235 is divisible by 2, 5, or 10.

STEP 1 Write the number. Look at the last digit.   5,235

STEP 2 Is the number even?   No.   It is not divisible by 2.

STEP 3 Is the last digit a 0 or 5?   Yes.   It is divisible by 5.

STEP 4 Is the last digit a 0?   No.   It is not divisible by 10.

The number 5,235 is only divisible by 5.

Practice A

Common Error Not all divisibility tests are applied. Have students make a list of the tests asked for. Then, check that each test was done for a number.

Tell if each number is divisible by 2. Write *Yes* or *No*.

1. 875 no   **2.** 634 yes   **3.** 7,301 no   **4.** 37,598 yes   **5.** 268,180 yes

Practice B

Tell if each number is divisible only by 5 or by both 5 and 10.

6. 67,475
only by 5

7. 390,740
by 5 and 10

8. 89,370
by 5 and 10

9. 456,785
only by 5

10. 700,005
only by 5

Practice C

Tell if each number is divisible by 2, 5, or 10.

11. 48,296
by 2

12. 9,990
by 2, by 5, by 10

13. 16,005
by 5

14. 55,558
by 2

15. 800,000
by 2, by 5, by 10

16. 2,615
by 5

17. 3,180
by 2, by 5, by 10

18. 1,274
by 2

19. 2,695
by 5

20. 7,312
by 2

Everyday Problem Solving

Mika is a camp director. She uses the floor plans to assign campers to cabins. She does not want any empty beds in a cabin she assigns.

1. There will be 45 campers in June. Mika wants to assign them all to the same type of cabin. Is 45 divisible by 2, 5, or 10? Which type of cabin could she use?
45 is divisible by 5; Cabin B

2. In August, there will be 70 campers. Which type of cabin could she use if all the campers were in the same type of cabin?
Cabins A, B, or C

3. There are 8 camp counselors. Which cabins could they use? How many cabins of that type would they need?
Cabin A; 4

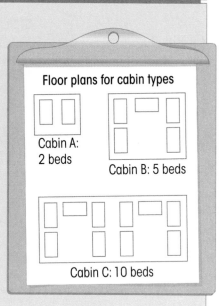

Floor plans for cabin types

Cabin A: 2 beds

Cabin B: 5 beds

Cabin C: 10 beds

Extra Practice for this lesson is provided on page 421.

More Practice is provided in Exercise 46 of the *Workbook*.

6·2 ▶ Divisibility Tests for 3, 6, and 9

Number Sense
List multiples of 6 from 6 to 60. Point out that these numbers are divisible by 6. Then, circle those numbers that are also divisible by 9.

You can use divisibility tests to quickly see if numbers are divisible by 3, 6, or 9.

Divisible by 3   A number is divisible by 3 if the sum of the digits is also divisible by 3. Try 471.

$$4 + 7 + 1 = 12 \qquad 12 \div 3 = 4 \text{ R0}$$
So, 471 is divisible by 3.

You can apply the divisibility tests for 2 and 3 to test for 6.

Divisible by 6   A number is divisible by 6 if it is divisible by both 2 and 3. Try 108.

$$108 \div 2 = 54 \text{ R0} \quad 108 \div 3 = 36 \text{ R0}$$
So, 108 is divisible by 6.

Divisible by 9   A number is divisible by 9 if the sum of the digits is also divisible by 9. Try 513.

$$5 + 1 + 3 = 9 \qquad 9 \div 9 = 1 \text{ R0}$$
So, 513 is divisible by 9.

▶ **EXAMPLE 1**

Is 255 divisible by 6?

STEP 1 Find the sum of the digits.		$2 + 5 + 5 = 12$
STEP 2 Is 12 divisible by 3?	Yes.	$12 \div 3 = 4 \text{ R0}$
STEP 3 Is 255 divisible by 2?	No.	It is not even.

Avoiding Errors
Students may be weak in the basic multiplication and division facts. Quickly review basic facts.

The number 255 is not divisible by 6.

▶ **EXAMPLE 2**

Is 7,431 divisible by 3 or 9?

STEP 1 Find the sum of the digits.		$7 + 4 + 3 + 1 = 15$
STEP 2 Is 15 divisible by 3?	Yes.	$15 \div 3 = 5 \text{ R0}$
STEP 3 Is 15 divisible by 9?	No.	$15 \div 9 = 1 \text{ R6}$

The number 7,431 is divisible by 3 but not by 9.

Practice A

Tell if each number is divisible by 6. Write *Yes* or *No.*

1. 243 no   **2.** 66 yes   **3.** 3,783 no   **4.** 5,940 yes   **5.** 7,602 yes

6. 7,458 yes   **7.** 15,555 no   **8.** 9,720 yes   **9.** 578,564 no **10.** 21,864 yes

Practice B

Tell if each number is divisible by 3, 9, or both.
Write *3, 9,* or *Both 3 and 9.*

11. 1,524
3

12. 7,470
Both 3 and 9

13. 3,141
Both 3 and 9

14. 2,568
3

15. 6,246
Both 3 and 9

16. 333
Both 3 and 9

17. 5,109
3

18. 8,883
Both 3 and 9

19. 78,777
Both 3 and 9

20. 4,953
3

21. 498
3

22. 52,668
Both 3 and 9

23 101,904
3

24. 525,000
3

25. 258,129
Both 3 and 9

Everyday Problem Solving

Alyse makes jewelry for craft fairs. She uses the chart
for the beads she needs. When she orders, she does
not want to have any beads left over.

1. Alyse needs 183 dozen black beads.
What size boxes could she order? small boxes

2. Alyse needs 249 dozen yellow beads.
What size boxes could she order? small boxes
How many boxes could she order? 83 boxes

3. Alyse needs 756 dozen green beads.
What size boxes could she order? small, medium, or large

4. Alyse needs 162 dozen red beads. She can order
any size box. She wants the least number of boxes.
Which size boxes should she order? large boxes

Beads by the Dozens	
Size of Box (any color)	Number of Dozens
Small	3
Medium	6
Large	9

Extra Practice for this lesson
is provided on page 421.

More Practice is provided in Exercise 47 of the *Workbook*.

6-3 ▸ Divisibility Test for 4

If a number can be divided by 4 with a remainder of 0, it is divisible by 4. You can use a divisibility test to quickly see if numbers are divisible by 4.

Divisible by 4   A number is divisible by 4 if the number formed by the last two digits is divisible by 4.

▸ **EXAMPLE**

Tell if 845,628 is divisible by 4.

STEP 1	Write the number.	845,628
STEP 2	Look at the last two digits.	845,628
STEP 3	Is this number divisible by 4? Yes.	$28 \div 4 = 7$ R0

The number 845,628 is divisible by 4.

Practice

Tell if each number is divisible by 4. Write *Yes* or *No*.

1. 5,890 no

2. 784 yes

3. 45,032 yes

4. 349,821 no

5. 20 yes

6. 6,000 yes

7. 128,530 no

8. 1,245,904 yes

9. 540 yes

10. 6,981 no

11. 7,504 yes

12. 1,980 yes

13. 87,664 yes

14. 210,971 no

15. 923,456 yes

16. 79,894 no

17. 4,440,413 no

18. 678,004 yes

19. 4 yes

20. 42 no

21. 444,500 yes

22. 78,992 yes

23. 64,992,824 yes

24. 4,956 yes

USING YOUR CALCULATOR
Test for Divisibility

You can use a calculator to quickly test for divisibility.

Is 8,679 divisible by 6?

Divide 8,679 by 6.

PRESS $\boxed{8}\boxed{6}\boxed{7}\boxed{9}\boxed{\div}\boxed{6}$ $\boxed{1446.5}$

↑
This dot means that
the number is not
a whole number

The quotient 1,446.5 is not a whole number. This means that 8,679 is not divisible by 6.

Is 12,468 divisible by 3?

Divide 12,468 by 3.

PRESS $\boxed{1}\boxed{2}\boxed{4}\boxed{6}\boxed{8}\boxed{\div}\boxed{3}$ $\boxed{4156.}$

The quotient 4,156 is a whole number. This means that 12,468 is divisible by 3.

Use a calculator to tell if each number is divisible by 2, 3, 4, 5, 6, 9, or 10. Copy the table and write *Yes* or *No*. The first one has been done for you.

		Divisible by					
	2	3	4	5	6	9	10
1. 132	Yes	Yes	Yes	No	Yes	No	No
2. 1,756	yes	no	yes	no	no	no	no
3. 18,921	no	yes	no	no	no	no	no
4. 27,150	yes	yes	no	yes	yes	no	yes
5. 540	yes	yes	yes	yes	yes	yes	yes

More Practice is provided in Exercise 48 of the *Workbook*.

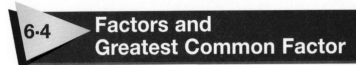

6·4 ▶ Factors and Greatest Common Factor

Number Sense
Have students do a quick review of basic division facts.

The two numbers you multiply are **factors** of the product. When you divide, the divisor and the quotient are the factors.

$$3 \times 4 = 12$$
Factor × Factor = Product

$$\begin{array}{r} 4 \leftarrow \text{Factor} \\ \text{Factor} \rightarrow 3\overline{)12} \\ \uparrow \\ \text{Product} \end{array}$$

You can divide to find all the factors of a number. The remainder must be 0. Divide by 1, 2, 3, and so on. Stop dividing when the factors repeat.

$$\begin{array}{cccc} 12 & 6 & 4 & 3 \\ 1\overline{)12} & 2\overline{)12} & 3\overline{)12} & 4\overline{)12} \text{ STOP!} \end{array}$$

The symbol F_{12} means the factors of 12.

You can list the factors of 12 from least to greatest.

$$F_{12} = \{1, 2, 3, 4, 6, 12\}$$

▶ **EXAMPLE 1**

Avoiding Errors
Remind students that as soon as the factors repeat, you can stop dividing.

Find the factors of 20.

STEP 1 Divide starting with the whole number 1.

$$\begin{array}{ccccc} 20 & 10 & 6\text{ R2} & 5 & 4 \\ 1\overline{)20} & 2\overline{)20} & 3\overline{)20} & 4\overline{)20} & 5\overline{)20} \text{ STOP!} \end{array}$$

STEP 2 List the factors from least to greatest without repeating any numbers.

$$F_{20} = \{1, 2, 4, 5, 10, 20\}$$

The factors of 20 are 1, 2, 4, 5, 10, and 20.

If you list the factors for each of two numbers, you may find that some of their factors are the same. They are called common factors. The **greatest common factor (GCF)** is the largest of the common factors.

EXAMPLE 2

Find the greatest common factor of 18 and 24.

STEP 1 Find the factors of each number.

$F_{18} = \{1, 2, 3, 6, 9, 18\}$
$F_{24} = \{1, 2, 3, 4, 6, 8, 12, 24\}$

STEP 2 List the common factors.

1, 2, 3, 6

STEP 3 Find the greatest common factor.

6

The greatest common factor of 18 and 24 is 6.

Practice A

Common Error The greatest common factor is not chosen. Make sure that all the common factors are circled, including the number itself if needed.

Find the factors of each number.

1. 10
1, 2, 5, 10

2. 21
1, 3, 7, 21

3. 64
1, 2, 4, 8, 16, 32, 64

4. 48
1, 2, 3, 4, 6, 8, 12, 16, 24, 48

5. 51 1, 3, 17, 51

6. 81
1, 3, 9, 27, 81

7. 32
1, 2, 4, 8, 16, 32

8. 5
1, 5

9. 50
1, 2, 5, 10, 25, 50

10. 75
1, 3, 5, 15, 25, 75

Practice B

Find the greatest common factor of each pair of numbers.

11. 10   8 2

12. 15   45 15

13. 20   10 10

14. 17   51 17

15. 13   4 1

16. 50   75 25

17. 22   66 22

18. 36   54 18

19. 16   30 2

20. 12   28 4

Everyday Problem Solving

Jena is planning a party for 120 people. She needs to rent chairs and tables. She wants to use only one size table. She does not want any empty chairs at a table.

1. If she uses 4-person tables, how many tables will she need?   30 tables

2. If she uses 5-person tables, how many tables will she need? What will it cost for the tables?
24 tables; $360

3. What will it cost to rent 6-person tables? What is the total cost with chairs? $400; $640

Seating for Party	
Table Sizes	Cost
4-person table	$13.00 each
5-person table	$15.00 each
6-person table	$20.00 each
8-person table	$25.00 each
Chairs	$2.00 each

Extra Practice for this lesson is provided on page 421.

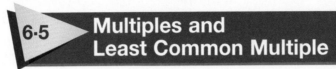

6·5 Multiples and Least Common Multiple

The **multiples** of a number are the products you get when you multiply that number by whole numbers. The numbers in blue are some multiples of 12.

$$12 \times 1 = 12 \qquad 12 \times 2 = 24 \qquad 12 \times 3 = 36$$
$$12 \times 4 = 48 \qquad 12 \times 5 = 60 \qquad 12 \times 6 = 72$$

You can list some multiples of 12.

$$M_{12} = \{12, 24, 36, 48, 60, 72 \ldots\}$$

The three dots show that the multiples go on.

To find the multiples of a number, multiply that number by the whole numbers. Begin with 1.

▶ **EXAMPLE 1**

Find the first five multiples of 9.

STEP 1 Multiply the given number by 1, 2, 3, 4, and 5.

$$9 \times 1 = 9 \qquad 9 \times 2 = 18$$
$$9 \times 3 = 27 \qquad 9 \times 4 = 36$$
$$9 \times 5 = 45$$

STEP 2 List these multiples from least to greatest.

$$M_9 = \{9, 18, 27, 36, 45\ldots\}$$

The first five multiples of 9 are 9, 18, 27, 36, and 45.

For two different numbers, you may find that some multiples are the same. These are called common multiples. The **least common multiple (LCM)** is the smallest of the common multiples.

▶ **EXAMPLE 2**

Find the least common multiple of 5 and 15.

STEP 1 List some multiples of each number.

$$M_5 = \{5, 10, 15, 20, 25, 30\ldots\}$$
$$M_{15} = \{15, 30, 45, 60\ldots\}$$

STEP 2 List the common multiples.   15, 30

STEP 3 Find the least common multiple.   15

The least common multiple of 5 and 15 is 15.

Practice A

Find the first five multiples of each number. List them from least to greatest.

1. 7
7, 14, 21, 28, 35,

2. 10
10, 20, 30 ,40, 50

3. 6
6, 12, 18, 24, 30

4. 25
25, 50, 75, 100, 125

5. 50
50, 100, 150, 200, 250

6. 22
22, 44, 66, 88, 110

7. 40
40, 80, 120, 160, 200

8. 16
16, 32, 48, 64, 80

9. 18
18, 36, 54, 72, 90

10. 1
1, 2, 3, 4, 5

Practice B

Find the least common multiple of each pair of numbers.

11. 8   12 24

12. 10   18 90

13. 13   3 39

14. 15   25 75

15. 10   25 50

16. 6   15 30

17. 14   21 42

18. 40   50 200

19. 9   15 45

20. 16   40 80

21. 21   6 42

22. 60   80 240

23. 12   40 120

24. 72   32 288

25. 4   42 84

26. 16   24 48

Everyday Problem Solving

Alfonso and Adena want to go to the beach together. Alfonso has every fifth day off from work, and Adena has every third day off.

1. They both began work on June 1. What is the first day they will have off together? June 15

2. What is the LCM of 3 and 5? 15

Jen has every sixth day off. Bob has every eighth day off.

3. They both began work on June 1. What is the first day they will have off together? June 24

4. What is the LCM of 6 and 8? 24

| | | •JUNE• | | | | |
SUN	MON	TUES	WED	THURS	FRI	SAT
		1 START WORK	2	3	4	5
6	7	8	9	10	11	12
13	14	15	16	17	18	19
20	21	22	23	24	25	26
27	28	29	30			

6-6 ▶ Prime Numbers

Number Sense
Have students factor the whole numbers from 1 to 10.

A **prime number** has only two factors. The two factors are the number itself and 1. A **composite number** has more than two factors.

$$17 = 1 \times 17 \qquad 15 = 1 \times 15 \text{ and } 15 = 3 \times 5$$
$$F_{17} = \{1, 17\} \qquad F_{15} = \{1, 3, 5, 15\}$$
$$\text{Prime} \qquad\qquad\qquad \text{Composite}$$

Every composite number can be shown as the product of prime numbers. This is called *prime factorization*. You can make a factor tree.

▶ **EXAMPLE**

Avoiding Errors
Have students memorize all the prime numbers through 20: 1, 2, 3, 5, 7, 11, 13, 17,19.

Write the prime factorization of 60.

STEP 1 Write the number.   60

STEP 2 Choose two factors. These factors do not have to be prime numbers.

$$60$$
$$6 \times 10$$

STEP 3 Factor each number again until all the factors are prime numbers. If a factor is a prime, bring it down to the next line.

$$60$$
$$6 \quad \times \quad 10$$
$$2 \times 3 \times 2 \times 5$$

STEP 4 Write the prime factors in order from least to greatest.

$$2 \times 2 \times 3 \times 5$$

The prime factorization of 60 is $2 \times 2 \times 3 \times 5$.

Practice A

Common Error Students do not recognize larger prime numbers. Let them check for factors using a calculator.

Tell if each number is *prime* or *composite*. Test by factoring each number.

1. 13
prime

2. 15
composite

3. 99
composite

4. 41
prime

5. 57
composite

Practice B

Write the prime factorization of each number. Use a factor tree.

6. 8
$2 \times 2 \times 2$

7. 18
$2 \times 3 \times 3$

8. 24
$2 \times 2 \times 2 \times 3$

9. 75
$3 \times 5 \times 5$

10. 28
$2 \times 2 \times 7$

Extra Practice for this lesson is provided on page 421.

More Practice is provided in Exercise 51 of the *Workbook*.

Exponents

Number Sense
Have students copy this long multiplication: $4 \times 4 \times 4 \times 4 \times 4 \times 4$. Then, show them how useful exponents can be.

Some expressions ask you to multiply a number by itself one or more times. An **exponent** tells you how many times the number is used as a factor.

$$2^3 \leftarrow \text{Exponent}$$

You can find the value of expressions that contain exponents.

$$2^3 = 2 \times 2 \times 2 = 8$$
2^3 is read, *two to the third power*.

▶ **EXAMPLE**

Avoiding Errors
Make sure that students use repeated multiplication, not repeated addition.

Find the value of the expression 4^3.

STEP 1 Rewrite the expression as a product of the number without exponents. $4 \times 4 \times 4$

STEP 2 Multiply. $4 \times 4 \times 4 = 64$

The value of 4^3 is 64.

An expression that has a zero as the exponent has a value of 1. The expression 8^0 equals 1.

$$5,432^0 = 1$$

Practice

Common Error Students multiply the base number by the exponent. Encourage them to rewrite the expression as repeated multiplication.

Find the value of each expression.

1. 5^3 125

2. 2^5 32

3. 100^2 10,000

4. 8^2 64

5. 11^1 11

6. 10^3 1,000

7. 1^0 1

8. 3^3 27

9. 0^4 0

10. 9^1 9

11. 1^{22} 1

12. 20^2 400

13. 400^0 1

14. 15^2 225

15. 12^2 144

Extra Practice for this lesson is provided on page 421.

More Practice is provided in Exercise 52 of the *Workbook*.

6·8 Squares and Square Roots

Number Sense
Write the number 25 on the board. Ask students, "What number multiplied by itself gives 25 as the product?" Help students remember that $5 \times 5 = 25$.

When you multiply a number by itself, the product is called the **square** of the number.

The square of 4 is 16. $4 \times 4 = 4^2 = 16$.

The symbol for square is the exponent ^{2}. The number that was squared is called the **square root**.

The square root of 16 is 4, because 4^2 equals 16.

The symbol for square root is $\sqrt{}$.

EXAMPLE

Avoiding Errors
Students sometimes mistake 7^2 for 7×2. Reinforce the meaning of 7^2 as 7×7.

Find $\sqrt{49}$.

STEP 1	Think: "What number squared equals 49?"	Try 6. $6^2 = 6 \times 6 = 36$
STEP 2	Decide if the product is too big or too small.	36 is too small.
STEP 3	If the product is too small, try the next largest whole number. If the product is too large, try the next smallest whole number.	Try 7. $7^2 = 7 \times 7 = 49$

The correct answer is 7. So, $\sqrt{49} = 7$.

Common Error Students arrive at the wrong value for a square root. Make sure students understand that they can find the square root of 49 either by remembering that $7 \times 7 = 49$ or by looking it up in the table.

Practice A

Find the square of each number.

1. 6^2 36   **2.** 8^2 64   **3.** 9^2 81   **4.** 3^2 9   **5.** 13^2 169

Practice B

Find the square root of each number.

6. $\sqrt{4}$ 2   **7.** $\sqrt{25}$ 5   **8.** $\sqrt{10,000}$ 100   **9.** $\sqrt{16}$ 4

10. $\sqrt{121}$ 11   **11.** $\sqrt{49}$ 7   **12.** $\sqrt{900}$ 30   **13.** $\sqrt{196}$ 14

Extra Practice for this lesson is provided on page 421.

ON-THE-JOB MATH
Electric Meter Reader

Sharon reads meters for a power company. Your electric meter shows how many kilowatt-hours of electricity you use. An electric meter has five dials. The dials are read from left to right.

| 2 | 3 | 5 | 4 | 8 |

The meter above shows 23,548 kilowatt-hours. If you know the reading for the month before, you can tell how much electricity you used that month.

Read the numbers on the meter to solve the first word problem.

1. The meter below is an August 1 reading. On July 1, the same meter showed 10,455. How many kilowatt-hours were used during the month? Subtract to find out. 2,410

2. Electricity costs 8¢ a kilowatt-hour. This is $8 for 100 kilowatt-hours. How much does 1,000 kilowatt-hours cost? $80

Critical Thinking

Mr. Miller is away. Sharon cannot read the meter. The electric company wants to send Mr. Miller a bill for the month. Sharon needs to estimate how much electricity he used. How can she do this?

Critical Thinking
One possible answer is that Sharon can base her estimate on the amount of electricity Mr. Miller used that month in previous years.

More Practice is provided in Exercise 53 of the *Workbook*.

Problem Solving: Extra Information

Some word problems give you more information than you need. To solve a problem with extra information, first decide what facts are needed.

Ms. Cohen spent 8 hours shopping for party supplies. She bought 5 packages of white paper plates for $3 each. What was the total cost for the paper plates?

STEP 1 **READ** **What do you need to find out?**
You need to find the total cost of the paper plates.

STEP 2 **PLAN** **What do you need to do?**
What information do you need?
The number of packages.
The cost of each package.
Multiply to find the total cost.

STEP 3 **DO** **Follow the plan.**
Multiply.

$$
\begin{array}{r}
5 \quad \text{packages} \\
\times \ \ \$3 \quad \text{each} \\
\hline
\$15 \quad \text{for paper plates}
\end{array}
$$

STEP 4 **CHECK** **Does your answer make sense?**
Check to see that you used only the numbers you needed.
5 packages × $3 ✓

What information was not needed?
8 hours spent shopping

The total cost of the paper plates was $15.

Problem Solving

Common Error Students use the wrong information. Have the students ask themselves, "What do I need to know? Will this fact help me find it?"

READ the problem. Answer the questions under PLAN.
DO the plan to solve the problem. Remember to use
only the information you need.

1. Danielle bought 3 CDs for $15 each. She bought a CD
   case for $20. How much did the CDs cost altogether? $45

   PLAN   the number of CDs; the cost of each CD
   What information do you need to solve the problem? DO $3 \times 15 = 45$
   What operation will you use? multiplication

2. Cal had 59 boxes to pack and 10 pieces of furniture
   to move. By noon, he had packed 43 boxes. How
   many boxes does he still have to pack? 16 boxes

   PLAN   the total number of boxes to pack; the number of boxes already packed
   What information do you need to solve the problem? DO $59 - 43 = 16$
   What operation will you use? subtraction

3. Ms. Kelly earns $630 a week. She travels 12 miles to
   work each day. She works 35 hours each week. How
   much does Mrs. Kelly earn an hour? $18

   PLAN   the amount Ms. Kelly earns a week; the number of hours she works a week
   What information do you need to solve the problem? DO $630 \div 35 = 18$
   What operation will you use? division

Problem Solving Strategy

You can have different problems for the same situation.

> Mrs. Lee is having a New Year's Eve party for
> 73 guests. She bought 8 packages of noisemakers
> for $5 each. There are 10 noisemakers in a package.

1. How much did all the packages of noisemakers cost? $40

2. How many noisemakers did she buy? 80 noisemakers

3. Each guest got 1 noisemaker. How many noisemakers were left over?
   7 noisemakers

Chapter

6 ▷ Review

composite number
divisible
exponent
factors
greatest common factor
least common multiple
multiples
prime number
square
square root

Vocabulary Review

True or false? If the statement is false, change the underlined word to make the statement true.

1. 21 is <u>divisible</u> by 7 true

2. 2 and 4 are <u>factors</u> of 16. true

3. The <u>greatest</u> common multiple of 12 and 24 is 24. false; least

4. 81 is a <u>multiple</u> of 9. true

5. 22 is a <u>prime number</u>. false; composite number

6. In the expression 4^5, 5 is the <u>exponent</u>. true

7. 18 is a <u>composite</u> number. true

8. The <u>least</u> common factor of 12 and 18 is 6. false; greatest

9. The <u>square</u> of 6 is 6×6, or 36. true

10. The <u>square root</u> of 36 is 6. true

11. **Writing** Choose one word from the vocabulary list. Explain the meaning of the word to a classmate. Answers will vary.

Chapter Quiz

LESSONS 6·1 to 6·3

Test Tip
Use long division to check for divisibility. If the remainder is 0, the number is divisible by the divisor.

Using Divisibility Tests

Use a divisibility test to answer each question.

1. Is 3,258 divisible by 6? yes

2. Is 59,848 divisible by 4? yes

3. Is 10,319 divisible by 9? no

4. Is 4,235 divisible by 5? yes

The marchers can be arranged in different ways: 3 rows of 45 or 45 rows of 3; 5 rows of 27 or 27 rows of 5; 9 rows of 15 or 15 rows of 9; 1 row of 135 or 135 rows of 1. You can use divisibility tests to find the factors of 135.

LESSON 6·4

Test Tip
Divide by 1, 2, 3, and so on to find factors. The remainder must be zero.

Finding Greatest Common Factors

Find the greatest common factor of each pair of numbers.

5. 18   24 6   **6.** 12   15 3   **7.** 4   12 4

LESSON 6·5

Test Tip
Multiply by 1, 2, 3, and so on to find multiples.

Finding Least Common Multiples

Find the least common multiple of each pair of numbers.

8. 6   7 42   **9.** 9   12 36   **10.** 6   8 24

LESSON 6·6

Test Tip
Use a factor tree to write the prime factors of a number.

Writing Prime Factorizations

Find the prime factorization of each number.

11. 12 $2 \times 2 \times 3$ **12.** 50 $2 \times 5 \times 5$ **13.** 30 $2 \times 3 \times 5$

LESSONS 6·7 and 6·8

Test Tip
Think of a perfect square to find the square root.

Finding Exponents, Squares, and Square Roots

Find the value of each expression.

14. 3^3 27   **15.** 2^4 16   **16.** 4^3 64

17. $\sqrt{64}$ 8   **18.** $\sqrt{81}$ 9   **19.** $\sqrt{16}$ 4

LESSON 6·9

Test Tip
Use only the information you need.

Solving Problems with Extra Information

Solve.

20. Jon drove 12 miles to the shore. He then drove 25 miles to the Cape. He had 12 gallons of gas. How far did he drive in all? 37 miles

---

Group Activity See the *Teacher Planning Guide* for a Scoring Rubric.

Work with your group to solve the following problem. The school marching band is marching in a parade. There are 135 band members. Arrange the marchers so that there are an equal number of students in each row. How many different ways can the marchers be arranged? Explain. See above.

Unit 1 Review

Choose the letter for the correct answer.

Use the table to answer Questions 1–3.

Favorite Books	
Book	Pages
Mystery	576
Adventure	804
Drama	813
Biography	528

1. Which book has an odd number of pages?

A. Mystery
B. Adventure
C. Drama Correct.
D. Biography

2. How many more pages does the drama book have than the mystery book?

A. 237 Correct.
B. 347 Incorrect; subtracted without regrouping.
C. 363 Incorrect; regrouping.
D. None of the above Incorrect.

3. Which list is in order from the least to the greatest number of pages?

A. Mystery, Biography, Adventure
B. Biography, Mystery, Adventure
C. Adventure, Drama, Biography
D. Drama, Adventure, Mystery

3. A. Incorrect.
   B. Correct.
   C. Incorrect; hundreds places out of order.
   D. Incorrect; ordered from greatest to least.

4. Bryan drove 348 miles in 4 days. He drove the same number of miles each day. How many miles did Bryan drive each day?

A. 87 miles Correct.
B. 344 miles Incorrect; subtracted the numbers.
C. 352 miles Incorrect; added the numbers.
D. None of the above Incorrect.

5. Neil ate 1,212 calories for breakfast, 1,057 calories for lunch, and 1,172 calories for dinner. How many calories did he eat in the 3 meals?

A. 2,229 calories Incorrect; added lunch and dinner.
B. 2,269 calories See below.
C. 3,331 calories Incorrect; did not regroup.
D. 3,441 calories Correct.
   Incorrect; added breakfast and lunch.

6. Each of 8 shipments weighs 73 pounds. What is the total weight?

A. About 9 pounds Incorrect; divided the numbers.
B. 81 pounds Incorrect; added the numbers.
C. 584 pounds Correct.
D. None of the above Incorrect.

> **Critical Thinking**
> Use the Favorite Books chart above. Which two books have a total of 1,104 pages?
> **CHALLENGE** You want to read at least 1,500 pages. Which books can you read? Why?

Critical Thinking Answer: Biography and Mystery   Challenge Possible Answers: Adventure and Drama; Mystery, Adventure, and Biography; Mystery, Drama, and Biography.

Unit 2 ▷ Fractions

Chapter 7 **Fractions and Mixed Numbers**

Chapter 8 **Multiplying and Dividing Fractions**

Chapter 9 **Adding and Subtracting Fractions**

Opening the Unit Along the chalkboard, write the different name brands of orange juice. Have each student write an X above the brand he or she prefers. These X's will form a bar graph. Have the students copy this graph and save it for later to create and compare fractions for each brand.

After being picked, about 900 pounds of oranges have been sent to a packaging plant. Here the oranges will wait to be cleaned, checked, packaged, and sent to food stores and juice plants.

Type of Fruit	Amount of Juice Produced
1 medium orange	$\frac{1}{3}$ cup
1 medium lemon	$\frac{1}{6}$ cup
1 medium grapefruit	$\frac{2}{3}$ cup
1 medium tangerine	$\frac{1}{4}$ cup

Number of Fruit Needed to Produce 1 Cup of Juice	
Orange	◯◯◯
Lemon	◯◯◯◯◯◯
Grapefruit	◯(
Tangerine	◯◯◯◯

Key: ◯ =1 whole fruit   (= $\frac{1}{2}$ fruit

The graph and table above give information about four types of fruit and the amount of juice that each one can produce.

1. How many grapefruit are needed for 1 cup of juice? $1\frac{1}{2}$ grapefruit

2. How much juice can you get from one medium lemon? $\frac{1}{6}$ cup

3. Which fruit needs the largest number to make 1 cup of juice? lemon

The people in the picture are working at the Pacific Stock Exchange. They buy, sell, and trade stocks. They use mixed numbers and fractions in their work. A mixed number is a whole number together with a fraction. The last stock today went up two and a half points. What would this mixed number look like?

Caption $2\frac{1}{2}$ points

Chapter **7**

Fractions and Mixed Numbers

ESL Note Draw examples of fractions and mixed numbers, and label the different parts. Have students use terms in sentences to describe the pictures.

Words to Know

fraction	a form of a number that shows part of a whole
numerator	the top number in a fraction
denominator	the bottom number in a fraction
equivalent fractions	fractions with different numbers but equal values
lowest terms	when only 1 divides evenly into both the numerator and denominator of a fraction
like fractions	fractions with the same denominator
unlike fractions	fractions with different denominators
mixed number	a number made up of a whole number and a fraction

Words to Know Give a few examples and have the students use the words to label each.

Fraction and Mixed Number Journal Project

Keep a daily journal of every fraction and mixed number you see. Look for them in different places. Read containers, signs, newspapers, and magazines. Write what each one is about and where you found it.

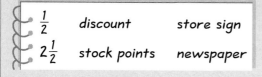

Learning Objectives

- Identify fractions and their parts.
- Recognize equivalent fractions.
- Write fractions in lowest terms and in higher terms.
- Find common denominators.
- Compare and order fractions and other numbers.
- Change mixed numbers and fractions.
- Solve problems using patterns.
- Apply fractions to cooking.

Project Answers will vary. More examples are: miles on maps or recipes.

More Practice is provided in Exercise 54 of the *Workbook*.

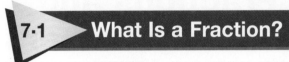

7·1 ▶ What Is a Fraction?

Number Sense
Place three clear chips and two colored chips on the overhead. Ask students for the number of chips that are clear and the total number of chips. Then, ask for the fractional amount of chips that are clear.

A **fraction** is part of a whole or part of a set. Every fraction has a numerator and a denominator.

$\dfrac{3}{4}$ ← Numerator
← Denominator

The **numerator** is the top number. It tells how many parts of the whole are being used.

The **denominator** is the bottom number. It tells how many parts there are in the whole.

▶ **EXAMPLE 1**

Write a fraction to tell what part of the square is blue.

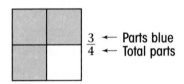

$\dfrac{3}{4}$ ← Parts blue
← Total parts

Three-fourths of the square is blue.

▶ **EXAMPLE 2**

Write a fraction for the situation.

Avoiding Errors
Point out the difference between $\frac{2}{3}$ and $\frac{3}{2}$. Have students orally explain the meaning of each fraction.

There are **four students in the Math Club. Three of the students are girls.** Write a fraction to tell what part of the Math Club is girls.

$\dfrac{3}{4}$ ← Girls in Math Club
← Total students in Math Club

Three-fourths of the club is girls.

Common Error Fractions show blue regions to white regions. Encourage students to use the words "out of" when writing a fraction. For example, $\frac{3}{4}$ means 3 blue "out of" 4 total.

Practice

Write a fraction to tell what part of the whole is blue.

1. 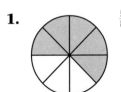 $\frac{5}{8}$

2. ◯ ◯ ◯ ◯ ◯ $\frac{3}{10}$
◯ ◯ ◯ ◯ ◯

3. There are 24 hours in a day. What fraction of the day is 8 hours?
$\frac{8}{24}$ or $\frac{1}{3}$

More Practice is provided in Exercise 55 of the *Workbook*.

7·2 Recognizing Equivalent Fractions

Number Sense
Show $\frac{4}{4} = \frac{8}{8}$ using models.

Equivalent fractions have the same value. Three equivalent fractions are pictured below.

 = =

$$\frac{1}{2} \quad = \quad \frac{2}{4} \quad = \quad \frac{3}{6}$$

▶ **EXAMPLE**

Avoiding Errors
Be sure students look at the size and shape of the area that is shaded when comparing. Tell them not to try to compare the numbers.

Each shape is equivalent. The shaded area in each shape is the same. This means that each fraction has the same value. $\frac{1}{2}$, $\frac{2}{4}$, and $\frac{3}{6}$ are equivalent fractions.

Common Error Numbers instead of shapes are compared. Have the students trace the shapes onto separate pieces of paper and overlay them to compare the shaded areas.

Practice

Tell if each pair of fractions is equivalent. Write *Equivalent* or *Not equivalent*.

1. equivalent

$$\frac{3}{6} \qquad \frac{4}{8}$$

2. not equivalent

$$\frac{1}{4} \qquad \frac{3}{8}$$

3. equivalent

$$\frac{1}{3} \qquad \frac{2}{6}$$

4. not equivalent

$$\frac{1}{2} \qquad \frac{1}{3}$$

5. equivalent

$$\frac{3}{4} \qquad \frac{6}{8}$$

6. equivalent

$$\frac{2}{3} \qquad \frac{4}{6}$$

7. 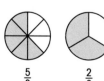 not equivalent

$$\frac{5}{8} \qquad \frac{2}{3}$$

8. equivalent

$$\frac{2}{5} \qquad \frac{4}{10}$$

More Practice is provided in Exercise 56 of the *Workbook*.

7·3 Reducing Fractions to Lowest Terms

Number Sense
Show that $\frac{2}{3}$ is in lowest terms because 1 is the GCF of 2 and 3.

To reduce a fraction, you divide the numerator and denominator by the same factor. A fraction is in **lowest terms** if you cannot divide any further.

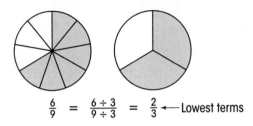

$$\frac{6}{9} = \frac{6 \div 3}{9 \div 3} = \frac{2}{3} \longleftarrow \text{Lowest terms}$$

You can reduce a fraction to lowest terms. Divide both numerator and denominator by their GCF.

> **EXAMPLE**

The Greatest Common Factor, or GCF, is the largest of the common factors of two or more numbers.

Reduce $\frac{15}{20}$ to lowest terms.

STEP 1 List the factors of numerator and denominator.

$F_{15} = \{1, 3, 5, 15\}$
$F_{20} = \{1, 2, 4, 5, 10, 20\}$

STEP 2 Find the greatest common factor.

$GCF = 5$

Avoiding Errors
Remind students to divide numerator and denominator by the *same* number.

STEP 3 Divide numerator and denominator by the GCF.

$\frac{15 \div 5}{20 \div 5} = \frac{3}{4}$

The fraction $\frac{15}{20}$ in lowest terms is $\frac{3}{4}$.

Practice A

Decide if each fraction is reduced to lowest terms. Write *Yes* or *No*.

1. $\frac{1}{3}$ yes

2. $\frac{3}{9}$ no

3. $\frac{2}{3}$ yes

4. $\frac{3}{3}$ no

5. $\frac{1}{4}$ yes

6. $\frac{3}{5}$ yes

7. $\frac{4}{8}$ no

8. $\frac{6}{9}$ no

9. $\frac{3}{4}$ yes

10. $\frac{2}{10}$ no

Practice B

Common Error Fractions are not completely reduced. Have students check that the GCF of the numerator and denominator of the final fraction is 1.

Reduce each fraction to lowest terms.

11. $\frac{4}{8}$ $\frac{1}{2}$ **12.** $\frac{5}{35}$ $\frac{1}{7}$ **13.** $\frac{9}{24}$ $\frac{3}{8}$ **14.** $\frac{8}{32}$ $\frac{1}{4}$ **15.** $\frac{3}{9}$ $\frac{1}{3}$

16. $\frac{12}{27}$ $\frac{4}{9}$ **17.** $\frac{6}{15}$ $\frac{2}{5}$ **18.** $\frac{6}{8}$ $\frac{3}{4}$ **19.** $\frac{5}{10}$ $\frac{1}{2}$ **20.** $\frac{7}{49}$ $\frac{1}{7}$

21. $\frac{13}{39}$ $\frac{1}{3}$ **22.** $\frac{4}{16}$ $\frac{1}{4}$ **23.** $\frac{8}{12}$ $\frac{2}{3}$ **24.** $\frac{49}{56}$ $\frac{7}{8}$ **25.** $\frac{6}{10}$ $\frac{3}{5}$

26. $\frac{10}{80}$ $\frac{1}{8}$ **27.** $\frac{6}{9}$ $\frac{2}{3}$ **28.** $\frac{9}{12}$ $\frac{3}{4}$ **29.** $\frac{8}{24}$ $\frac{1}{3}$ **30.** $\frac{7}{63}$ $\frac{1}{9}$

31. $\frac{15}{18}$ $\frac{5}{6}$ **32.** $\frac{6}{18}$ $\frac{1}{3}$ **33.** $\frac{12}{24}$ $\frac{1}{2}$ **34.** $\frac{7}{21}$ $\frac{1}{3}$ **35.** $\frac{3}{12}$ $\frac{1}{4}$

36. $\frac{4}{10}$ $\frac{2}{5}$ **37.** $\frac{8}{16}$ $\frac{1}{2}$ **38.** $\frac{12}{18}$ $\frac{2}{3}$ **39.** $\frac{15}{20}$ $\frac{3}{4}$ **40.** $\frac{4}{24}$ $\frac{1}{6}$

Everyday Problem Solving

At Rita's Pizza Place, the same sized pizza pie can be sliced in eighths or sixths.

1. A pizza pie was sliced into 8 equal pieces. Sam ate 2 pieces. What fraction of the pie did he eat? Write the fraction in lowest terms. $\frac{1}{4}$ pie

2. A pizza pie was sliced into 6 equal pieces. Irene ate 2 pieces. What fraction of the pie did she eat? Write the fraction in lowest terms. $\frac{1}{3}$ pie

3. Bill ate $\frac{4}{8}$ of one pie. Bonnie ate $\frac{3}{6}$ of another pie. Did both Bill and Bonnie eat $\frac{1}{2}$ a pie? How do you know? yes; Both $\frac{4}{8}$ and $\frac{3}{6}$ are equivalent to $\frac{1}{2}$.

Extra Practice for this lesson is provided on page 422.

Chapter 7 • Fractions and Mixed Numbers   133

More Practice is provided in Exercise 57 of the *Workbook*.

7·4 Changing Fractions to Higher Terms

Number Sense
Stress that the given fraction and the higher-term fraction are equivalent.

Sometimes, you need to write a fraction in higher terms. This will change the numbers, but keep the value the same.

$$\frac{4}{5} = \frac{4 \times 2}{5 \times 2} = \frac{8}{10} \leftarrow \text{Higher terms}$$

The fractions $\frac{4}{5}$ and $\frac{8}{10}$ are equivalent fractions.

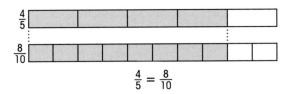

$$\frac{4}{5} = \frac{8}{10}$$

Sometimes, you know the denominator you want to use for the higher-term fraction.

▶ **EXAMPLE**

Write $\frac{3}{4}$ in higher terms.

Use the denominator 12. $\frac{3}{4} = \frac{?}{12}$

Avoiding Errors
Remind students that they must multiply numerator and denominator by the *same* number.

STEP 1 Divide the new higher denominator by the given denominator. $12 \div 4 = 3$

STEP 2 Multiply the numerator and denominator of the given fraction by the quotient from step 1. $\frac{3 \times 3}{4 \times 3} = \frac{9}{12}$

The fraction $\frac{3}{4}$ can be written as $\frac{9}{12}$.

Practice

Common Error Division in the first step is wrong. Have students use a multiplication table to find factors.

Change each fraction to higher terms. Use the higher denominator shown.

1. $\frac{1}{2} = \frac{?}{8}$ 4

2. $\frac{5}{9} = \frac{?}{18}$ 10

3. $\frac{6}{10} = \frac{?}{30}$ 18

4. $\frac{2}{9} = \frac{?}{27}$ 6

5. $\frac{2}{7} = \frac{?}{35}$ 10

6. $\frac{1}{3} = \frac{?}{21}$ 7

7. $\frac{1}{12} = \frac{?}{60}$ 5

8. $\frac{4}{9} = \frac{?}{36}$ 16

9. $\frac{3}{7} = \frac{?}{42}$ 18

10. $\frac{7}{9} = \frac{?}{45}$ 35

11. $\frac{1}{5} = \frac{?}{25}$ 5

12. $\frac{5}{7} = \frac{?}{49}$ 35

13. $\frac{1}{4} = \frac{?}{20}$ 5

14. $\frac{2}{8} = \frac{?}{24}$ 6

15. $\frac{2}{3} = \frac{?}{15}$ 10

16. $\frac{4}{6} = \frac{?}{36}$ 24

17. $\frac{2}{5} = \frac{?}{50}$ 20

18. $\frac{3}{15} = \frac{?}{45}$ 9

19. $\frac{3}{8} = \frac{?}{32}$ 12

20. $\frac{1}{6} = \frac{?}{54}$ 9

21. $\frac{7}{9} = \frac{?}{63}$ 49

22. $\frac{1}{2} = \frac{?}{18}$ 9

23. $\frac{3}{11} = \frac{?}{22}$ 6

24. $\frac{3}{4} = \frac{?}{24}$ 18

Everyday Problem Solving

The cooking class made sheet cakes.

1. Mary sliced her cake into 4 equal pieces. She put chocolate frosting on 3 of the pieces. What part of the cake has chocolate frosting? $\frac{3}{4}$ cake

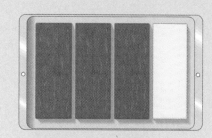

2. Mary then sliced the same cake into 3 equal parts the other way. Now how many parts are there? What part of the cake has chocolate frosting? 12 parts; $\frac{9}{12}$ cake

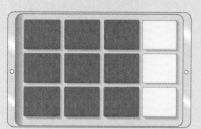

Extra Practice for this lesson is provided on page 422.

7·5 Finding Common Denominators

Number Sense
Point out that like fractions
are not equivalent fractions.

Like fractions have the same denominators.
Unlike fractions have different denominators.

Like fractions	Unlike fractions
$\frac{1}{15}$ $\frac{4}{15}$ $\frac{6}{15}$ $\frac{7}{15}$	$\frac{3}{2}$ $\frac{5}{4}$ $\frac{9}{11}$ $\frac{8}{15}$

You can change unlike fractions to like fractions.

Change $\frac{5}{6}$ and $\frac{3}{8}$ to like fractions.

▶ **EXAMPLE**

The Least Common Multiple, or
LCM, is the smallest multiple
that two or more numbers have
in common.

STEP 1 Find the least
common multiple of
the given denominators.

$M_6 = \{6, 12, 18, 24, ...\}$
$M_8 = \{8, 16, 24, ...\}$
$LCM = 24$

STEP 2 Use the least
common multiple as
the new denominator.

$\frac{5}{6} = \frac{?}{24}$ $\frac{3}{8} = \frac{?}{24}$

Avoiding Errors
Point out that multiples of a
number are the products
found in one row of the
multiplication table.

STEP 3 Divide the LCM by
the given denominators.

$24 \div 6 = 4$
$24 \div 8 = 3$

STEP 4 Multiply the
numerator and
denominator of
each fraction by the
quotients from Step 3.

$\frac{5 \times 4}{6 \times 4} = \frac{20}{24}$ $\frac{3 \times 3}{8 \times 3} = \frac{9}{24}$

You can write $\frac{5}{6}$ and $\frac{3}{8}$ as $\frac{20}{24}$ and $\frac{9}{24}$. The new fractions
have the same denominator. They are like fractions.

Practice A

Write the like fractions from each exercise.

1. $\frac{2}{5}$ $\frac{2}{15}$ $\frac{3}{5}$ $\frac{2}{5}, \frac{3}{5}$

2. $\frac{5}{12}$ $\frac{7}{12}$ $\frac{3}{11}$ $\frac{5}{12}, \frac{7}{12}$

3. $\frac{3}{10}$ $\frac{2}{20}$ $\frac{6}{10}$ $\frac{3}{10}, \frac{6}{10}$

4. $\frac{3}{4}$ $\frac{6}{7}$ $\frac{1}{7}$ $\frac{6}{7}, \frac{1}{7}$

5. $\frac{7}{8}$ $\frac{2}{9}$ $\frac{4}{9}$ $\frac{2}{9}, \frac{4}{9}$

6. $\frac{3}{8}$ $\frac{3}{5}$ $\frac{1}{8}$ $\frac{3}{8}, \frac{1}{8}$

Practice B

Change each pair of fractions to like fractions.

7. $\frac{2}{3}$ $\frac{3}{4}$ $\frac{8}{12}, \frac{9}{12}$

8. $\frac{4}{5}$ $\frac{5}{6}$ $\frac{24}{30}, \frac{25}{30}$

9. $\frac{3}{8}$ $\frac{7}{10}$ $\frac{15}{40}, \frac{28}{40}$

10. $\frac{1}{7}$ $\frac{4}{5}$ $\frac{5}{35}, \frac{28}{35}$

11. $\frac{3}{9}$ $\frac{3}{4}$ $\frac{12}{36}, \frac{27}{36}$

12. $\frac{5}{8}$ $\frac{7}{12}$ $\frac{15}{24}, \frac{14}{24}$

13. $\frac{1}{2}$ $\frac{1}{11}$ $\frac{11}{22}, \frac{2}{22}$

14. $\frac{1}{3}$ $\frac{5}{9}$ $\frac{3}{9}, \frac{5}{9}$

15. $\frac{2}{3}$ $\frac{4}{7}$ $\frac{14}{21}, \frac{12}{21}$

16. $\frac{1}{2}$ $\frac{1}{9}$ $\frac{9}{18}, \frac{2}{18}$

17. $\frac{1}{5}$ $\frac{2}{7}$ $\frac{7}{35}, \frac{10}{35}$

18. $\frac{3}{4}$ $\frac{1}{10}$ $\frac{15}{20}, \frac{2}{20}$

19. $\frac{2}{5}$ $\frac{1}{3}$ $\frac{6}{15}, \frac{5}{15}$

20. $\frac{1}{6}$ $\frac{4}{9}$ $\frac{3}{18}, \frac{8}{18}$

21. $\frac{7}{10}$ $\frac{1}{5}$ $\frac{7}{10}, \frac{2}{10}$

22. $\frac{8}{9}$ $\frac{2}{3}$ $\frac{8}{9}, \frac{6}{9}$

23. $\frac{3}{4}$ $\frac{2}{7}$ $\frac{21}{28}, \frac{8}{28}$

24. $\frac{1}{4}$ $\frac{5}{6}$ $\frac{3}{12}, \frac{10}{12}$

25. $\frac{2}{3}$ $\frac{3}{8}$ $\frac{16}{24}, \frac{9}{24}$

26. $\frac{7}{15}$ $\frac{3}{10}$ $\frac{14}{30}, \frac{9}{30}$

27. $\frac{1}{2}$ $\frac{3}{4}$ $\frac{2}{4}, \frac{3}{4}$

28. $\frac{5}{6}$ $\frac{5}{9}$ $\frac{15}{18}, \frac{10}{18}$

29. $\frac{2}{5}$ $\frac{3}{4}$ $\frac{8}{20}, \frac{15}{20}$

30. $\frac{3}{5}$ $\frac{2}{3}$ $\frac{9}{15}, \frac{10}{15}$

Everyday Problem Solving

At the supermarket, Carmine bought $\frac{1}{2}$ pound of cherries, $\frac{7}{8}$ pound of pears, and $\frac{5}{8}$ pound of apples.

1. Name the like fractions. $\frac{7}{8}, \frac{5}{8}$

2. Change all three fractions to like fractions. $\frac{4}{8}, \frac{7}{8}, \frac{5}{8}$

More Practice is provided in Exercise 59 of the *Workbook*.

7-6 ▶ Comparing Fractions

Number Sense
Point out that like fractions can be compared as follows:

$\frac{5}{8}$ = 5 eighths

$\frac{3}{8}$ = 3 eighths

Since the unit is the same, compare only 5 and 3.

You can compare like and unlike fractions.

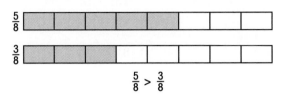

$\frac{5}{8} > \frac{3}{8}$

If the fractions are like fractions, compare the numerators.

▶ EXAMPLE 1

Review the symbols below.
< means *less than*
> means *greater than*

Compare $\frac{5}{8}$ and $\frac{3}{8}$. Use <, >, or =.

STEP 1 Are the fractions like fractions? Yes.

$\frac{5}{8}$ $\qquad$ $\frac{3}{8}$
Like fractions

STEP 2 Compare the numerators.

5 > 3
is greater than

STEP 3 Write the fractions in the same order.

$\frac{5}{8}$ > $\frac{3}{8}$

The fraction $\frac{5}{8}$ is greater than the fraction $\frac{3}{8}$.

To compare unlike fractions, you first need to change the fractions to like fractions.

▶ EXAMPLE 2

Avoiding Errors
Remind students that fractions can be compared only if they are like fractions.

When you compare fractions, order is important.

$\frac{5}{8} < \frac{5}{6}$

$\frac{5}{6} > \frac{5}{8}$

Compare $\frac{5}{8}$ and $\frac{5}{6}$. Use <, >, or =.

STEP 1 Are the fractions like fractions? No.

$\frac{5}{8}$ $\qquad$ $\frac{5}{6}$
Unlike fractions

STEP 2 Change the fractions to like fractions. Use the common denominator of 24.

$\frac{5 \times 3}{8 \times 3} = \frac{15}{24}$ $\qquad$ $\frac{5 \times 4}{6 \times 4} = \frac{20}{24}$

STEP 3 Compare the like fractions.

$\frac{15}{24}$ < $\frac{20}{24}$
is less than

STEP 4 Rewrite using the given fractions.

$\frac{5}{8}$ < $\frac{5}{6}$

The fraction $\frac{5}{8}$ is less than the fraction $\frac{5}{6}$.

Practice A

Common Error Signs for > and < are reversed. The arrow always points to the smaller number.

Compare each pair of fractions. Use >, <, or =.

1. $\frac{3}{8}$ < $\frac{7}{8}$

2. $\frac{5}{12}$ = $\frac{5}{12}$

3. $\frac{7}{9}$ > $\frac{5}{9}$

4. $\frac{5}{5}$ > $\frac{4}{5}$

5. $\frac{9}{10}$ = $\frac{9}{10}$

6. $\frac{2}{7}$ < $\frac{3}{7}$

7. $\frac{11}{12}$ > $\frac{7}{12}$

8. $\frac{1}{3}$ = $\frac{1}{3}$

9. $\frac{1}{4}$ < $\frac{3}{4}$

Practice B

Change the fractions to like fractions. Then, compare each pair of fractions. Use >, <, or =.

10. $\frac{2}{8}$ = $\frac{1}{4}$

11. $\frac{5}{8}$ < $\frac{4}{5}$

12. $\frac{1}{3}$ > $\frac{4}{15}$

13. $\frac{5}{6}$ > $\frac{3}{4}$

14. $\frac{2}{9}$ > $\frac{1}{8}$

15. $\frac{1}{6}$ < $\frac{5}{9}$

16. $\frac{9}{10}$ > $\frac{5}{6}$

17. $\frac{5}{15}$ = $\frac{1}{3}$

18. $\frac{3}{10}$ > $\frac{1}{15}$

19. $\frac{3}{8}$ > $\frac{2}{7}$

20. $\frac{3}{4}$ < $\frac{7}{8}$

21. $\frac{2}{3}$ < $\frac{3}{4}$

Everyday Problem Solving

Sometimes you compare fractions in everyday situations.

1. Mora hiked $\frac{3}{4}$ mile. Jan hiked $\frac{3}{8}$ mile.
Who hiked further? Mora

2. Sam used $\frac{3}{4}$ cup of flour for baking.
Brian used $\frac{2}{3}$ cup of flour. Who used
less flour? Brian

3. Joe drew a line that was $\frac{6}{16}$ inch long.
Ling drew a line that was $\frac{3}{8}$ inch long.
Who drew the longer line? neither student; both lines are the same length.

More Practice is provided in Exercise 60 of the *Workbook*.

7·7 Ordering Fractions

Number Sense
Review ordering numbers from least to greatest.

▶ **EXAMPLE**

You can place fractions in order from least to greatest. Use what you know about comparing fractions.

Write these fractions in order from least to greatest.

$$\frac{3}{5}, \frac{1}{2}, \frac{7}{10}$$

STEP 1 Change the fractions to like fractions. Use the least common denominator.

$$\frac{3 \times 2}{5 \times 2} = \frac{6}{10}$$
$$\frac{1 \times 5}{2 \times 5} = \frac{5}{10}$$

Avoiding Errors
Remind students that all three fractions must be like fractions so they can be ordered. Students need to find the LCM of all three numbers.

STEP 2 Look at the numerators. Write the like fractions in order from least to greatest.

$$\frac{5}{10} \qquad \frac{6}{10} \qquad \frac{7}{10}$$

STEP 3 Write the given fractions in order from least to greatest.

$$\frac{1}{2} \qquad \frac{3}{5} \qquad \frac{7}{10}$$

The fractions in order are $\frac{1}{2}, \frac{3}{5}, \frac{7}{10}$.

Common Error Students cannot translate like fractions to original fractions. Encourage the use of index cards. Write each original and higher-term fraction as pairs on separate cards, then order.

Practice

Write the fractions in order from least to greatest.

1. $\frac{1}{2}$ $\frac{3}{8}$ $\frac{3}{4}$ $\frac{3}{8}, \frac{1}{2}, \frac{3}{4}$

2. $\frac{7}{10}$ $\frac{3}{5}$ $\frac{8}{15}$ $\frac{8}{15}, \frac{3}{5}, \frac{7}{10}$

3. $\frac{2}{3}$ $\frac{3}{4}$ $\frac{5}{8}$ $\frac{5}{8}, \frac{2}{3}, \frac{3}{4}$

4. $\frac{1}{3}$ $\frac{3}{10}$ $\frac{2}{5}$ $\frac{3}{10}, \frac{1}{3}, \frac{2}{5}$

5. $\frac{2}{9}$ $\frac{1}{6}$ $\frac{2}{15}$ $\frac{2}{15}, \frac{1}{6}, \frac{2}{9}$

6. $\frac{4}{5}$ $\frac{1}{2}$ $\frac{3}{4}$ $\frac{1}{2}, \frac{3}{4}, \frac{4}{5}$

7. $\frac{3}{7}$ $\frac{1}{3}$ $\frac{2}{21}$ $\frac{2}{21}, \frac{1}{3}, \frac{3}{7}$

8. $\frac{3}{8}$ $\frac{3}{4}$ $\frac{3}{11}$ $\frac{3}{11}, \frac{3}{8}, \frac{3}{4}$

9. $\frac{2}{3}$ $\frac{5}{8}$ $\frac{7}{9}$ $\frac{5}{8}, \frac{2}{3}, \frac{7}{9}$

10. $\frac{4}{9}$ $\frac{2}{3}$ $\frac{1}{2}$ $\frac{4}{9}, \frac{1}{2}, \frac{2}{3}$

11. $\frac{5}{7}$ $\frac{3}{4}$ $\frac{5}{14}$ $\frac{5}{14}, \frac{5}{7}, \frac{3}{4}$

12. $\frac{3}{5}$ $\frac{7}{20}$ $\frac{1}{4}$ $\frac{1}{4}, \frac{7}{20}, \frac{3}{5}$

13. $\frac{7}{10}$ $\frac{2}{5}$ $\frac{1}{3}$ $\frac{1}{3}, \frac{2}{5}, \frac{7}{10}$

14. $\frac{5}{7}$ $\frac{5}{9}$ $\frac{5}{6}$ $\frac{5}{9}, \frac{5}{7}, \frac{5}{6}$

15. $\frac{3}{4}$ $\frac{11}{20}$ $\frac{1}{5}$ $\frac{1}{5}, \frac{11}{20}, \frac{3}{4}$

16. $\frac{2}{9}$ $\frac{2}{3}$ $\frac{2}{5}$ $\frac{2}{9}, \frac{2}{5}, \frac{2}{3}$

17. $\frac{3}{7}$ $\frac{1}{4}$ $\frac{5}{14}$ $\frac{1}{4}, \frac{5}{14}, \frac{3}{7}$

18. $\frac{2}{5}$ $\frac{3}{8}$ $\frac{1}{2}$ $\frac{3}{8}, \frac{2}{5}, \frac{1}{2}$

USING YOUR CALCULATOR
Comparing Fractions

Here is another way to compare fractions.

Compare $\frac{7}{8}$ and $\frac{5}{6}$.

Multiply the numerator of one fraction by the denominator of the other fraction. Start with the first numerator.

PRESS $\boxed{7}$ $\boxed{\times}$ $\boxed{6}$ $\boxed{=}$ $\boxed{\quad 42.}$

PRESS $\boxed{5}$ $\boxed{\times}$ $\boxed{8}$ $\boxed{=}$ $\boxed{\quad 40.}$

Calculator Tip
Write down the products from the calculator after you multiply. Press CLEAR between products.

Compare the products. Compare the fractions.

42 > 40

Replace the products with the given fractions.

$\frac{7}{8}$ > $\frac{5}{6}$

Compare $\frac{2}{7}$ and $\frac{6}{21}$.

PRESS $\boxed{2}$ $\boxed{\times}$ $\boxed{2}$ $\boxed{1}$ $\boxed{=}$ $\boxed{\quad 42.}$

PRESS $\boxed{6}$ $\boxed{\times}$ $\boxed{7}$ $\boxed{=}$ $\boxed{\quad 42.}$

42 = 42

$\frac{2}{7}$ = $\frac{6}{21}$

Use a calculator to compare the fractions. Use >, <, or =.

1. $\frac{5}{9}$ < $\frac{7}{8}$

2. $\frac{16}{20}$ = $\frac{28}{35}$

3. $\frac{2}{11}$ < $\frac{2}{7}$

4. $\frac{9}{10}$ > $\frac{3}{4}$

5. $\frac{3}{17}$ > $\frac{2}{15}$

6. $\frac{8}{9}$ > $\frac{15}{19}$

7. $\frac{9}{11}$ < $\frac{11}{13}$

8. $\frac{11}{12}$ > $\frac{15}{19}$

9. $\frac{9}{19}$ > $\frac{7}{17}$

More Practice is provided in Exercise 61 of the *Workbook*.

7·8 Changing Fractions to Mixed Numbers

Number Sense
Remind students that 1 whole is 2 halves, 3 thirds, 4 fourths, etc. Draw circles and divide them into halves, thirds, etc.

A proper fraction is a fraction whose numerator is smaller than its denominator.

$\frac{1}{2}$ is a proper fraction.

An improper fraction is a fraction whose numerator is larger than or equal to its denominator.

$\frac{8}{3}$ is an improper fraction.

A **mixed number** is a whole number and a fraction.

$2\frac{2}{3}$ is a mixed number.

You can change an improper fraction to a mixed number.

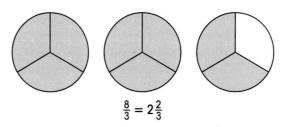

$$\frac{8}{3} = 2\frac{2}{3}$$

To change an improper fraction to a mixed number, divide the numerator by the denominator.

▶ **EXAMPLE 1**

Avoiding Errors
Emphasize that the denominator of the improper fraction will be the denominator of the fractional part in the mixed number before it is reduced to lowest terms.

Change $\frac{8}{3}$ to a mixed number.

STEP 1 Divide the numerator by the denominator.

$$\begin{array}{r} 2 \\ 3\overline{)8} \\ -6 \\ \hline \end{array}$$ 2 out of 3 parts

STEP 2 Write the remainder as a fraction.

$$\begin{array}{r} 2\frac{2}{3} \\ 3\overline{)8} \\ -6 \\ \hline 2 \end{array}$$

The fraction $\frac{8}{3}$ is the mixed number $2\frac{2}{3}$.

Sometimes, the fraction part of the mixed number needs to be reduced to lowest terms.

► EXAMPLE 2

Change $\frac{28}{8}$ to a mixed number.

STEP 1 Divide the numerator by the denominator.

$$\begin{array}{r} 3 \\ 8\overline{)28} \\ -24 \\ \hline \text{4 out of 8 parts} \end{array}$$

STEP 2 Write the remainder as a fraction.

$$\begin{array}{r} 3\frac{4}{8} \\ 8\overline{)28} \\ -24 \\ \hline 4 \end{array}$$

STEP 3 Reduce the fraction part to lowest terms.

$$3\frac{4}{8} = 3\frac{1}{2}$$

The fraction $\frac{28}{8}$ is the mixed number $3\frac{1}{2}$.

Sometimes an improper fraction can be written as a whole number.

$$\frac{15}{3} \rightarrow 3\overline{)15}^{\,5} \rightarrow \frac{15}{3} = 5$$

Common Error Fractional parts of mixed numbers are not reduced to lowest terms. Have students review their answers to be sure all fractions are in lowest terms. The GCF of the numerator and denominator must be 1.

Practice

Change each fraction to a mixed number or a whole number.

1. $\frac{17}{9}$ $1\frac{8}{9}$ **2.** $\frac{8}{5}$ $1\frac{3}{5}$ **3.** $\frac{10}{3}$ $3\frac{1}{3}$ **4.** $\frac{16}{8}$ 2 **5.** $\frac{18}{3}$ 6

6. $\frac{22}{7}$ $3\frac{1}{7}$ **7.** $\frac{54}{8}$ $6\frac{3}{4}$ **8.** $\frac{29}{3}$ $9\frac{2}{3}$ **9.** $\frac{42}{6}$ 7 **10.** $\frac{20}{4}$ 5

11. $\frac{80}{9}$ $8\frac{8}{9}$ **12.** $\frac{65}{3}$ $21\frac{2}{3}$ **13.** $\frac{14}{11}$ $1\frac{3}{11}$ **14.** $\frac{70}{12}$ $5\frac{5}{6}$ **15.** $\frac{35}{5}$ 7

16. $\frac{9}{4}$ $2\frac{1}{4}$ **17.** $\frac{25}{3}$ $8\frac{1}{3}$ **18.** $\frac{82}{9}$ $9\frac{1}{9}$ **19.** $\frac{63}{7}$ 9 **20.** $\frac{56}{6}$ $9\frac{1}{3}$

 **7·9** **Changing Mixed Numbers to Fractions**

Number Sense
Draw 3 circles on the board and divide each into fourths. Shade 11 fourths. Count as each fourth is shaded. Explain that 11 fourths = $\frac{11}{4} = 2\frac{3}{4}$.

Mixed numbers can be changed to improper fractions. Change the whole number part to a fraction. Then, add the fraction part.

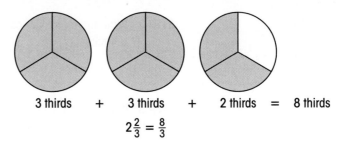

3 thirds + 3 thirds + 2 thirds = 8 thirds

$$2\frac{2}{3} = \frac{8}{3}$$

▶ **EXAMPLE**

Avoiding Errors
Be sure that students use the denominator from the mixed number as the denominator for the fraction.

Change $5\frac{2}{3}$ to a fraction.

STEP 1 Multiply the whole number by the denominator of the fraction.

$5\frac{2}{3}$
$5 \times 3 = 15$

STEP 2 Add the numerator to the product from Step 1.

$15 + 2 = 17$

STEP 3 Write the sum as the numerator of the fraction. The denominator is the same.

$\frac{17}{3}$

The mixed number $5\frac{2}{3}$ is the improper fraction $\frac{17}{3}$.

You can write a whole number as a fraction. $3 = \frac{3}{1}$

Common Error Students reverse the addition and multiplication processes. Have the students circle the denominator and draw an arrow to the whole number with a times sign. Write a plus sign next to the numerator with the product.

Practice

Change each mixed number or whole number to an improper fraction.

1. $4\frac{3}{4}$ $\frac{19}{4}$

2. 4 $\frac{4}{1}$

3. $5\frac{2}{5}$ $\frac{27}{5}$

4. $3\frac{6}{7}$ $\frac{27}{7}$

5. $9\frac{4}{5}$ $\frac{49}{5}$

6. $7\frac{3}{4}$ $\frac{31}{4}$

7. 9 $\frac{9}{1}$

8. $8\frac{5}{9}$ $\frac{77}{9}$

9. $5\frac{8}{9}$ $\frac{53}{9}$

10. $6\frac{7}{12}$ $\frac{79}{12}$

11. $12\frac{1}{3}$ $\frac{37}{3}$

12. 6 $\frac{6}{1}$

Extra Practice for this lesson is provided on page 422.

MATH IN YOUR LIFE
Cooking

In a few minutes, Nina's guests will be arriving for her party. She still needs to prepare the spinach dip. Nina can only find her measuring cup marked $\frac{1}{8}$ cup. She uses equivalent fractions to help her.

$\frac{1}{2}$ cup = $\frac{4}{8}$ cup soft cream cheese

This means that Nina will fill the measuring cup 4 times to measure the cream cheese.

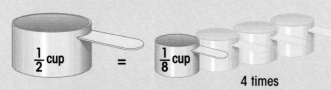

4 times

Spinach Dip

$\frac{1}{2}$ cup soft cream cheese
$\frac{1}{8}$ cup half-and-half
1 cup shredded cheese
$\frac{1}{4}$ cup chopped onion
$\frac{3}{4}$ cup chopped spinach
Option: 3 Tbsp chopped olives

1. How many times must she fill the measuring cup to measure each of the other ingredients?
   half-and-half, 1; shredded cheese, 8; onion, 2; spinach, 6

2. A recipe option calls for 3 tablespoons of chopped olives. Nina remembers that this is about $\frac{1}{16}$ of a cup. How can she measure the olives using the $\frac{1}{8}$ cup? fill the $\frac{1}{8}$ cup half full

3. Nina plans to serve the dip with tortilla chips. She wants $\frac{1}{4}$ bag of chips for each guest. How many guests can be served with 2 bags of chips? 8 guests

Critical Thinking

The next day Nina's $\frac{1}{8}$-cup cracked. She found her $\frac{1}{4}$-cup measuring cup. If she used this cup to make more spinach dip, what will she need to do differently?

Critical Thinking
Nina will need to use different numbers of $\frac{1}{4}$-cups for each ingredient. She'll need to estimate one-half of the $\frac{1}{4}$-cup for the half-and-half.

More Practice is provided in Exercise 63 of the *Workbook*.

7·10 ▶ Ordering Numbers You Know

Sometimes, you will need to order numbers in different forms from least to greatest. Order mixed numbers and fractions as you would whole numbers.

Write the numbers in order from least to greatest.

$$2\tfrac{1}{2} \quad \tfrac{9}{4} \quad 3$$

▶ **EXAMPLE**

STEP 1 Change the improper fraction to a mixed number.

$$\begin{array}{r} 2\tfrac{1}{4} \\ 4\overline{)9} \\ -8 \\ \hline 1 \end{array}$$

STEP 2 Change the mixed numbers to like mixed numbers.

$$2\tfrac{1}{2} = 2\tfrac{2}{4}$$
$$2\tfrac{1}{4} = 2\tfrac{1}{4}$$

STEP 3 List the numbers vertically. Find the least and the greatest numbers.

$$2\tfrac{2}{4}$$
$$2\tfrac{1}{4} \leftarrow \text{least}$$
$$3 \leftarrow \text{greatest}$$

STEP 4 Write the numbers in order from least to greatest.

$$2\tfrac{1}{4}, 2\tfrac{2}{4}, 3$$

STEP 5 Rewrite the numbers in the given form.

$$\tfrac{9}{4}, 2\tfrac{1}{2}, 3$$

The numbers from least to greatest are: $\tfrac{9}{4}$, $2\tfrac{1}{2}$, 3

Practice A

Write each group of numbers in order from least to greatest.

1. $3\tfrac{1}{2}$ $\tfrac{3}{2}, 3, 3\tfrac{1}{2}$

3

$\tfrac{3}{2}$

2. 4 $\tfrac{5}{2}, 3\tfrac{1}{2}, 4$

$\tfrac{5}{2}$

$3\tfrac{1}{2}$

3. $2\tfrac{3}{4}$ $2\tfrac{1}{4}, 2\tfrac{1}{2}, 2\tfrac{3}{4}$

$2\tfrac{1}{2}$

$2\tfrac{1}{4}$

4. $\tfrac{7}{3}$ $1\tfrac{2}{3}, 2, \tfrac{7}{3}$

$1\tfrac{2}{3}$

2

Practice B

Write each group of numbers in order from least to greatest.

5. $3, 2\frac{2}{3}, \frac{10}{3}$ $2\frac{2}{3}, 3, \frac{10}{3}$

6. $1\frac{5}{6}, 1\frac{1}{2}, \frac{5}{3}$ $1\frac{1}{2}, \frac{5}{3}, 1\frac{5}{6}$

7. $4\frac{1}{4}, \frac{9}{2}, 4$ $4, 4\frac{1}{4}, \frac{9}{2}$

8. $3\frac{2}{3}, \frac{7}{2}, 3\frac{5}{6}$ $\frac{7}{2}, 3\frac{2}{3}, 3\frac{5}{6}$

9. $2\frac{3}{4}, 2\frac{1}{2}, 2\frac{3}{8}$ $2\frac{3}{8}, 2\frac{1}{2}, 2\frac{3}{4}$

10. $1\frac{1}{3}, 1\frac{1}{4}, 1\frac{1}{2}$ $1\frac{1}{4}, 1\frac{1}{3}, 1\frac{1}{2}$

11. $5\frac{3}{5}, 5\frac{1}{2}, 5\frac{3}{10}$ $5\frac{3}{10}, 5\frac{1}{2}, 5\frac{3}{5}$

12. $\frac{6}{2}, 2\frac{1}{2}, \frac{11}{4}$ $2\frac{1}{2}, \frac{11}{4}, \frac{6}{2}$

13. $10, \frac{10}{3}, 3\frac{1}{2}$ $\frac{10}{3}, 3\frac{1}{2}, 10$

14. $8\frac{3}{4}, \frac{24}{4}, 8\frac{3}{8}$ $\frac{24}{4}, 8\frac{3}{8}, 8\frac{3}{4}$

Everyday Problem Solving

Hiking trails were built in a local park.
Use the chart to answer the questions.

1. Which trail is the longest? Field

2. Which trail is the shortest? Pleasant

3. List the distances in order from least to greatest. $3\frac{3}{8}, 3\frac{1}{2}, 3\frac{5}{8}, 3\frac{3}{4}$

4. List the names of the trails in order from shortest to longest. Pleasant, Vista, Stream, Field

5. Cindy walked the entire distance of one of the trails. She walked $3\frac{9}{12}$ miles. Which trail did she walk? Field

Trail	Distance
Vista	$3\frac{1}{2}$
Pleasant	$3\frac{3}{8}$
Field	$3\frac{3}{4}$
Stream	$3\frac{5}{8}$

7·11 Problem Solving: Patterns

Sometimes, you need to solve problems that are not word problems. You may need to find and complete a pattern. You can use the same problem-solving steps.

▶ **EXAMPLE**

Copy and complete the sequence. Write each fraction in lowest terms.

$$\frac{1}{8}, \frac{1}{4}, \frac{3}{8}, \frac{1}{2}, \underline{\quad?\quad}, \underline{\quad?\quad}, \underline{\quad?\quad}, 1$$

STEP 1 READ What do you need to find out?
Find the three missing fractions.

STEP 2 PLAN What do you need to do?
Write each fraction with a **common denominator**. Then, look for the **pattern** and complete it. Reduce to lowest terms where needed.

Change the fractions to like fractions

$$\frac{1}{4} = \frac{1 \times 2}{4 \times 2} = \frac{2}{8}$$

$$\frac{1}{2} = \frac{1 \times 4}{2 \times 4} = \frac{4}{8}$$

$$1 = \frac{1 \times 8}{1 \times 8} = \frac{8}{8}$$

STEP 3 DO Follow the plan.
Write each fraction with a **common denominator of 8.**

$$\frac{1}{8}, \frac{1}{4}, \frac{3}{8}, \frac{1}{2}, \underline{\quad?\quad}, \underline{\quad?\quad}, \underline{\quad?\quad}, 1$$

$$\frac{1}{8}, \frac{2}{8}, \frac{3}{8}, \frac{4}{8}, \underline{\quad?\quad}, \underline{\quad?\quad}, \underline{\quad?\quad}, \frac{8}{8}$$

Look for a **pattern** and complete it.

$$\frac{1}{8}, \frac{2}{8}, \frac{3}{8}, \frac{4}{8}, \frac{5}{8}, \frac{6}{8}, \frac{7}{8}, \frac{8}{8}$$

Reduce to the lowest terms, where needed.

$$\frac{6}{8} = \frac{3}{4}$$

STEP 4 CHECK Does your answer make sense?
The fractions $\frac{5}{8}, \frac{6}{8}, \frac{7}{8}$ complete a pattern. ✓

The complete sequence is: $\frac{1}{8}, \frac{1}{4}, \frac{3}{8}, \frac{1}{2}, \frac{5}{8}, \frac{3}{4}, \frac{7}{8}, 1$

Problem Solving

READ each problem. Answer the questions under PLAN. DO the plan to solve the problem.

1. $\frac{1}{6}, \frac{1}{3}, \frac{1}{2}, \underline{\quad?\quad}, \underline{\quad?\quad}, \underline{\quad?\quad}, 1\frac{1}{6}$

PLAN

What is the least common denominator? 6

What is the pattern? $\frac{1}{6}, \frac{2}{6}, \frac{3}{6}, \frac{4}{6}, \frac{5}{6}, \frac{6}{6}, \frac{7}{6}$

What are the fractions in lowest terms? $\frac{1}{6}, \frac{1}{3}, \frac{1}{2}, \frac{2}{3}, \frac{5}{6}, 1, 1\frac{1}{6}$

2. $1, \frac{7}{8}, \frac{3}{4}, \underline{\quad?\quad}, \frac{1}{2}, \underline{\quad?\quad}, \frac{1}{4}, \underline{\quad?\quad}$

PLAN

What is the least common denominator? 8

What is the pattern? $\frac{8}{8}, \frac{7}{8}, \frac{6}{8}, \frac{5}{8}, \frac{4}{8}, \frac{3}{8}, \frac{2}{8}, \frac{1}{8}$

What are the fractions in lowest terms? $1, \frac{7}{8}, \frac{3}{4}, \frac{5}{8}, \frac{1}{2}, \frac{3}{8}, \frac{1}{4}, \frac{1}{8}$

3. $1\frac{1}{2}, 1\frac{3}{4}, 2, \underline{\quad?\quad}, 2\frac{1}{2}, \underline{\quad?\quad}, \underline{\quad?\quad}$

PLAN

What is the least common denominator? 4

What is the pattern? $1\frac{2}{4}, 1\frac{3}{4}, 2, 2\frac{1}{4}, 2\frac{2}{4}, 2\frac{3}{4}, 3$

What are the fractions in lowest terms? $1\frac{1}{2}, 1\frac{3}{4}, 2, 2\frac{1}{4}, 2\frac{1}{2}, 2\frac{3}{4}, 3$

Problem Solving Strategy

Sometimes, you need to find one number in a pattern.

Find the 10th number in this pattern.

$\frac{1}{3}, \frac{2}{3}, 1, 1\frac{1}{3}, 1\frac{2}{3}, 2, \ldots$

Count the numbers. Continue the pattern. Stop at the 10th number.

$\frac{1}{3}, \frac{2}{3}, 1, 1\frac{1}{3}, 1\frac{2}{3}, 2, 2\frac{1}{3}, 2\frac{2}{3}, 3, 3\frac{1}{3}$

$\phantom{\frac{1}{3}}1\ 2\ 3\ 4\ 5\ 6\ 7\ 8\ 9\ 10$

| denominator |
| equivalent fraction |
| fraction |
| like fractions |
| lowest terms |
| improper fraction |
| mixed number |
| numerator |
| unlike fractions |

Vocabulary Review

Choose a word from the list to complete each sentence.

1. The __?__ of $\frac{3}{4}$ is 3. numerator
2. The fraction $\frac{20}{40}$ in __?__ is $\frac{1}{2}$. lowest terms
3. A(n) __?__ for $\frac{6}{8}$ is $\frac{3}{4}$. equivalent fraction
4. The __?__ of $\frac{7}{8}$ is 8. denominator
5. If 3 circles out of 5 are shaded, then the __?__ of shaded circles is $\frac{3}{5}$. fraction
6. $\frac{5}{6}$ and $\frac{1}{6}$ are __?__. like fractions
7. $\frac{3}{7}$ and $\frac{1}{2}$ are __?__. unlike fractions
8. $7\frac{1}{2}$ is the __?__ for $\frac{15}{2}$. mixed number
9. $\frac{19}{3}$ is an __?__. improper fraction
10. **Writing** Explain why an improper fraction is always greater than or equal to 1.

Chapter Quiz

LESSONS 7·1 and 7·2

Test Tip
The top number of a fraction tells the part. The bottom number tells the whole.

Identifying Fractions

Write a fraction to tell what part of each whole is blue. Is each fraction pair equivalent?

1.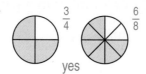
   $\frac{3}{4}$ $\frac{6}{8}$
   yes

2.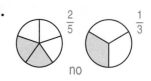
   $\frac{2}{5}$ $\frac{1}{3}$
   no

LESSONS 7·3 and 7·4

Test Tip
Multiply or divide the numerator and denominator by the same number.

Writing in Lowest Terms and Higher Terms

Write each fraction in lowest terms.

3. $\frac{16}{18}$ $\frac{8}{9}$
4. $\frac{9}{27}$ $\frac{1}{3}$
5. $\frac{6}{10}$ $\frac{3}{5}$

Write each fraction in higher terms.

6. $\frac{1}{6} = \frac{?}{18}$ $\frac{3}{18}$
7. $\frac{2}{3} = \frac{?}{30}$ $\frac{20}{30}$

Finding Common Denominators
Change the fractions to like fractions.

8. $\frac{4}{5}$ $\frac{7}{10}$ $\frac{8}{10}, \frac{7}{10}$ **9.** $\frac{5}{6}$ $\frac{1}{4}$ $\frac{10}{12}, \frac{3}{12}$ **10.** $\frac{1}{3}$ $\frac{4}{9}$ $\frac{3}{9}, \frac{4}{9}$

Comparing and Ordering
Compare. Use >, <, or =.

11. $\frac{6}{7} > \frac{5}{7}$ **12.** $\frac{2}{3} < \frac{5}{6}$

13. $\frac{1}{3} > \frac{1}{4}$ **14.** $\frac{3}{4} = \frac{6}{8}$

Write the fractions in order from least to greatest.

15. $\frac{1}{2}$ $\frac{3}{8}$ $\frac{3}{4}$ $\frac{3}{8}, \frac{1}{2}, \frac{3}{4}$ **16.** $\frac{5}{6}$ $\frac{2}{3}$ $\frac{1}{2}$ $\frac{1}{2}, \frac{2}{3}, \frac{5}{6}$

Changing Mixed Numbers and Fractions
Change to a mixed number or a whole number.

17. $\frac{34}{5}$ $6\frac{4}{5}$ **18.** $\frac{18}{4}$ $4\frac{1}{2}$ **19.** $\frac{15}{3}$ 5

Change to an improper fraction.

20. $2\frac{1}{3}$ $\frac{7}{3}$ **21.** $5\frac{1}{2}$ $\frac{11}{2}$ **22.** $3\frac{3}{4}$ $\frac{15}{4}$

Write the numbers in order from least to greatest.

23. $\frac{7}{4}$ 2 $1\frac{1}{2}$ $1\frac{1}{2}, \frac{7}{4}, 2$ **24.** $\frac{7}{3}$ 2 $2\frac{1}{2}$ $2, \frac{7}{3}, 2\frac{1}{2}$

Finding Patterns
Complete the pattern.

25. $\frac{1}{4}$, _____ ?, $\frac{3}{4}$, 1, _____ ?, $1\frac{1}{2}$, $1\frac{3}{4}$, _____ $\frac{1}{2}, 1\frac{1}{4}, 2$

Group Activity See the *Teacher Planning Guide* for a Scoring Rubric for this activity.
With your group, look at the Business section of a newspaper. See how fractions and mixed numbers are used on the stock exchange. Pick three stocks. List the closing price for each stock. List the stock prices in order from least to greatest.

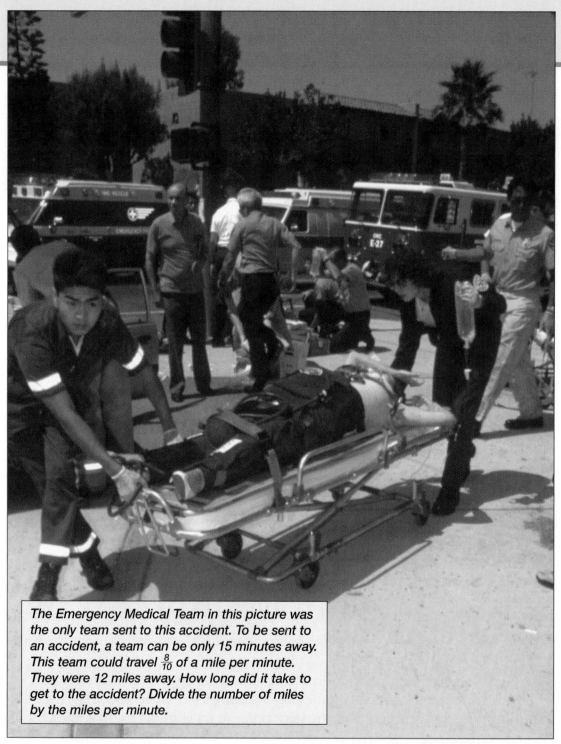

The Emergency Medical Team in this picture was the only team sent to this accident. To be sent to an accident, a team can be only 15 minutes away. This team could travel $\frac{8}{10}$ of a mile per minute. They were 12 miles away. How long did it take to get to the accident? Divide the number of miles by the miles per minute.

Caption They arrived in 15 minutes.

Chapter 8 ▷ Multiplying and Dividing Fractions

ESL Note Show examples of each word. Use each in a sentence.

Words to Know

canceling	dividing a numerator and a denominator by the same number
invert	to reverse the positions of the numerator and denominator of a fraction

Words to Know Provide examples of each word. Relate "canceling" to "regrouping" in whole number operations.

Recipe Project

Look through several magazines or cookbooks for recipes that have fractions and mixed numbers. Choose 3 of your favorite recipes. Find out how many servings the recipe makes when it is completed. Now, cut the ingredients to serve only one person.

Project Answers will vary based on recipes. Students can gather recipes for a few weeks. This project will be hard for students. Be sure they know that they have to divide by the current number of servings. Save recipes so they can be used in the Group Activity at the end of the chapter.

Learning Objectives

- Multiply fractions.
- Multiply fractions using canceling.
- Multiply fractions, whole numbers, and mixed numbers.
- Divide fractions by fractions.
- Divide whole numbers, mixed numbers, and fractions.
- Apply multiplying fractions to finding gallons of gasoline.
- Solve word problems by multiplying and dividing fractions.

More Practice is provided in Exercise 65 of the *Workbook*.

8·1 ▶ Multiplying Fractions

Number Sense
Cut out circles to demonstrate multiplying fractions. Fold $\frac{1}{2}$ of a $\frac{1}{2}$ to show that $\frac{1}{2} \times \frac{1}{2} = \frac{1}{4}$.

What is one-half of one-third? This means $\frac{1}{2} \times \frac{1}{3}$.

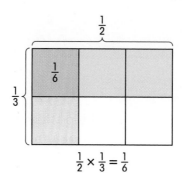

$$\frac{1}{2} \times \frac{1}{3} = \frac{1}{6}$$

One-half of one-third is one-sixth.

Knowing the basic multiplication facts will help you to multiply fractions.

▶ **EXAMPLE 1**

Multiply. $\frac{1}{2} \times \frac{1}{3}$

Avoiding Errors
Remind students that no common denominators are needed. "Go across" the fractions to get the product.

STEP 1 Multiply the numerators. $\qquad \frac{1}{2} \times \frac{1}{3} = \frac{1}{\underline{}}$

STEP 2 Multiply the denominators. $\qquad \frac{1}{2} \times \frac{1}{3} = \frac{1}{6}$

STEP 3 Reduce to lowest terms. $\qquad \frac{1}{6}$ is in lowest terms.

The product of $\frac{1}{2}$ and $\frac{1}{3}$ is $\frac{1}{6}$.

▶ **EXAMPLE 2**

Multiply. $\frac{3}{4} \times \frac{2}{5}$

The Greatest Common Factor of 6 and 20 is 2. Divide 6 and 20 by 2 to reduce $\frac{6}{20}$ to lowest terms.

STEP 1 Multiply the numerators. $\qquad \frac{3}{4} \times \frac{2}{5} = \frac{6}{\underline{}}$

STEP 2 Multiply the denominators. $\qquad \frac{3}{4} \times \frac{2}{5} = \frac{6}{20}$

STEP 3 Reduce to lowest terms. $\qquad \frac{6 \div 2}{20 \div 2} = \frac{3}{10}$

The product of $\frac{3}{4}$ and $\frac{2}{5}$ is $\frac{3}{10}$.

Practice

Multiply. Write each product in lowest terms.

1. $\frac{1}{3} \times \frac{3}{4}$ $\frac{1}{4}$

2. $\frac{5}{6} \times \frac{1}{2}$ $\frac{5}{12}$

3. $\frac{2}{3} \times \frac{2}{3}$ $\frac{4}{9}$

4. $\frac{3}{5} \times \frac{2}{3}$ $\frac{2}{5}$

5. $\frac{3}{4} \times \frac{1}{2}$ $\frac{3}{8}$

6. $\frac{2}{5} \times \frac{3}{5}$ $\frac{6}{25}$

7. $\frac{3}{5} \times \frac{3}{4}$ $\frac{9}{20}$

8. $\frac{2}{3} \times \frac{5}{6}$ $\frac{5}{9}$

9. $\frac{4}{7} \times \frac{3}{4}$ $\frac{3}{7}$

10. $\frac{5}{8} \times \frac{1}{5}$ $\frac{1}{8}$

11. $\frac{2}{3} \times \frac{3}{4}$ $\frac{1}{2}$

12. $\frac{3}{4} \times \frac{3}{4}$ $\frac{9}{16}$

13. $\frac{2}{3} \times \frac{2}{5}$ $\frac{4}{15}$

14. $\frac{1}{2} \times \frac{2}{3}$ $\frac{1}{3}$

15. $\frac{4}{5} \times \frac{1}{2}$ $\frac{2}{5}$

16. $\frac{2}{5} \times \frac{5}{6}$ $\frac{1}{3}$

17. $\frac{3}{4} \times \frac{4}{5}$ $\frac{3}{5}$

18. $\frac{2}{3} \times \frac{4}{5}$ $\frac{8}{15}$

19. $\frac{3}{5} \times \frac{5}{6}$ $\frac{1}{2}$

20. $\frac{5}{6} \times \frac{3}{4}$ $\frac{5}{8}$

21. $\frac{2}{3} \times \frac{3}{8}$ $\frac{1}{4}$

22. $\frac{3}{4} \times \frac{4}{9}$ $\frac{1}{3}$

23. $\frac{3}{5} \times \frac{5}{12}$ $\frac{1}{4}$

24. $\frac{7}{8} \times \frac{4}{7}$ $\frac{1}{2}$

Everyday Problem Solving

This is a drawing of Lee's garden.

1. What fraction of the garden is planted in corn? $\frac{1}{2}$ of the garden

2. What fraction of the corn is white corn? $\frac{3}{4}$ of the garden

3. What fraction of the garden is white corn? Multiply $\frac{1}{2} \times \frac{3}{4}$. $\frac{3}{8}$ of the corn

4. What fraction of the garden is yellow corn? $\frac{1}{8}$ of the garden

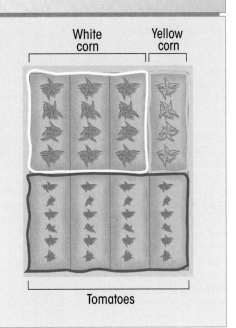

White corn   Yellow corn

Tomatoes

Extra Practice for this lesson is provided on page 423.

More Practice is provided in Exercise 66 of the *Workbook*.

8·2 Canceling

Number Sense
Write on the board: $\frac{2}{3} \times \frac{3}{4}$.
Ask students to identify the numbers that have 2 as a common factor, then 3 as a common factor.

► **EXAMPLE**

Avoiding Errors
Knowing the multiplication facts will help students recognize common factors.

Canceling is dividing the numerator of one fraction and the denominator of another fraction by the same number. Cancel fractions whenever you can before multiplying. Look for common factors.

Multiply. $\frac{2}{3} \times \frac{3}{4}$

STEP 1 Divide the numerator 2 and the denominator 4 by 2.
$2 \div 2 = 1$ Cross out 2 and write 1.
$4 \div 2 = 2$ Cross out 4 and write 2.

$\frac{\overset{1}{\cancel{2}}}{3} \times \frac{3}{\underset{2}{\cancel{4}}}$

STEP 2 Divide the numerator 3 and the denominator 3 by 3.
$3 \div 3 = 1$ Cross out each 3 and write 1.

$\frac{\overset{1}{\cancel{2}}}{\underset{1}{\cancel{3}}} \times \frac{\cancel{3}}{\underset{2}{\cancel{4}}}$

STEP 3 Multiply the new fractions.

$\frac{1}{1} \times \frac{1}{2} = \frac{1}{2}$

The product of $\frac{2}{3}$ and $\frac{3}{4}$ is $\frac{1}{2}$.

Without canceling, you would have to reduce $\frac{6}{12}$ to lowest terms, $\frac{6}{12} = \frac{1}{2}$.

Common Error Cross multiplication is used instead of cross canceling to find the products. Remind students to multiply the numerators. Then, multiply the denominators.

Practice A

Multiply. Remember to cancel before you multiply.

1. $\frac{2}{3} \times \frac{6}{7}$ $\frac{4}{7}$

2. $\frac{2}{5} \times \frac{9}{10}$ $\frac{9}{25}$

3. $\frac{3}{4} \times \frac{2}{9}$ $\frac{1}{6}$

4. $\frac{3}{7} \times \frac{14}{15}$ $\frac{2}{5}$

5. $\frac{5}{6} \times \frac{12}{25}$ $\frac{2}{5}$

6. $\frac{4}{7} \times \frac{7}{8}$ $\frac{1}{2}$

7. $\frac{1}{3} \times \frac{9}{10}$ $\frac{3}{10}$

8. $\frac{4}{5} \times \frac{5}{18}$ $\frac{2}{9}$

9. $\frac{3}{5} \times \frac{5}{9}$ $\frac{1}{3}$

10. $\frac{5}{8} \times \frac{2}{5}$ $\frac{1}{4}$

11. $\frac{8}{15} \times \frac{5}{12}$ $\frac{2}{9}$

12. $\frac{3}{4} \times \frac{8}{9}$ $\frac{2}{3}$

Practice B

Multiply. You will not need to cancel in every problem.

13. $\frac{3}{10} \times \frac{8}{21}$ $\frac{4}{35}$

14. $\frac{7}{8} \times \frac{16}{49}$ $\frac{2}{7}$

15. $\frac{5}{9} \times \frac{9}{10}$ $\frac{1}{2}$

16. $\frac{3}{8} \times \frac{6}{7}$ $\frac{9}{28}$

17. $\frac{7}{9} \times \frac{18}{19}$ $\frac{14}{19}$

18. $\frac{1}{5} \times \frac{1}{4}$ $\frac{1}{20}$

19. $\frac{4}{9} \times \frac{3}{28}$ $\frac{1}{21}$

20. $\frac{1}{4} \times \frac{8}{9}$ $\frac{2}{9}$

21. $\frac{4}{5} \times \frac{1}{3}$ $\frac{4}{15}$

22. $\frac{3}{8} \times \frac{16}{17}$ $\frac{6}{17}$

23. $\frac{5}{12} \times \frac{4}{5}$ $\frac{1}{3}$

24. $\frac{8}{9} \times \frac{3}{10}$ $\frac{4}{15}$

25. $\frac{2}{5} \times \frac{1}{2}$ $\frac{1}{5}$

26. $\frac{3}{13} \times \frac{1}{2}$ $\frac{3}{26}$

27. $\frac{7}{18} \times \frac{6}{7}$ $\frac{1}{3}$

28. $\frac{7}{15} \times \frac{12}{21}$ $\frac{4}{15}$

29. $\frac{7}{8} \times \frac{1}{4}$ $\frac{7}{32}$

30. $\frac{9}{10} \times \frac{15}{24}$ $\frac{9}{16}$

Everyday Problem Solving

Gina has a recipe for Power Cereal. She wants to make $\frac{3}{4}$ of the recipe. Remember that *of* means to multiply.

Power Cereal

2 Cups Quick Oatmeal

$\frac{2}{3}$ Cup Wheat Germ

$\frac{3}{4}$ Cup Raisins

$\frac{1}{3}$ Cup Sunflower Seeds

1 Tablespoon Brown Sugar

Serves 2 people

1. How much wheat germ will she need? Multiply $\frac{2}{3}$ by $\frac{3}{4}$. $\frac{1}{2}$ cup wheat germ

2. How many cups of raisins will she need? $\frac{9}{16}$ cup raisins

3. How many cups of sunflower seeds will she need? $\frac{1}{4}$ cup sunflower seeds

4. Will she need more or less than 2 cups of quick oatmeal? Why? less; $\frac{3}{4}$ of 2 is less than 2

Extra Practice for this lesson is provided on page 423.

8-3 Multiplying Fractions and Whole Numbers

Number Sense
Ask students to draw rectangles and shade the fractions $\frac{2}{1}$ and $\frac{1}{2}$. This shows that they are not the same quantity.

Avoiding Errors
Remind students that with fractions you just multiply across to find the product.

▶ **EXAMPLE**

To change $\frac{16}{3}$ to a mixed number, divide the numerator by the denominator:

$$\begin{array}{r} 5\frac{1}{3} \\ 3\overline{)16} \\ -15 \\ \hline 1 \end{array}$$

To multiply a fraction and a whole number, first change the whole number to a fraction.

You can change any whole number to a fraction. Make the whole number the numerator. Make the denominator 1.

$$2 = \frac{2}{1} \qquad 16 = \frac{16}{1} \qquad 39 = \frac{39}{1}$$

Multiply. $8 \times \frac{2}{3}$

STEP 1 Change the whole number to a fraction. $8 = \frac{8}{1}$

STEP 2 Multiply numerators and denominators. $\frac{8}{1} \times \frac{2}{3} = \frac{16}{3}$

STEP 3 Change the product to a mixed number in lowest terms. $\frac{16}{3} = 5\frac{1}{3}$

The product of 8 and $\frac{2}{3}$ is $5\frac{1}{3}$.

Practice

Common Error Products are not reduced to lowest terms. Remind students to use cancellation within the problem to make it easier to solve.

Multiply. Cancel, if possible.

1. $5 \times \frac{3}{4}$ $3\frac{3}{4}$

2. $\frac{7}{8} \times 5$ $4\frac{3}{8}$

3. $\frac{3}{4} \times 7$ $5\frac{1}{4}$

4. $\frac{4}{5} \times 7$ $5\frac{3}{5}$

5. $\frac{3}{10} \times 7$ $2\frac{1}{10}$

6. $15 \times \frac{2}{7}$ $4\frac{2}{7}$

7. $\frac{8}{9} \times 5$ $4\frac{4}{9}$

8. $7 \times \frac{3}{4}$ $5\frac{1}{4}$

9. $\frac{2}{3} \times 9$ 6

10. $12 \times \frac{5}{6}$ 10

11. $81 \times \frac{5}{9}$ 45

12. $22 \times \frac{3}{8}$ $8\frac{1}{4}$

13. $36 \times \frac{5}{12}$ 15

14. $\frac{1}{8} \times 20$ $2\frac{1}{2}$

15. $\frac{5}{6} \times 11$ $9\frac{1}{6}$

16. $32 \times \frac{7}{16}$ 14

17. $15 \times \frac{1}{3}$ 5

18. $\frac{2}{5} \times 10$ 4

19. $\frac{5}{12} \times 8$ $3\frac{1}{3}$

20. $6 \times \frac{3}{8}$ $2\frac{1}{4}$

Extra Practice for this lesson is provided on page 423.

You can use your calculator to find the product of a whole number and a fraction.

Multiply. $\frac{3}{8} \times 24$

First, multiply the whole number and the numerator.

PRESS [2] [4] [×] [3] [=] 72.

Calculator Tip
Do not press clear between steps.

Do not press CLEAR. Leave the product on the screen. Divide it by the denominator of the fraction.

PRESS [÷] [8] [=] 9.

The product of $\frac{3}{8}$ and 24 is 9.

Copy each problem on paper. Then, use your calculator to multiply.

1. $500 \times \frac{4}{5}$ 400

2. $\frac{5}{8} \times 6,400$ 4,000

3. $\frac{2}{3} \times 1,500$ 1,000

4. $312 \times \frac{5}{8}$ 195

5. $\frac{5}{6} \times 84$ 70

6. $\frac{27}{4} \times 4$ 27

7. $\frac{3}{5} \times 600$ 360

8. $1,400 \times \frac{4}{7}$ 800

9. $\frac{5}{9} \times 270$ 150

10. $330 \times \frac{2}{3}$ 220

11. $\frac{1}{2} \times 900$ 450

12. $\frac{2}{3} \times 9$ 6

13. $\frac{3}{4} \times 1,600$ 1,200

14. $1,800 \times \frac{5}{6}$ 1,500

15. $\frac{7}{10} \times 1,200$ 840

More Practice is provided in Exercise 68 of the *Workbook*.

8-4 ▶ Multiplying Mixed Numbers

Number Sense
Use manipulatives and repeated addition to show that $1\frac{1}{2} \times 2 = 1\frac{1}{2} + 1\frac{1}{2} = 3$

Before you can multiply mixed numbers, you have to change each mixed number to an improper fraction.

Here is how you can change $5\frac{1}{3}$ and $2\frac{1}{2}$ to improper fractions:

$$5\frac{1}{3} = \frac{3 \times 5 + 1}{3} = \frac{16}{3} \qquad 2\frac{1}{2} = \frac{2 \times 2 + 1}{2} = \frac{5}{2}$$

▶ **EXAMPLE**

Multiply. $5\frac{1}{3} \times 2\frac{1}{2}$

In an improper fraction, the numerator is larger than the denominator.

STEP 1 Change each mixed number to an improper fraction.
$5\frac{1}{3} = \frac{16}{3} \quad 2\frac{1}{2} = \frac{5}{2}$

$5\frac{1}{3} \times 2\frac{1}{2}$

$\frac{16}{3} \times \frac{5}{2}$

Avoiding Errors
Review how to change a mixed number to an improper fraction using multiplication and addition.

STEP 2 Cancel if you can. Then, multiply.

$\overset{8}{\cancel{\frac{16}{3}}} \times \frac{5}{\underset{1}{\cancel{2}}} = \frac{40}{3}$

STEP 3 Change the product to a mixed number.

$\frac{40}{3} = 13\frac{1}{3}$

The product of $5\frac{1}{3}$ and $2\frac{1}{2}$ is $13\frac{1}{3}$.

Before you can multiply a mixed number and a whole number, you have to change each number to an improper fraction.

Common Error Multiplying is done without first changing the mixed numbers to improper fractions. Have students cross out each mixed number as they change it to a fraction.

Practice A

Multiply. Be sure to change mixed numbers.

1. $6\frac{2}{3} \times 1\frac{1}{8}$ $7\frac{1}{2}$

2. $3\frac{1}{7} \times 2\frac{1}{10}$ $6\frac{3}{5}$

3. $1\frac{2}{3} \times 4\frac{1}{5}$ 7

4. $3\frac{1}{3} \times 3\frac{1}{2}$ $11\frac{2}{3}$

5. $2\frac{3}{4} \times 3\frac{1}{9}$ $8\frac{5}{9}$

6. $4\frac{1}{2} \times 7\frac{1}{3}$ 33

Practice B

Multiply.

7. $3\frac{1}{8} \times 2$ $6\frac{1}{4}$

8. $5\frac{3}{5} \times 2\frac{1}{2}$ 14

9. $1\frac{3}{4} \times 1\frac{3}{5}$ $2\frac{4}{5}$

10. $\frac{3}{4} \times \frac{3}{10}$ $\frac{9}{40}$

11. $\frac{6}{7} \times \frac{5}{12}$ $\frac{5}{14}$

12. $20 \times \frac{4}{5}$ 16

13. $10 \times 2\frac{1}{2}$ 25

14. $12 \times \frac{5}{24}$ $2\frac{1}{2}$

15. $\frac{2}{5} \times \frac{2}{5}$ $\frac{4}{25}$

16. $\frac{3}{4} \times 3\frac{5}{6}$ $2\frac{7}{8}$

17. $\frac{5}{6} \times \frac{3}{15}$ $\frac{1}{6}$

18. $\frac{2}{3} \times 15$ 10

19. $16 \times 2\frac{3}{4}$ 44

20. $24 \times 3\frac{1}{2}$ 84

21. $\frac{6}{7} \times \frac{1}{2}$ $\frac{3}{7}$

22. $2\frac{4}{9} \times 1\frac{1}{2}$ $3\frac{2}{3}$

23. $2\frac{5}{6} \times \frac{2}{5}$ $1\frac{2}{15}$

24. $1\frac{7}{8} \times 5\frac{1}{9}$ $9\frac{7}{12}$

Everyday Problem Solving

Ms. Cruz went food shopping. At the meat department, she saw this sign.

1. How much will $2\frac{1}{2}$ pounds of prime steak cost? Multiply $2\frac{1}{2} \times \$10$. $25

2. How much will $3\frac{1}{2}$ pounds of hamburger cost? $7

3. Which costs more: $2\frac{1}{2}$ pounds of prime steak or $4\frac{1}{2}$ pounds of veal cutlet? veal cutlet

4. Ms. Cruz buys a package of hamburger that costs \$3. How much does the package weigh? $1\frac{1}{2}$ pounds

☆**Today's Specials**☆

Prime Steak	\$10 per pound
Veal Cutlet	\$ 8 per pound
Hamburger	\$ 2 per pound

Extra Practice for this lesson is provided on page 423.

More Practice is provided in Exercise 69 of the *Workbook*.

8·5   Dividing by Fractions

Number Sense
Review the meaning of division. $\frac{3}{4} \div \frac{1}{4}$ means "How many fourths are in 3 fourths?" Show that $\frac{3}{4} \div \frac{1}{4}$ means $\frac{3}{4} \times \frac{4}{1}$, or 3. Thus, there are 3 fourths in $\frac{3}{4}$.

You can use fraction strips to divide by a fraction. What is $1 \div \frac{1}{3}$? How many $\frac{1}{3}$s are in 1?

1 whole		
$\frac{1}{3}$	$\frac{1}{3}$	$\frac{1}{3}$

$$1 \div \frac{1}{3} = 3$$

There are three $\frac{1}{3}$s in 1.

You can link division by a fraction to multiplication.

$$1 \div \frac{1}{3} = 1 \times \frac{3}{1} = 3$$

invert

To divide by a fraction, first you **invert** the second number. Then, you multiply.

► **EXAMPLE**

Avoiding Errors
Remind students to first invert the second fraction and then multiply across numerators and denominators.

Divide. $5 \div \frac{2}{3}$

STEP 1 Write the whole number as a fraction. $5 = \frac{5}{1}$ Change the division sign to a multiplication sign.

$5 \div \frac{2}{3}$

$\frac{5}{1} \times$

STEP 2 Invert the second fraction. Do NOT change the first fraction.

$\frac{5}{1} \times \frac{3}{2}$

STEP 3 Multiply. Simplify the product, if possible.

$\frac{5}{1} \times \frac{3}{2} = \frac{15}{2} = 7\frac{1}{2}$

The quotient of 5 and $\frac{2}{3}$ is $7\frac{1}{2}$.

Follow the same steps to divide a fraction by a fraction.

$$\frac{1}{2} \div \frac{2}{3} = \frac{1}{2} \times \frac{3}{2} = \frac{3}{4}$$

Practice A

Common Errors Second fraction is not inverted. Have students circle the fraction to be inverted before writing the problem with multiplication.

Divide. Remember to invert the second number. Then, multiply.

1. $3 \div \frac{1}{4}$ 12

2. $4 \div \frac{1}{8}$ 32

3. $5 \div \frac{1}{2}$ 10

4. $9 \div \frac{1}{3}$ 27

5. $6 \div \frac{3}{4}$ 8

6. $8 \div \frac{2}{3}$ 12

7. $10 \div \frac{5}{6}$ 12

8. $9 \div \frac{3}{5}$ 15

Practice B

Divide. Be sure that each answer is in lowest terms.

9. $\frac{2}{3} \div \frac{1}{3}$ 2

10. $\frac{7}{12} \div \frac{1}{5}$ $2\frac{11}{12}$

11. $\frac{12}{13} \div \frac{4}{5}$ $1\frac{2}{13}$

12. $\frac{9}{24} \div \frac{2}{3}$ $\frac{9}{16}$

13. $\frac{4}{5} \div \frac{2}{5}$ 2

14. $\frac{9}{10} \div \frac{6}{7}$ $1\frac{1}{20}$

15. $\frac{4}{10} \div \frac{1}{5}$ 2

16. $\frac{12}{20} \div \frac{1}{2}$ $1\frac{1}{5}$

17. $\frac{3}{4} \div \frac{2}{3}$ $1\frac{1}{8}$

18. $\frac{2}{5} \div \frac{3}{5}$ $\frac{2}{3}$

19. $\frac{4}{5} \div \frac{4}{5}$ 1

20. $\frac{2}{3} \div \frac{8}{15}$ $1\frac{1}{4}$

21. $\frac{3}{7} \div \frac{9}{10}$ $\frac{10}{21}$

22. $\frac{2}{7} \div \frac{3}{14}$ $1\frac{1}{3}$

23. $\frac{1}{2} \div \frac{1}{7}$ $3\frac{1}{2}$

24. $\frac{9}{10} \div \frac{1}{2}$ $1\frac{4}{5}$

Everyday Problem Solving

In music, there are whole notes, half notes, quarter notes, and eighth notes. These notes tell you how long you need to hold a note.

1. How many half notes are in a whole note? Divide. $1 \div \frac{1}{2}$ 2 half notes

2. How many quarter notes are in a whole note? 4 quarter notes

3. How many quarter notes are in a half note? 2 quarter notes

4. How many eighth notes are in a half note? Divide. $\frac{1}{2} \div \frac{1}{8}$ 4 eighth notes

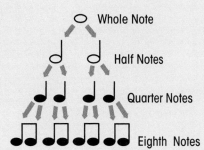

Whole Note

Half Notes

Quarter Notes

Eighth Notes

Extra Practice for this lesson is provided on page 424.

8-6 ▷ Dividing Fractions by Whole Numbers

Number Sense
Show students :
$\frac{1}{2} \div 3 = \frac{1}{2} \times \frac{1}{3} = \frac{1}{6}$
$3 \div \frac{1}{2} = \frac{3}{1} \times \frac{2}{1} = 6$

▶ **EXAMPLE**

Avoiding Errors
Emphasize that all whole numbers have denominators of 1.

You can divide a fraction by a whole number. First, change the whole number to an improper fraction.

Divide. $\frac{7}{8} \div 5$

STEP 1 Change the whole number to an improper fraction. $5 = \frac{5}{1}$ Do NOT change the first fraction.	$\frac{7}{8} \div 5$ $\frac{7}{8} \div \frac{5}{1}$
STEP 2 Change the sign to multiplication.	$\frac{7}{8} \times$
STEP 3 Invert the second fraction.	$\frac{7}{8} \times \frac{1}{5}$
STEP 4 Multiply. Cancel, if possible.	$\frac{7}{8} \times \frac{1}{5} = \frac{7}{40}$

The quotient of $\frac{7}{8}$ divided by 5 is $\frac{7}{40}$.

Common Error Quotients are found without inverting the second fraction or by inverting the first fraction. Encourage students to write the work next to the steps.

Practice

Divide. Remember to invert the second number and multiply.

1. $\frac{2}{3} \div 3$ $\frac{2}{9}$ **2.** $\frac{1}{2} \div 4$ $\frac{1}{8}$ **3.** $\frac{3}{4} \div 5$ $\frac{3}{20}$ **4.** $3 \div \frac{7}{8}$ $3\frac{3}{7}$

5. $25 \div \frac{1}{5}$ 125 **6.** $\frac{1}{2} \div 7$ $\frac{1}{14}$ **7.** $\frac{2}{3} \div 18$ $\frac{1}{27}$ **8.** $\frac{4}{5} \div 20$ $\frac{1}{25}$

9. $20 \div \frac{5}{12}$ 48 **10.** $16 \div \frac{6}{7}$ $18\frac{2}{3}$ **11.** $\frac{7}{9} \div 6$ $\frac{7}{54}$ **12.** $52 \div \frac{2}{3}$ 78

13. $49 \div \frac{7}{10}$ 70 **14.** $10 \div \frac{1}{8}$ 80 **15.** $\frac{1}{3} \div 10$ $\frac{1}{30}$ **16.** $6 \div \frac{3}{4}$ 8

17. $\frac{3}{4} \div 6$ $\frac{1}{8}$ **18.** $\frac{5}{7} \div 13$ $\frac{5}{91}$ **19.** $\frac{8}{9} \div 24$ $\frac{1}{27}$ **20.** $\frac{10}{11} \div 20$ $\frac{1}{22}$

21. $18 \div \frac{2}{3}$ 27 **22.** $\frac{5}{6} \div 5$ $\frac{1}{6}$ **23.** $20 \div \frac{4}{5}$ 25 **24.** $16 \div \frac{1}{2}$ 32

Extra Practice for this lesson is provided on page 424.

ON-THE-JOB MATH
Car Rental Agent

Jason works at a car rental agency. He checks the cars when they are returned. The fuel tank should be full. If the fuel tank is not full, the customer must pay to fill the tank.

Jason needs to know how many gallons are needed to fill the tank. Here is how Jason finds out.

Car A: The tank holds 20 gallons.

The gauge reads $\frac{1}{4}$ tank.

Jason multiplies to find how many gallons are in the tank.

$$20 \times \tfrac{1}{4} = 5 \text{ gallons}$$

Then he subtracts to find how many more gallons are needed to fill the tank.

$$20 - 5 = 15 \text{ gallons}$$

The customer pays for 15 gallons of gasoline to fill the tank.

Find out how many gallons are needed to fill each tank. The gauge shows the amount of gasoline in each tank.

Critical Thinking
How could Jason quickly figure the cost for a customer who just returned a car that is almost empty?

Critical Thinking
Jason can estimate the number of gallons based on the size of the tank.

1.

Holds 20 gallons
10 gallons

2.

Holds 24 gallons
18 gallons

3.

Holds 16 gallons
8 gallons

More Practice is provided in Exercise 71 of the *Workbook*.

8-7 ▶ Problem Solving: Solve a Simpler Problem

Some word problems can seem confusing. Use simpler whole numbers to help you decide which operation to use. Then use the numbers in the problem to solve.

▶ **EXAMPLE**

Number Sense
Allow students to select other, "simpler" numbers to use in the problem. Have them orally explain why they chose the numbers and how the numbers help them decide which operation to use.

Avoiding Errors
Remind students to use the original numbers, not the ones they chose as replacements.

Remember that when you divide, you invert the second fraction and mulitply.

At Mike's Auto Body Shop, it takes $\frac{5}{6}$ of an hour to polish one car. How many cars can be polished in 10 hours?

STEP 1 READ What do you need to find out?
You need to find the number of cars that can be polished in 10 hours.

STEP 2 PLAN What do you need to do?
Make the problem simpler. Use simple whole numbers.

Pretend it takes 2 hours to polish one car. How many cars can be polished in 10 hours?

Divide the total hours by the amount of hours to polish one car.
10 hours ÷ 2 hours for one car

STEP 3 DO Follow the plan.
Now, use the numbers from the original problem.

10 hours ÷ $\frac{5}{6}$ hour for one car
$\frac{10}{1} \times \frac{6}{5} = 12$ cars

STEP 4 CHECK Does your answer make sense?
Work backward. If one car takes $\frac{5}{6}$ hour, how long does it take 12 cars?

$$12 \times \frac{5}{6} = \frac{12}{1} \times \frac{5}{6} = 10 \text{ hours } ✓$$

In 10 hours, 12 cars can be polished.

Problem Solving

READ the problem. Replace the fraction with a whole number. Make a PLAN. Now use the original numbers to DO the plan to solve the problem.

1. Jon has a board that is $\frac{2}{3}$ yard long. He cuts the board into 6 equal pieces. How long is each piece? $\frac{1}{9}$ yard

PLAN
Pretend the board is 12 yards long. What would you divide? $12 \div 6 \rightarrow \frac{2}{3} \div 6 = \frac{1}{9}$

2. Four people want to equally share $\frac{4}{5}$ pound of nuts. How much will each person have? $\frac{1}{5}$ pound

PLAN
Pretend there are 8 pounds of nuts. What would you divide? $8 \div 4 \rightarrow \frac{4}{5} \div 4 = \frac{1}{5}$

3. At Ann's Auto Body Shop, it takes $\frac{3}{4}$ of an hour to paint one car. How long will it take to paint 8 cars? 6 hours

PLAN
Pretend it takes 2 hours to paint one car. Would you multiply or divide? multiply; $\frac{3}{4} \times 8 = 6$

Problem Solving Strategy

Sometimes, you can draw a picture to solve a problem.

> Diane found $\frac{1}{2}$ of a pie on the table. She ate $\frac{1}{4}$ of the $\frac{1}{2}$. How much of the pie did Diane eat?

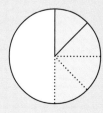

Draw a picture of $\frac{1}{2}$ pie. Then, split this piece into $\frac{1}{4}$s. How much of the whole pie is $\frac{1}{4}$ of $\frac{1}{2}$?
$\frac{1}{8}$ of the pie

More Practice is provided in Exercise 72 of the *Workbook*.

8·8 Dividing Mixed Numbers

Number Sense
A fraction divided by a mixed number is always less than 1. $\frac{1}{2} \div 1\frac{1}{2} = \frac{1}{3}$

▶ **EXAMPLE**

Remember:
$4\frac{2}{3} = \frac{3 \times 4 + 2}{3} = \frac{14}{3}$

Avoiding Errors
Remind students to change mixed numbers into fractions before dividing.

Dividing a mixed number by a fraction is like dividing a fraction by another fraction.

Divide. $4\frac{2}{3} \div \frac{7}{9}$

STEP 1	Change the mixed number to an improper fraction.	$\frac{14}{3} \div \frac{7}{9}$
STEP 2	Change the sign to multiplication.	$\frac{14}{3} \times$
STEP 3	Invert the second fraction. Do NOT change the first fracton.	$\frac{14}{3} \times \frac{9}{7}$
STEP 4	Multiply. Simplify the quotient, if possible.	$\overset{2}{\cancel{\frac{14}{3}}} \times \overset{3}{\cancel{\frac{9}{7}}} = \frac{6}{1} = 6$

The quotient of $4\frac{2}{3}$ divided by $\frac{7}{9}$ is 6.

Practice A

Common Error The first number in the division problem is inverted. Stress that division is really "multiplying <u>by</u> the inverted number."

Divide. Remember to change the mixed numbers to fractions.

1. $\frac{2}{3} \div 1\frac{2}{3}$ $\frac{2}{5}$ **2.** $4\frac{2}{5} \div \frac{2}{5}$ 11   **3.** $2\frac{2}{7} \div \frac{4}{5}$ $2\frac{6}{7}$ **4.** $\frac{3}{4} \div 1\frac{1}{3}$ $\frac{9}{16}$

5. $\frac{7}{8} \div 2\frac{3}{8}$ $\frac{7}{19}$ **6.** $2\frac{2}{3} \div \frac{1}{6}$ 16   **7.** $\frac{7}{9} \div 3\frac{1}{2}$ $\frac{2}{9}$ **8.** $2\frac{1}{12} \div \frac{5}{6}$ $2\frac{1}{2}$

9. $1\frac{1}{5} \div \frac{1}{5}$ 6   **10.** $\frac{5}{6} \div 2\frac{1}{2}$ $\frac{1}{3}$ **11.** $2\frac{2}{7} \div \frac{6}{7}$ $2\frac{2}{3}$ **12.** $\frac{5}{8} \div 1\frac{1}{2}$ $\frac{5}{12}$

13. $\frac{3}{5} \div 2\frac{1}{4}$ $\frac{4}{15}$ **14.** $1\frac{1}{9} \div \frac{5}{9}$ 2   **15.** $\frac{2}{7} \div 1\frac{1}{3}$ $\frac{3}{14}$ **16.** $2\frac{1}{3} \div \frac{5}{6}$ $2\frac{4}{5}$

Practice B

Divide. Remember to change the mixed numbers or whole numbers to fractions.

17. $8 \div \frac{4}{5}$ 10

18. $\frac{3}{5} \div 2\frac{2}{3}$ $\frac{9}{40}$

19. $\frac{2}{7} \div \frac{3}{4}$ $\frac{8}{21}$

20. $\frac{3}{8} \div 4$ $\frac{3}{32}$

21. $\frac{3}{5} \div \frac{1}{5}$ 3

22. $\frac{7}{8} \div 1\frac{1}{2}$ $\frac{7}{12}$

23. $9 \div \frac{2}{3}$ $13\frac{1}{2}$

24. $\frac{1}{3} \div \frac{4}{5}$ $\frac{5}{12}$

25. $\frac{1}{3} \div \frac{8}{9}$ $\frac{3}{8}$

26. $\frac{4}{5} \div 2\frac{3}{5}$ $\frac{4}{13}$

27. $12 \div \frac{5}{6}$ $14\frac{2}{5}$

28. $\frac{2}{3} \div 6$ $\frac{1}{9}$

29. $15 \div \frac{3}{5}$ 25

30. $\frac{9}{10} \div 1\frac{2}{5}$ $\frac{9}{14}$

31. $\frac{7}{9} \div 21$ $\frac{1}{27}$

32. $\frac{3}{14} \div \frac{6}{7}$ $\frac{1}{4}$

Everyday Problem Solving

The gym displays a chart of daily running times. It shows the number of days each person runs in a month. It also shows the monthly total for each person. Some of the data are missing from the chart.

Running Times			
Name	Daily Time	Number of Days	Monthly Total
Bly	$\frac{3}{4}$ hour	?	$7\frac{1}{2}$ hours
Aki	$\frac{2}{3}$ hour	?	$10\frac{2}{3}$ hours
Tracy	$\frac{1}{2}$ hour	20 days	?
Lani	$\frac{7}{8}$ hour	24 days	?

1. How many days did Bly run on the track that month? Divide the monthly total by the daily time.   10 days

2. How many days did Aki run on the track that month?   16 days

3. Tracy ran $\frac{1}{2}$ hour each day for 20 days that month. What was her total running time for that month? Multiply 20 days by $\frac{1}{2}$ hour.   10 hours

4. Lani ran $\frac{7}{8}$ hour each day for 24 days that month. What was his total running time for that month?   21 hours

Extra Practice for this lesson is provided on page 424.

8-9 Dividing Mixed Numbers by Mixed Numbers

Number Sense
Have the students use the steps they know from the last section to communicate the steps to solving: $4\frac{2}{3} \div \frac{7}{9}$.

You can divide a mixed number by another mixed number.

▶ **EXAMPLE**

Divide. $6\frac{1}{2} \div 5\frac{7}{9}$

STEP 1 Change the mixed numbers to improper fractions.

$$\frac{13}{2} \div \frac{52}{9}$$

STEP 2 Change the sign to multiplication.

$$\frac{13}{2} \times$$

Avoiding Errors
Review and practice changing a mixed number to a fraction.

STEP 3 Invert the second fraction. Do NOT change the first fraction.

$$\frac{13}{2} \times \frac{9}{52}$$

STEP 4 Multiply. Simplify the quotient, if possible.

$$\overset{1}{\cancel{\frac{13}{2}}} \times \frac{9}{\underset{4}{\cancel{52}}} = \frac{9}{8} = 1\frac{1}{8}$$

The quotient of $6\frac{1}{2}$ divided by $5\frac{7}{9}$ is $1\frac{1}{8}$.

Practice A

Common Error Students divide the whole number parts of the mixed number, then the fractions. Have students circle each mixed number to emphasize that it is one number.

Divide. Remember to change the mixed numbers to improper fractions.

1. $6\frac{1}{8} \div 3\frac{1}{2}$ $1\frac{3}{4}$ **2.** $4\frac{2}{5} \div \frac{2}{5}$ 11 **3.** $3\frac{1}{8} \div \frac{7}{8}$ $3\frac{4}{7}$ **4.** $5\frac{1}{7} \div 1\frac{1}{3}$ $3\frac{6}{7}$

5. $7\frac{1}{5} \div 2\frac{2}{5}$ 3 **6.** $2\frac{1}{9} \div 1\frac{2}{3}$ $1\frac{4}{15}$ **7.** $9\frac{3}{8} \div 4\frac{1}{2}$ $2\frac{1}{12}$ **8.** $4\frac{1}{3} \div 2\frac{1}{6}$ 2

9. $8\frac{1}{8} \div 2\frac{1}{2}$ $3\frac{1}{4}$ **10.** $4\frac{2}{5} \div \frac{3}{10}$ $14\frac{2}{3}$ **11.** $8\frac{1}{2} \div 5\frac{2}{3}$ $1\frac{1}{2}$ **12.** $4\frac{3}{8} \div 3\frac{1}{8}$ $1\frac{2}{5}$

13. $2\frac{1}{3} \div \frac{3}{5}$ $3\frac{8}{9}$ **14.** $3\frac{4}{7} \div 3\frac{4}{7}$ 1 **15.** $5\frac{4}{9} \div 3\frac{1}{2}$ $1\frac{5}{9}$ **16.** $4\frac{1}{6} \div \frac{7}{12}$ $7\frac{1}{7}$

17. $2\frac{1}{4} \div \frac{3}{8}$ 6 **18.** $3\frac{7}{8} \div 1\frac{1}{2}$ $2\frac{7}{12}$ **19.** $5\frac{1}{10} \div \frac{7}{10}$ $7\frac{2}{7}$ **20.** $9\frac{4}{5} \div 3\frac{1}{2}$ $2\frac{4}{5}$

Practice B

Divide or multiply.

21. $\frac{4}{5} \times 2\frac{3}{4}$ $2\frac{1}{5}$ **22.** $10 \div \frac{2}{5}$ 25 **23.** $\frac{1}{2} \div 1\frac{3}{4}$ $\frac{2}{7}$ **24.** $\frac{4}{5} \div 2$ $\frac{2}{5}$

25. $5\frac{1}{4} \times 8$ 42 **26.** $3\frac{2}{3} \times \frac{5}{9}$ $2\frac{1}{27}$ **27.** $3\frac{1}{4} \div \frac{3}{4}$ $4\frac{1}{3}$ **28.** $\frac{3}{5} \times \frac{6}{7}$ $\frac{18}{35}$

29. $10 \div \frac{1}{7}$ 70 **30.** $9 \times \frac{2}{3}$ 6 **31.** $\frac{3}{5} \times 5\frac{1}{2}$ $3\frac{3}{10}$ **32.** $\frac{5}{6} \div \frac{2}{3}$ $1\frac{1}{4}$

33. $\frac{5}{6} \div 3$ $\frac{5}{18}$ **34.** $2\frac{2}{5} \times 1\frac{4}{5}$ $4\frac{8}{25}$ **35.** $\frac{7}{9} \times 81$ 63 **36.** $3\frac{3}{8} \div 1\frac{1}{4}$ $2\frac{7}{10}$

Everyday Problem Solving

Jena's regular pay is $12 per hour at her job. She usually works 40 hours a week. Some weeks, she may work overtime. Overtime is any time more than 40 hours. For overtime, she is paid $1\frac{1}{2}$ times her regular pay. The time card shows her hours for three weeks.

1. How much is Jena paid for 1 hour of overtime? Multiply her regular pay by $1\frac{1}{2}$. $12 \times 1\frac{1}{2} = $18

Name:	Jena
Week	Number of hours worked
1	45
2	48
3	40

2. How many hours of overtime did Jena work during Week 1? Subtract 40 from the hours worked. 45 hours − 40 hours = 5 hours

3. How much was she paid for overtime during Week 1? Multiply the overtime pay for 1 hour by the overtime hours. 5 hours × $18 = $90

4. How much was Jena paid for the overtime in Week 2? 48 hours − 40 hours = 8 hours overtime × $18 = $144

Extra Practice for this lesson is provided on page 424.

8·10 ▶ Problem Solving: Does the Answer Make Sense?

Number Sense
Review clue words for multiplication. Review clue words for division.

▶ **EXAMPLE**

It is important to check your answer to a word problem. You should be sure it makes sense.

Mr. Harris bought a large sub sandwich for a family picnic. He wants to cut the sandwich into slices $1\frac{4}{5}$ inches long. The sub is 72 inches long. How many slices will he have?

STEP 1   READ   What do you need to find out?
You need to find how many slices Mr. Harris can cut.

STEP 2   PLAN   What do you need to do?
Divide the length of the sub by the size of each slice.

Remember to change the mixed number to a fraction.
$$1\frac{4}{5} = \frac{9}{5}$$

STEP 3   DO   Follow the plan.

72 inches ÷ $\frac{9}{5}$ inches
↑   ↑
length of sub   size of each piece

$$\frac{72}{1} \times \frac{5}{9} = 40 \text{ slices}$$
↑
number of slices

Avoiding Errors
After reading each problem, have students decide which operation will solve the problem. Encourage oral discussion.

STEP 4   CHECK   Does your answer make sense?
Did you use the right operation in the right order? To check, reverse the order in the division problem.

$$1\frac{4}{5} \div 72 = \frac{1}{40} \text{ slice}$$

Does $\frac{1}{40}$ slice make sense? No.

So, 40 slices is correct. ✓

Mr. Harris can cut 40 slices.

Problem Solving

Common Error Answers do not make sense. Tell students they need to check their answer with the original question to see that answers are reasonable.

READ the problem. Determine if you will use multiplication or division for the PLAN. DO the plan to solve each problem. Answer the questions under CHECK.

1. It took Robert $6\frac{3}{4}$ hours to repair his car. Dave said that he could do it in $\frac{1}{2}$ the time. How long would it take Dave? $3\frac{3}{8}$ hours

   CHECK
   Did you use the right numbers in the right order? $6\frac{3}{4} \times \frac{1}{2}$
   Does the answer make sense? Yes. $13\frac{1}{2}$ is too big and $\frac{2}{27}$ is too small.

2. Gloria made 96 cookies for the bake sale. She sold $\frac{2}{3}$ of them. How many cookies did she sell? 64 cookies

   CHECK
   Did you use the right numbers in the right order? $96 \times \frac{2}{3}$
   Does the answer make sense? Yes. 144 is too big and $\frac{1}{144}$ is too small.

3. The bookshelf is 40 inches long. Each book is $1\frac{1}{4}$ inches wide. How many books will fit on the shelf? 32 books

   CHECK
   Did you use the right numbers in the right order? $40 \div 1\frac{1}{4}$
   Does the answer make sense? Yes. 50 is too big and $\frac{1}{32}$ is too small.

Problem Solving Strategy

Sometimes, choosing the correct answer to a word problem is thinking about what makes sense.

David had to answer this problem on a test:

About how many dogs could be groomed in one week?

(a) $\frac{1}{50}$ dog   (b) 50 weeks   (c) 50 dogs   (d) $\frac{1}{50}$ week

Eliminate choices that don't make sense. Ask yourself:
Can you have $\frac{1}{50}$ of a dog? no; eliminate (a)
Should your answer be about dogs or weeks? dogs; eliminate (b) and (d)
What is the only answer that makes sense? (c)

canceling
invert

Vocabulary Review

Answer each question.

1. Give an example of canceling when multiplying two fractions. Examples will vary.

2. How do you invert a fraction? When is it necessary to invert a fraction? Give an example. Examples wil

3. **Writing** Pretend you are tutoring someone. How would you show the student how to cancel? Answers will vary.

Chapter Quiz

LESSONS 8·1 and 8·2

Test Tip
Use a common factor to cancel. Multiply numerators, then denominators.

Multiplying Fractions

Multiply. Cancel, if possible.

1. $\frac{1}{2} \times \frac{6}{7}$ $\frac{3}{7}$

2. $\frac{5}{6} \times \frac{12}{13}$ $\frac{10}{13}$

3. $\frac{3}{4} \times \frac{1}{8}$ $\frac{3}{32}$

4. $\frac{8}{9} \times \frac{1}{4}$ $\frac{2}{9}$

5. $\frac{3}{8} \times \frac{1}{8}$ $\frac{3}{64}$

6. $\frac{12}{17} \times \frac{17}{20}$ $\frac{3}{5}$

LESSONS 8·3 and 8·4

Test Tip
Change mixed numbers and whole numbers to improper fractions before multiplying.

Multiplying Whole Numbers, Mixed Numbers, and Fractions

Multiply. Cancel, if possible.

7. $45 \times \frac{5}{9}$ 25

8. $\frac{3}{4} \times 36$ 27

9. $\frac{2}{3} \times 3\frac{5}{6}$ $2\frac{5}{9}$

10. $6\frac{3}{7} \times \frac{7}{8}$ $5\frac{5}{8}$

11. $4\frac{3}{5} \times 2\frac{11}{23}$ $11\frac{2}{5}$

12. $14 \times 3\frac{1}{2}$ 49

13. $3\frac{7}{9} \times 2\frac{3}{17}$ $8\frac{2}{9}$

14. $5\frac{3}{4} \times 5\frac{1}{3}$ $30\frac{2}{3}$

LESSONS 8·5 and 8·6

Dividing with Fractions and Whole Numbers

Divide. Cancel, if possible.

Test Tip
To divide fractions, invert the second fraction and then multiply.

15. $\frac{9}{10} \div 20$ $\frac{9}{200}$

16. $\frac{3}{4} \div \frac{3}{8}$ 2

17. $\frac{4}{5} \div \frac{1}{5}$ 4

18. $6 \div \frac{2}{3}$ 9

19. $\frac{2}{5} \div \frac{9}{10}$ $\frac{4}{9}$

20. $36 \div \frac{3}{4}$ 48

LESSONS 8·8 and 8·9

Dividing with Mixed Numbers

Divide. Cancel, if possible.

Test Tip
Change mixed numbers and whole numbers to improper fractions before dividing.

21. $2\frac{1}{2} \div \frac{3}{4}$ $3\frac{1}{3}$

22. $\frac{5}{6} \div 3\frac{1}{12}$ $\frac{10}{37}$

23. $\frac{7}{9} \div 3\frac{5}{6}$ $\frac{14}{69}$

24. $4\frac{3}{7} \div \frac{3}{14}$ $20\frac{2}{3}$

25. $3\frac{5}{8} \div 1\frac{1}{2}$ $2\frac{5}{12}$

26. $5\frac{1}{9} \div 3\frac{2}{3}$ $1\frac{13}{33}$

LESSONS 8·7 and 8·10

Solving Problems

Solve.

Test Tip
Check that your answers make sense.

Group Activity Note that baking times and oven temperatures should not be changed when increasing a recipe.

27. Jan bought $2\frac{5}{8}$ pounds of hamburger meat. Each pound is 16 ounces. How many ounces did she buy? 42 ounces

28. It took Jason $3\frac{3}{4}$ hours to cut the grass. Frank says he can cut the grass in $\frac{2}{3}$ the time. How long would it take Frank to cut the grass? $2\frac{1}{2}$ hours

Group Activity See the *Teacher Planning Guide* for a Scoring Rubric for this activity.
With your group, choose three favorite recipes. Double the first recipe. Find the new amount of each ingredient needed. Triple the second recipe. Find the new amounts of each ingredient. For the third recipe, find the ingredients for $2\frac{1}{2}$ times the recipe. Give the new number of servings for each recipe. What items or directions should not be changed?

This draftswoman is a skilled worker. She often needs to work with fractions on the job. She is looking at a blueprint. It tells her that she needs $50\frac{1}{2}$ feet of wood to build part of a wall. She has $25\frac{1}{2}$ feet of wood on order. How much more wood does she need to order?

Caption She needs 25 more feet of wood.

Chapter 9 ▶ Adding and Subtracting Fractions

ESL Note Have students discuss meanings of *like*. For example, *same as* and *similar to*. Then have them show examples of "like" items. The students can then discuss "unlike" as the opposite of "like."

Words to Know

like fractions	fractions that have the same denominator
unlike fractions	fractions that have different denominators

Words to Know Have students create examples for each word. Then, have the students compare and contrast the different types of fractions.

Activities Project

During the week, you have activities after school. You may have band practice, play basketball, or work. Make a list of the days that you have activities after school. For one week, write how long you do each activity. Use fractions of an hour, if you need to. Find the total hours for one week. Try this for one month.

Mon.	Band practice	$1\frac{1}{2}$ h
Tues.	Part-time job	$3\frac{1}{4}$ h
Wed.	Make dinner	$\frac{1}{2}$ h
Thurs.	Read book	$1\frac{1}{4}$ h
Fri.	Part-time job	$2\frac{3}{4}$ h
	TOTAL	$9\frac{1}{4}$ h

Learning Objectives

- Add and subtract like fractions.
- Add and subtract like mixed numbers.
- Subtract mixed numbers and fractions from whole numbers.
- Add and subtract unlike fractions.
- Add and subtract unlike mixed numbers.
- Solve multi-part fraction problems.
- Apply adding and subtracting fractions to find work hours.

Project
You may want students to list the times they start and finish each activity. Help them convert time to fractions of an hour, such as 15 minutes $= \frac{1}{4}$ hour.

More Practice is provided in Exercise 75 of the *Workbook*.

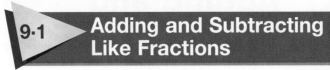

9·1 Adding and Subtracting Like Fractions

Number Sense
Have students make fraction strips with the same denominator. Encourage them to use the fraction strips to add and subtract like fractions. Have them record the results and look for a pattern.

Like fractions have the same denominators. The fraction strips below show how to add or subtract like fractions.

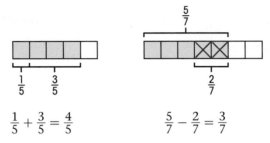

$$\frac{1}{5} + \frac{3}{5} = \frac{4}{5} \qquad \frac{5}{7} - \frac{2}{7} = \frac{3}{7}$$

To add or subtract like fractions, add or subtract only the numerators. Use the common denominator as the denominator of your answer.

▶ **EXAMPLE 1**

If the answer is an improper fraction, change it to a mixed number. To change $\frac{15}{9}$, divide 15 by 9.

$$\begin{array}{r} 1\frac{6}{9} \\ 9\overline{)15} \\ \underline{-9} \\ 6 \end{array}$$

Add. $\frac{8}{9} + \frac{7}{9}$

STEP 1
Add the numerators. Keep the common denominator.

$$\begin{array}{r} \frac{8}{9} \\ + \frac{7}{9} \\ \hline \frac{15}{9} \end{array}$$

STEP 2
Write the answer in lowest terms.

$$\begin{array}{r} \frac{8}{9} \\ + \frac{7}{9} \\ \hline \frac{15}{9} = 1\frac{6}{9} \\ = 1\frac{2}{3} \end{array}$$

The sum of $\frac{8}{9}$ and $\frac{7}{9}$ is $1\frac{2}{3}$.

▶ **EXAMPLE 2**

Avoiding Errors
Remind students that a fraction is in lowest terms when the greatest common factor of the numerator and denominator is 1.

Subtract. $\frac{7}{8} - \frac{3}{8}$

STEP 1
Subtract the numerators. Keep the common denominator.

$$\begin{array}{r} \frac{7}{8} \\ - \frac{3}{8} \\ \hline \frac{4}{8} \end{array}$$

STEP 2
Write the answer in lowest terms.

$$\begin{array}{r} \frac{7}{8} \\ - \frac{3}{8} \\ \hline \frac{4}{8} = \frac{1}{2} \end{array}$$

The difference between $\frac{7}{8}$ and $\frac{3}{8}$ is $\frac{1}{2}$.

Practice A

Add. Write the answer in lowest terms.

1. $\frac{1}{3}$ $\frac{2}{3}$ $+\frac{1}{3}$

2. $\frac{2}{7}$ $\frac{6}{7}$ $+\frac{4}{7}$

3. $\frac{7}{8}$ 1 $+\frac{1}{8}$

4. $\frac{4}{9}$ $\frac{2}{3}$ $+\frac{2}{9}$

5. $\frac{2}{5}$ $1\frac{1}{5}$ $+\frac{4}{5}$

6. $\frac{5}{6}$ $1\frac{1}{3}$ $+\frac{3}{6}$

7. $\frac{7}{12}$ 1 $+\frac{5}{12}$

8. $\frac{5}{20}$ $\frac{3}{5}$ $+\frac{7}{20}$

9. $\frac{3}{4}$ $1\frac{1}{2}$ $+\frac{3}{4}$

10. $\frac{7}{10}$ $1\frac{3}{5}$ $+\frac{9}{10}$

Practice B

Subtract. Write the answer in lowest terms.

11. $\frac{7}{9}$ $\frac{5}{9}$ $-\frac{2}{9}$

12. $\frac{13}{20}$ $\frac{3}{10}$ $-\frac{7}{20}$

13. $\frac{9}{10}$ $\frac{2}{5}$ $-\frac{5}{10}$

14. $\frac{11}{15}$ $\frac{1}{3}$ $-\frac{6}{15}$

15. $\frac{7}{15}$ $\frac{1}{3}$ $-\frac{2}{15}$

16. $\frac{11}{12}$ $\frac{2}{3}$ $-\frac{3}{12}$

17. $\frac{6}{7}$ $\frac{5}{7}$ $-\frac{1}{7}$

18. $\frac{4}{5}$ $\frac{3}{5}$ $-\frac{1}{5}$

19. $\frac{17}{18}$ $\frac{4}{9}$ $-\frac{9}{18}$

20. $\frac{13}{14}$ $\frac{1}{2}$ $-\frac{6}{14}$

Everyday Problem Solving

The bath shop sells perfumes in bottles of different sizes.

1. Tina bought a small bottle and a large bottle of perfume. How many ounces did she buy <u>in all</u>? $\frac{3}{4}$ ounce

2. <u>How much more</u> perfume is contained in the large bottle than in the medium bottle? $\frac{1}{4}$ ounce

Perfumes

SIZE	FLUID OUNCES
Small	$\frac{1}{8}$
Medium	$\frac{3}{8}$
Large	$\frac{5}{8}$

Extra Practice for this lesson is provided on page 425.

9·2   Adding Like Mixed Numbers

Now that you know how to add like fractions, you can add like mixed numbers.

▶ **EXAMPLE 1**

Number Sense
Encourage students to estimate the sums of mixed numbers by finding the sum of the whole numbers.

Avoiding Errors
A mixed number must have a whole number and a proper fraction. If the fraction is not proper, the mixed number needs to be reduced.

Add. $2\frac{1}{5} + 3\frac{2}{5}$

STEP 1   Add the fractions.

$$\begin{array}{r} 2\frac{1}{5} \\ + 3\frac{2}{5} \\ \hline \frac{3}{5} \end{array}$$

STEP 2   Add the whole numbers.

$$\begin{array}{r} 2\frac{1}{5} \\ + 3\frac{2}{5} \\ \hline 5\frac{3}{5} \end{array}$$

The sum of $2\frac{1}{5}$ and $3\frac{2}{5}$ is $5\frac{3}{5}$.

Sometimes, the fraction part of the answer is not a proper fraction. You need to simplify the answer.

▶ **EXAMPLE 2**

If the numerator and denominator of a fraction are the same, the fraction is equal to 1.

$\frac{2}{2} = 1 \quad \frac{5}{5} = 1 \quad \frac{12}{12} = 1$

Add. $2\frac{1}{2} + 3\frac{1}{2}$

STEP 1   Add the fractions.

$$\begin{array}{r} 2\frac{1}{2} \\ + 3\frac{1}{2} \\ \hline \frac{2}{2} \end{array}$$

STEP 2   Add the whole numbers.

$$\begin{array}{r} 2\frac{1}{2} \\ + 3\frac{1}{2} \\ \hline 5\frac{2}{2} \end{array}$$

STEP 3   Change the fraction to a whole number. Add the whole numbers.

$$\begin{array}{r} 2\frac{1}{2} \\ + 3\frac{1}{2} \\ \hline 5\frac{2}{2} = 5 + 1 = 6 \end{array}$$

The sum of $2\frac{1}{2}$ and $3\frac{1}{2}$ is 6.

Practice A

Add. Write the answer in lowest terms.

1. $3\frac{2}{7}$ $4\frac{4}{7}$
$+ 1\frac{2}{7}$

2. $4\frac{2}{4}$ $6\frac{3}{4}$
$+ 2\frac{1}{4}$

3. $1\frac{6}{7}$ $4\frac{2}{7}$
$+ 2\frac{3}{7}$

4. $3\frac{1}{6}$ $4\frac{2}{3}$
$+ 1\frac{3}{6}$

5. $4\frac{5}{8}$ 6
$+ 1\frac{3}{8}$

6. $3\frac{1}{9}$ $5\frac{2}{3}$
$+ 2\frac{5}{9}$

7. $7\frac{3}{4}$ $9\frac{1}{2}$
$+ 1\frac{3}{4}$

8. $6\frac{5}{9}$ $9\frac{1}{3}$
$+ 2\frac{7}{9}$

Practice B

Add. Write the answer in lowest terms.

9. $3\frac{2}{5} + 7\frac{3}{5}$ 11

10. $9\frac{2}{9} + 2\frac{1}{9}$ $11\frac{1}{3}$

11. $3\frac{4}{11} + 5\frac{5}{11}$ $8\frac{9}{11}$

12. $8\frac{5}{12} + 9\frac{5}{12}$ $17\frac{5}{6}$

13. $3\frac{2}{7} + 7\frac{2}{7}$ $10\frac{4}{7}$

14. $2\frac{19}{25} + 4\frac{3}{25}$ $6\frac{22}{25}$

15. $6\frac{4}{5} + 1\frac{1}{5}$ 8

16. $11\frac{2}{3} + 7$ $18\frac{2}{3}$

17. $4\frac{5}{6} + 8\frac{4}{6}$ $13\frac{1}{2}$

18. $5\frac{1}{8} + 4\frac{3}{8}$ $9\frac{1}{2}$

19. $7\frac{2}{7} + 3\frac{4}{7}$ $10\frac{6}{7}$

20. $1 + 4\frac{11}{13}$ $5\frac{11}{13}$

Everyday Problem Solving

The local swim teams practice once a week. The practice schedule is on the wall at the pool.

1. Anita is a member of the Dolphins and Stingrays teams. How long does she practice each week? Add the hours. $4\frac{1}{2}$ hours

2. Joe is on two teams. He practices $2\frac{1}{2}$ hours a week. Joe is on which two teams?
Minnows and Eels

POOL
Daily Practice Schedule

SWIM TEAM	DAY	HOURS
Dolphins	Mon.	$2\frac{3}{4}$
Sharks	Tues.	2
Stingrays	Wed.	$1\frac{3}{4}$
Minnows	Thurs.	$1\frac{1}{4}$
Eels	Fri.	$1\frac{1}{4}$

Extra Practice for this lesson is provided on page 425.

More Practice is provided in Exercise 77 of the *Workbook*.

9-3 ▶ Subtracting Like Mixed Numbers

Now that you know how to subtract like fractions, you can subtract like mixed numbers.

▶ **EXAMPLE 1**

Number Sense
Use manipulatives to review subtracting like fractions.

Subtract. $7\frac{3}{4} - 2\frac{1}{4}$

STEP 1 Subtract the fractions.

$$\begin{array}{r} 7\frac{3}{4} \\ -\ 2\frac{1}{4} \\ \hline \frac{2}{4} \end{array}$$

STEP 2 Subtract the whole numbers. Write the answer in lowest terms.

$$\begin{array}{r} 7\frac{3}{4} \\ -\ 2\frac{1}{4} \\ \hline 5\frac{2}{4} = 5\frac{1}{2} \end{array}$$

The difference between $7\frac{3}{4}$ and $2\frac{1}{4}$ is $5\frac{1}{2}$.

Sometimes, you need to regroup a mixed number for more fraction parts.

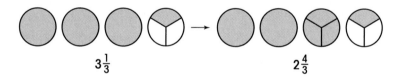

$3\frac{1}{3}$ $2\frac{4}{3}$

▶ **EXAMPLE 2**

Avoiding Errors
Explain that to regroup the mixed number, simply add the denominator of the fraction to the numerator. Then, decrease the whole number by 1.

Subtract. $3\frac{1}{3} - 1\frac{2}{3}$

STEP 1 Regroup so that you can subtract the fractions. Then, subtract the fractions.

$$\begin{array}{r} 3\frac{1}{3} = \quad 2\frac{4}{3} \\ -\ 1\frac{2}{3} = -1\frac{2}{3} \\ \hline \frac{2}{3} \end{array}$$

STEP 2 Subtract the whole numbers. Make sure the answer is in lowest terms.

$$\begin{array}{r} 3\frac{1}{3} = \quad 2\frac{4}{3} \\ -\ 1\frac{2}{3} = -1\frac{2}{3} \\ \hline 1\frac{2}{3} \end{array}$$

The difference between $3\frac{1}{3}$ and $1\frac{2}{3}$ is $1\frac{2}{3}$.

Practice A

Common Error Fractions are subtracted with unnecessary regrouping. Tell students that regrouping is needed <u>only</u> when the first numerator is smaller than the second numerator.

Subtract.

1. $4\frac{2}{3}$ $3\frac{1}{3}$
$-1\frac{1}{3}$

2. $7\frac{7}{8}$ $3\frac{1}{2}$
$-4\frac{3}{8}$

3. $9\frac{1}{2}$ 6
$-3\frac{1}{2}$

4. $6\frac{5}{6}$ $4\frac{1}{2}$
$-2\frac{2}{6}$

5. $9\frac{4}{5}$ $8\frac{2}{5}$
$-1\frac{2}{5}$

6. $15\frac{6}{11}$ $10\frac{3}{11}$
$-5\frac{3}{11}$

7. $9\frac{4}{5}$ $4\frac{2}{5}$
$-5\frac{2}{5}$

8. $12\frac{5}{9}$ $5\frac{1}{3}$
$-7\frac{2}{9}$

Practice B

Subtract. Be sure to regroup.

9. $6\frac{7}{11}$ $3\frac{10}{11}$
$-2\frac{8}{11}$

10. $11\frac{7}{9}$ $5\frac{8}{9}$
$-5\frac{8}{9}$

11. $24\frac{1}{10}$ $13\frac{4}{5}$
$-10\frac{3}{10}$

12. $6\frac{1}{6}$ $1\frac{1}{3}$
$-4\frac{5}{6}$

13. $7\frac{4}{9}-1\frac{5}{9}$ $5\frac{8}{9}$

14. $14\frac{3}{10}-5\frac{9}{10}$ $8\frac{2}{5}$

15. $8\frac{1}{4}-4\frac{3}{4}$ $3\frac{1}{2}$

16. $12\frac{2}{7}-5\frac{6}{7}$ $6\frac{3}{7}$

17. $9\frac{2}{6}-7\frac{5}{6}$ $1\frac{1}{2}$

18. $10\frac{7}{20}-8\frac{9}{20}$ $1\frac{9}{10}$

Everyday Problem Solving

Mountain climbing is Andrew's favorite sport. These are his favorite peaks.

1. How much higher is Borah than Washington? $1\frac{1}{5}$ miles

2. How much higher is King than Grand Teton? $\frac{3}{5}$ mile

3. What is the difference in height between the highest peak and the lowest peak? 2 miles

FAVORITE MOUNTAIN PEAKS

Peak	Location	Height (miles)
Grand Teton	WY	$2\frac{3}{5}$
King	Yukon	$3\frac{1}{5}$
Borah	ID	$2\frac{2}{5}$
Washington	NH	$1\frac{1}{5}$

Extra Practice for this lesson is provided on page 425.

More Practice is provided in Exercise 78 of the *Workbook*.

9-4 ▶ Subtracting from a Whole Number

Sometimes, you need to regroup a whole number as a mixed number. Look at the subtraction below.

$$5 - 2\frac{2}{3}$$

Number Sense
Students can use addition to check the subtraction.

$$5 \atop -2\frac{2}{3} \atop \overline{2\frac{1}{3}}$$

$$2\frac{2}{3} \atop +2\frac{1}{3} \atop \overline{5}$$

There are no thirds from which to subtract $\frac{2}{3}$. Regroup 5 to make thirds.

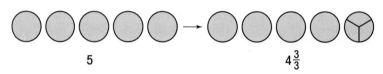

5       $4\frac{3}{3}$

▶ **EXAMPLE 1**

Subtract. $5 - 2\frac{2}{3}$

STEP 1 Regroup the whole number as a mixed number.

$$\begin{aligned} 5 &= 4\frac{3}{3} \\ -2\frac{2}{3} &= -2\frac{2}{3} \end{aligned}$$

STEP 2 Subtract. Be sure the answer is in lowest terms.

$$\begin{aligned} 5 &= 4\frac{3}{3} \\ -2\frac{2}{3} &= -2\frac{2}{3} \\ &\quad\ \ \overline{2\frac{1}{3}} \end{aligned}$$

The difference between 5 and $2\frac{2}{3}$ is $2\frac{1}{3}$.

▶ **EXAMPLE 2**

Subtract. $10 - \frac{1}{4}$

Avoiding Errors
Point out that the denominator of the given fraction tells which name for 1 is needed for subtracting the fractions, such as $\frac{2}{2}, \frac{3}{3}, \frac{4}{4}$, etc.

STEP 1 Regroup the whole number as a mixed number.

$$\begin{aligned} 10 &= 9\frac{4}{4} \\ -\frac{1}{4} &= -\frac{1}{4} \end{aligned}$$

STEP 2 Subtract. Be sure the answer is in lowest terms.

$$\begin{aligned} 10 &= 9\frac{4}{4} \\ -\frac{1}{4} &= -\frac{1}{4} \\ &\quad\ \ 9\frac{3}{4} \end{aligned}$$

The difference between 10 and $\frac{1}{4}$ is $9\frac{3}{4}$.

Practice A

Common Error The single fraction in the problem is brought down as part of the answer. Tell students to write a placeholder fraction using question marks next to the whole number.

Subtract. Remember to regroup the whole number.

1. 4 $1\frac{1}{4}$
$-\ 2\frac{3}{4}$

2. 7 $3\frac{1}{2}$
$-\ 3\frac{1}{2}$

3. 6 $5\frac{1}{6}$
$-\ \frac{5}{6}$

4. 8 $7\frac{3}{10}$
$-\ \frac{7}{10}$

5. 6 $5\frac{4}{7}$
$-\ \frac{3}{7}$

6. 10 $5\frac{7}{9}$
$-\ 4\frac{2}{9}$

7. 12 $2\frac{5}{8}$
$-\ 9\frac{3}{8}$

8. 20 $16\frac{1}{5}$
$-\ 3\frac{4}{5}$

Practice B

Subtract. Regroup, if necessary.

9. $9\frac{3}{4}$ $6\frac{1}{2}$
$-\ 3\frac{1}{4}$

10. 7 $1\frac{3}{5}$
$-\ 5\frac{2}{5}$

11. $18\frac{1}{6}$ $7\frac{1}{3}$
$-\ 10\frac{5}{6}$

12. 23 $22\frac{1}{8}$
$-\ \frac{7}{8}$

13. 11 $6\frac{2}{3}$
$-\ 4\frac{1}{3}$

14. $19\frac{2}{7}$ $10\frac{4}{7}$
$-\ 8\frac{5}{7}$

15. 8 $4\frac{3}{7}$
$-\ 3\frac{4}{7}$

16. $11\frac{3}{8}$ $4\frac{1}{4}$
$-\ 7\frac{1}{8}$

Everyday Problem Solving

This is Ms. Rhode's grocery list for making fruit salad. Use the list to answer the questions. Look for clue words to decide when to add or subtract.

1. How <u>many more</u> pounds of apples <u>than</u> pears will she buy? $\frac{3}{4}$ pound

2. How <u>many more</u> pounds of apples <u>than</u> plums will she buy? $1\frac{3}{4}$ pounds

3. How many pounds of fruit will she buy <u>altogether</u>? $6\frac{1}{2}$ pounds

——— Grocery list ———

For Fruit Salad

3 pounds Apples

$1\frac{1}{4}$ pounds Plums

$2\frac{1}{4}$ pounds Pears

Extra Practice for this lesson is provided on page 426.

9·5 Adding Unlike Fractions

Number Sense
Use fraction strips to show why you need like fractions to add.

Unlike fractions have different denominators. You know how to add like fractions. To add unlike fractions, you first need to rename one or both fractions to make like fractions.

▶ **EXAMPLE**

Add. $\frac{2}{3} + \frac{3}{5}$

Look for a common multiple of 3 and 5.
$M_3 = \{3, 6, 9, 12, 15, \ldots\}$
$M_5 = \{5, 10, 15, \ldots\}$

STEP 1 Make like fractions. Use 15 as the denominator.

$$\frac{2}{3} = \frac{2 \times 5}{3 \times 5} = \frac{10}{15}$$
$$\frac{3}{5} = \frac{3 \times 3}{5 \times 3} = \frac{9}{15}$$

Avoiding Errors
Review the steps on how to find equivalent fractions.

STEP 2 Add the like fractions. Write the answer in lowest terms.

$$\begin{array}{r} \frac{10}{15} \\ + \frac{9}{15} \\ \hline \frac{19}{15} = 1\frac{4}{15} \end{array}$$

The sum of $\frac{2}{3}$ and $\frac{3}{5}$ is $1\frac{4}{15}$.

Practice

Common Error Fractions are not renamed properly. Remind students that the denominator and the numerator are multiplied by the same number in order to rename a fraction.

Add. Remember to rename as like fractions.

1. $\begin{array}{r} \frac{3}{8} \\ + \frac{1}{4} \end{array}$ $\frac{5}{8}$

2. $\begin{array}{r} \frac{5}{12} \\ + \frac{3}{4} \end{array}$ $1\frac{1}{6}$

3. $\begin{array}{r} \frac{7}{9} \\ + \frac{6}{27} \end{array}$ 1

4. $\begin{array}{r} \frac{5}{7} \\ + \frac{11}{28} \end{array}$ $1\frac{3}{28}$

5. $\begin{array}{r} \frac{1}{3} \\ + \frac{1}{5} \end{array}$ $\frac{8}{15}$

6. $\begin{array}{r} \frac{7}{8} \\ + \frac{2}{3} \end{array}$ $1\frac{13}{24}$

7. $\begin{array}{r} \frac{5}{12} \\ + \frac{2}{3} \end{array}$ $1\frac{1}{12}$

8. $\begin{array}{r} \frac{2}{3} \\ + \frac{2}{5} \end{array}$ $1\frac{1}{15}$

9. $\frac{17}{20} + \frac{3}{10}$ $1\frac{3}{20}$

10. $\frac{3}{4} + \frac{1}{3}$ $1\frac{1}{12}$

11. $\frac{6}{15} + \frac{3}{5}$ 1

12. $\frac{5}{8} + \frac{5}{6}$ $1\frac{11}{24}$

13. $\frac{3}{5} + \frac{1}{2}$ $1\frac{1}{10}$

14. $\frac{2}{5} + \frac{3}{4}$ $1\frac{3}{20}$

15. $\frac{1}{4} + \frac{3}{16}$ $\frac{7}{16}$

16. $\frac{5}{6} + \frac{4}{9}$ $1\frac{5}{18}$

Extra Practice for this lesson is provided on page 426.

MATH IN YOUR LIFE
Pay Day

Paul works part-time at a department store. He keeps a record of the hours he works each day. At the end of the week, he totals his hours. This helps him determine the amount of his paycheck.

HOURS WORKED

	Mon.	Tues.	Wed.	Thurs.	Fri.
May 5	4	$3\frac{1}{2}$	5	$5\frac{1}{2}$	$6\frac{1}{2}$
May 12	5	4	$3\frac{1}{2}$	4	$5\frac{1}{2}$
May 19	$3\frac{1}{2}$	0	$4\frac{1}{2}$	4	4
May 26	6	$3\frac{1}{2}$	5	$3\frac{1}{2}$	6

Use Paul's records to answer the following questions.

1. Find the total number of hours Paul worked the week of May 12. 22 hours

2. Which week did Paul work the most hours? How many hours was that? week of May 5; $24\frac{1}{2}$ hours

3. Which week did Paul work the least number of hours? How many hours was that? week of May 19; 16 hours

4. How many more hours did Paul work during the week of May 5 than the week of May 12? $2\frac{1}{2}$ hours

---

Critical Thinking

Paul gets paid $8 per hour. How much money did he make the week of May 26? Show your work.

Critical Thinking

Paul worked 24 hours. 24 × $8. He made $192 the week of May 26.

More Practice is provided in Exercise 80 of the *Workbook*.

9-6 ▶ Subtracting Unlike Fractions

Number Sense
Use fraction strips to show why you need like denominators to subtract.

To subtract unlike fractions, you need to rename one or both fractions to make like fractions. Then, subtract the like fractions.

▶ **EXAMPLE**

Subtract. $\frac{2}{3} - \frac{1}{4}$

Look for a common multiple of 3 and 4.
$M_3 = \{3, 6, 9, 12, \ldots\}$
$M_4 = \{4, 8, 12, \ldots\}$

STEP 1 Make like fractions. Use 12 as the denominator.

$\frac{2}{3} = \frac{2 \times 4}{3 \times 4} = \frac{8}{12}$

$\frac{1}{4} = \frac{1 \times 3}{4 \times 3} = \frac{3}{12}$

STEP 2 Subtract the like fractions. Make sure the answer is in lowest terms.

$$\begin{array}{r} \frac{8}{12} \\ -\frac{3}{12} \\ \hline \frac{5}{12} \end{array}$$

Avoiding Errors
Remind students to use the new denominator in the answer.

The difference between $\frac{2}{3}$ and $\frac{1}{4}$ is $\frac{5}{12}$.

Practice

Common Error Fractions with unlike denominators are subtracted. Have students read problems aloud to check for like denominators. All fractions should have the same "last name."

Subtract. Remember to rename as like fractions.

1. $\frac{7}{8}$ $\frac{1}{8}$
   $-\frac{3}{4}$

2. $\frac{1}{2}$ $\frac{1}{6}$
   $-\frac{1}{3}$

3. $\frac{2}{5}$ $\frac{3}{10}$
   $-\frac{1}{10}$

4. $\frac{3}{4}$ $\frac{1}{4}$
   $-\frac{1}{2}$

5. $\frac{7}{9}$ $\frac{1}{9}$
   $-\frac{2}{3}$

6. $\frac{3}{5}$ $\frac{1}{5}$
   $-\frac{4}{10}$

7. $\frac{5}{6}$ $\frac{1}{12}$
   $-\frac{3}{4}$

8. $\frac{13}{20}$ $\frac{1}{4}$
   $-\frac{2}{5}$

9. $\frac{7}{18}$ $\frac{1}{18}$
   $-\frac{1}{3}$

10. $\frac{4}{5}$ $\frac{1}{2}$
    $-\frac{3}{10}$

11. $\frac{6}{7}$ $\frac{23}{35}$
    $-\frac{1}{5}$

12. $\frac{2}{5}$ $\frac{8}{45}$
    $-\frac{2}{9}$

13. $\frac{7}{10} - \frac{1}{4}$ $\frac{9}{20}$

14. $\frac{5}{6} - \frac{5}{8}$ $\frac{5}{24}$

15. $\frac{5}{6} - \frac{1}{5}$ $\frac{19}{30}$

16. $\frac{8}{9} - \frac{5}{6}$ $\frac{1}{18}$

Extra Practice for this lesson is provided on page 426.

USING YOUR CALCULATOR
Finding Common Denominators

To add or subtract unlike fractions, you need a common denominator. You can use your calculator to find a common denominator.

Add. $\frac{3}{4} + \frac{3}{10}$

First, find multiples for each denominator.

Begin by listing 4 as the first multiple of 4. $M_4 = \{4,$

Find the next multiple of 4.

PRESS [4] [+] [4] [=] [8.] $M_4 = \{4, 8,$

PRESS [=] [12.] $M_4 = \{4, 8, 12,$

Continue to press [=] for each new multiple of 4.
    $M_4 = \{4, 8, 12, 16, 20, 24, 28, 32, 36, 40...\}$

List 10 as the first multiple of 10. $M_{10} = \{10,$
Then use your calculator to find multiples of 10.

PRESS [1][0] [+] [1][0] [=] [20.] $M_{10} = \{10, 20,$

PRESS [=] [30.] $M_{10} = \{10, 20, 30,$

Continue to press [=] for each new multiple of 10.
    $M_{10} = \{10, 20, 30, 40, 50, ...\}$

Look at the two lists above. The least common multiple is 20.
The least common denominator of $\frac{3}{4}$ and $\frac{3}{10}$ is 20.

> **Calculator Tip**
> You can enter a problem.
> Press [4] [+] [4] [=]
> [8.]
> The calculator continues to add 4 each time you press [=].

**Use your calculator to find the common denominator.
Then, add or subtract.**

1. $\frac{5}{18}$ $\frac{25}{36}$
$+\frac{5}{12}$

2. $\frac{4}{9}$ $1\frac{1}{63}$
$+\frac{4}{7}$

3. $\frac{5}{21}$ $\frac{1}{42}$
$-\frac{3}{14}$

4. $\frac{3}{8}$ $\frac{5}{24}$
$-\frac{1}{6}$

5. $\frac{2}{15}$ $\frac{1}{75}$
$-\frac{3}{25}$

More Practice is provided in Exercise 81 of the *Workbook*.

9-7 Adding Unlike Mixed Numbers

Number Sense
Have students show how they can make two unlike fractions into like fractions.

Unlike mixed numbers have unlike fractions. You can add unlike mixed numbers. First, rename to make like fractions. Then, add the like mixed numbers.

▶ **EXAMPLE**

Add. $7\frac{5}{6} + 3\frac{1}{4}$

Think: $\frac{5}{6} = \frac{?}{12}$

$\frac{5}{6} = \frac{5 \times 2}{6 \times 2} = \frac{10}{12}$

STEP 1 Make like fractions. Use 12 as the denominator.

$$7\frac{5}{6} = 7\frac{10}{12}$$
$$+ 3\frac{1}{4} = 3\frac{3}{12}$$

Think: $\frac{1}{4} = \frac{?}{12}$

$\frac{1}{4} = \frac{1 \times 3}{4 \times 3} = \frac{3}{12}$

STEP 2 Add the like mixed numbers. Write the answer in lowest terms.

$$7\frac{10}{12}$$
$$+ 3\frac{3}{12}$$
$$10\frac{13}{12} = 11\frac{1}{12}$$

Avoiding Errors
Remind students to add the fractions first and then the whole numbers.

The sum of $7\frac{5}{6}$ and $3\frac{1}{4}$ is $11\frac{1}{12}$.

Common Error Unlike fractions are not renamed. Have students pay special attention to the fractional part of the mixed numbers. Stress that the fractions must have common denominators before adding.

Practice A

Add. Remember to rename as like mixed numbers.

1. $2\frac{1}{3}$ $5\frac{5}{6}$
$+ 3\frac{1}{2}$

2. $4\frac{2}{9}$ $9\frac{5}{9}$
$+ 5\frac{1}{3}$

3. $7\frac{1}{2}$ $12\frac{3}{4}$
$+ 5\frac{1}{4}$

4. $8\frac{2}{3}$ $10\frac{11}{15}$
$+ 2\frac{1}{15}$

5. $3\frac{2}{7}$ $7\frac{13}{21}$
$+ 4\frac{1}{3}$

6. $8\frac{3}{4}$ $13\frac{5}{12}$
$+ 4\frac{2}{3}$

7. $9\frac{3}{8}$ $14\frac{5}{24}$
$+ 4\frac{5}{6}$

8. $8\frac{1}{4}$ $16\frac{1}{12}$
$+ 7\frac{5}{6}$

9. $7\frac{2}{3}$ $10\frac{4}{9}$
$+ 2\frac{7}{9}$

10. $6\frac{3}{4}$ $15\frac{3}{8}$
$+ 8\frac{5}{8}$

11. $9\frac{3}{5}$ $15\frac{4}{15}$
$+ 5\frac{2}{3}$

12. $6\frac{7}{8}$ $14\frac{7}{24}$
$+ 7\frac{5}{12}$

Practice B

Add. Remember to write each problem in vertical form.

13. $12\frac{11}{20} + 4\frac{3}{5}$ $17\frac{3}{20}$

14. $5\frac{1}{3} + 6\frac{2}{5}$ $11\frac{11}{15}$

15. $1\frac{4}{15} + 2\frac{2}{5}$ $3\frac{2}{3}$

16. $4\frac{1}{2} + 5\frac{3}{4}$ $10\frac{1}{4}$

17. $8\frac{3}{4} + \frac{7}{8}$ $9\frac{5}{8}$

18. $4\frac{5}{12} + 1\frac{3}{4}$ $6\frac{1}{6}$

19. $2\frac{5}{9} + 1\frac{2}{3}$ $4\frac{2}{9}$

20. $5\frac{1}{6} + 2\frac{3}{4}$ $7\frac{11}{12}$

21. $6\frac{7}{10} + 9\frac{1}{2}$ $16\frac{1}{5}$

22. $19\frac{1}{3} + 5\frac{3}{4}$ $25\frac{1}{12}$

23. $8\frac{1}{6} + 1\frac{5}{8}$ $9\frac{19}{24}$

24. $7\frac{5}{9} + 2\frac{5}{6}$ $10\frac{7}{18}$

Everyday Problem Solving

This neighborhood map helps people plan their routes. Use the map to answer the questions.

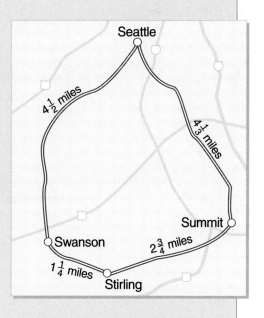

1. Brenda drove from Seattle to Summit and then to Stirling. How far did Brenda drive altogether? $7\frac{1}{12}$ miles

2. A bus route goes from Swanson to Seattle and then to Summit. How long is the route? $8\frac{5}{6}$ miles

3. Joe wants to jog 4 miles. What route should he jog? Summit to Stirling to Swanson

4. Dena wants to drive from Stirling to Seattle. She can drive through Swanson or through Summit. Which is the shorter route? Explain.
Stirling to Swanson to Seattle: This route is $5\frac{3}{4}$ miles long; the other route is $7\frac{1}{12}$ miles long.

Extra Practice for this lesson is provided on page 427.

More Practice is provided in Exercise 82 of the *Workbook*.

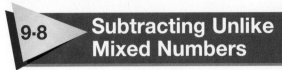

9·8 Subtracting Unlike Mixed Numbers

Number Sense
Review subtracting a mixed number from a whole number to show the regrouping.

You can subtract unlike mixed numbers. First, rename the fractions to make like mixed numbers. Then, subtract the like mixed numbers.

▶ **EXAMPLE 1**

Subtract. $6\frac{3}{4} - 2\frac{1}{3}$

Think: $\frac{3}{4} = \frac{?}{12}$

$\frac{3}{4} = \frac{3 \times 3}{4 \times 3} = \frac{9}{12}$

Think: $\frac{1}{3} = \frac{?}{12}$

$\frac{1}{3} = \frac{1 \times 4}{3 \times 4} = \frac{4}{12}$

STEP 1 Make like fractions. Use 12 as the denominator.

$$6\frac{3}{4} = 6\frac{9}{12}$$
$$- 2\frac{1}{3} = 2\frac{4}{12}$$

STEP 2 Subtract the like mixed numbers. Make sure the answer is in lowest terms.

$$6\frac{9}{12}$$
$$- 2\frac{4}{12}$$
$$4\frac{5}{12}$$

Avoiding Errors
Focus student attention on the operation involved; often, students may add when they should subtract.

The difference between $6\frac{3}{4}$ and $2\frac{1}{3}$ is $4\frac{5}{12}$.

Sometimes, you need to regroup the first mixed number to subtract the fractions.

▶ **EXAMPLE 2**

Subtract. $15\frac{1}{2} - 3\frac{4}{5}$

Regroup $15\frac{5}{10}$ for more tenths. Take 1 from 15.

$15\frac{5}{10} = 14 + 1 + \frac{5}{10}$

Rename 1 as $\frac{10}{10}$.

$= 14 + \frac{10}{10} + \frac{5}{10} = 14\frac{15}{10}$

STEP 1 Make like fractions. Use 10 as the denominator.

$$15\frac{1}{2} = 15\frac{5}{10}$$
$$- 3\frac{4}{5} = - 3\frac{8}{10}$$

STEP 2 Regroup so you can subtract. Make sure the answer is in lowest terms.

$$15\frac{5}{10} = 14\frac{15}{10}$$
$$- 3\frac{8}{10} = - 3\frac{8}{10}$$
$$11\frac{7}{10}$$

The difference between $15\frac{1}{2}$ and $3\frac{4}{5}$ is $11\frac{7}{10}$.

Common Error In a mixed number, the whole number is not decreased when it is regrouped. Have students cross out the whole number when they regroup. This will remind them to rewrite the whole number.

Subtract. Write the answer in lowest terms.

1. $5\frac{6}{7}$ $3\frac{5}{14}$

$\underline{-\ 2\frac{1}{2}}$

2. $8\frac{3}{5}$ $7\frac{4}{15}$

$\underline{-\ 1\frac{1}{3}}$

3. $4\frac{3}{4}$ $2\frac{3}{8}$

$\underline{-\ 2\frac{3}{8}}$

4. $9\frac{7}{10}$ $6\frac{3}{10}$

$\underline{-\ 3\frac{2}{5}}$

5. $4\frac{7}{9}$ $3\frac{4}{9}$

$\underline{-\ 1\frac{1}{3}}$

6. $5\frac{2}{3}$ $3\frac{7}{15}$

$\underline{-\ 2\frac{1}{5}}$

7. $10\frac{5}{6}$ $7\frac{1}{6}$

$\underline{-\ 3\frac{2}{3}}$

8. $5\frac{5}{9}$ $3\frac{7}{18}$

$\underline{-\ 2\frac{1}{6}}$

9. $10\frac{7}{8} - 5\frac{5}{6}$ $5\frac{1}{24}$

10. $5\frac{6}{7} - 2\frac{2}{3}$ $3\frac{4}{21}$

Practice B

Subtract. Remember to regroup.

11. $6\frac{1}{4}$ $3\frac{11}{12}$

$\underline{-\ 2\frac{1}{3}}$

12. $4\frac{1}{2}$ $2\frac{6}{7}$

$\underline{-\ 1\frac{9}{14}}$

13. $8\frac{1}{3}$ $7\frac{5}{6}$

$\underline{-\ \frac{1}{2}}$

14. $9\frac{1}{2}$ $4\frac{3}{4}$

$\underline{-\ 4\frac{3}{4}}$

15. $5\frac{1}{4}$ $\frac{5}{12}$

$\underline{-\ 4\frac{5}{6}}$

16. $6\frac{4}{9}$ $4\frac{7}{9}$

$\underline{-\ 1\frac{2}{3}}$

17. $7\frac{3}{10}$ $4\frac{7}{10}$

$\underline{-\ 2\frac{3}{5}}$

18. $12\frac{1}{3}$ $6\frac{1}{2}$

$\underline{-\ 5\frac{5}{6}}$

Everyday Problem Solving

Tracy saw this chart in the Business section of the newspaper. The closing price of a stock is the price for the stock at the end of the day.

1. How much higher was the closing price of Kanga than that of Big Tees? Subtract. $2\frac{1}{4}$

2. How much higher was the closing price of Top Mart than that of Big Tees? $2\frac{7}{8}$

APRIL 10

STOCK QUOTES

STOCK	CLOSING PRICE
Top Mart	$38\frac{3}{8}$
Big Tees	$35\frac{1}{2}$
Kanga	$37\frac{3}{4}$

Extra Practice for this lesson is provided on page 427.

9·9 Problem Solving: Multi-Part Problems

Solving multi-part word problems is easier if you work on one part at a time.

Number Sense
Show students other ways to solve the problem.

$3 \times \frac{3}{4} = 2\frac{1}{4}$ yards green

$3 \times 1\frac{1}{2} = 4\frac{1}{2}$ yards orange

Total: $2\frac{1}{4} + 4\frac{1}{2} = 6\frac{3}{4}$ yards

Avoiding Errors
Be sure students add like units, yards.

Ms. Torres is making 3 costumes for a play. Each costume requires $\frac{3}{4}$ yard of green fabric and $1\frac{1}{2}$ yards of orange fabric. How much fabric does she need altogether?

STEP 1 **READ** **What do you need to find out?**
You need to find how much fabric is needed for 3 costumes.

STEP 2 **PLAN** **What do you need to do?**
How much fabric is needed for 1 costume?
Add to find out.
How much fabric is needed for 3 costumes?
Multiply to find out.

STEP 3 **DO** **Follow the plan.**
Add.

$$\frac{3}{4} = \quad \frac{3}{4}$$
$$+ 1\frac{1}{2} = + 1\frac{2}{4}$$
$$\overline{}$$
$$1\frac{5}{4} = 2\frac{1}{4} \text{ yards}$$

Multiply.

$$2\frac{1}{4} \times 3 = \frac{9}{4} \times \frac{3}{1} = \frac{27}{4} = 6\frac{3}{4} \text{ yards}$$

Remember:
$3 \times 2 = 6$
So $3 \times 2\frac{1}{4} > 6$.

STEP 4 **CHECK** **Does your answer make sense?**
Notice that $2\frac{1}{4}$ is greater than 2.
This means that $3 \times 2\frac{1}{4}$ is greater than 6.
So, $6\frac{3}{4}$ yards makes sense. ✓

Ms. Torres needs $6\frac{3}{4}$ yards to make 3 costumes.

Common Error Correct operations with incorrect numbers are used. Encourage students to use units when they calculate, such as yards or dollars, to keep appropriate numbers together.

READ the problem. Answer the questions under PLAN. DO the plan to solve the problem.

1. Ms. Torres bought $5\frac{1}{4}$ yards of white fabric and $6\frac{3}{4}$ yards of red fabric. Each yard cost \$6. What is her total cost?

PLAN

How many yards of fabric did she buy? 12 yards

What is her total cost? \$72

DO

$5\frac{1}{4} + 6\frac{3}{4} = 12$

$12 \times \$6 = \$72$

2. Ms. Torres had $5\frac{2}{3}$ yards of black fabric. She used $2\frac{1}{3}$ yards for one skirt and $1\frac{3}{4}$ yards for slacks. How much fabric does she have left?

PLAN

How much fabric was used? $4\frac{1}{12}$ yards

How much fabric is left? $1\frac{7}{12}$ yards

DO

$2\frac{1}{3} + 1\frac{3}{4} = 4\frac{1}{12}$

$5\frac{2}{3} - 4\frac{1}{12} = 1\frac{7}{12}$

3. It takes Ms. Torres $3\frac{3}{4}$ hours to sew one adult's costume and $2\frac{1}{2}$ hours to sew one child's costume. How long will it take to sew two of each costume?

PLAN

How long does it take to sew one of each costume? $6\frac{1}{4}$ hours

How long does it take to sew two of each costume? $12\frac{1}{2}$ hours

DO

$3\frac{3}{4} + 2\frac{1}{2} = 6\frac{1}{4}$

$6\frac{1}{4} \times 2 = 12\frac{1}{2}$

Problem Solving Strategy

Sometimes, you can work backward to solve a problem.

Ms. Torres bought some fabric on sale. She used $1\frac{1}{2}$ yards for a costume. She has $\frac{1}{2}$ yard left. How much fabric did she buy?

Add to find how much fabric she bought.

$$\begin{array}{r} \blacksquare\blacksquare \\ -\ 1\frac{1}{2}\ \text{yards} \\ \hline \frac{1}{2}\ \text{yard} \end{array}$$

$$\begin{array}{r} 1\frac{1}{2}\ \text{yards} \\ +\ \frac{1}{2}\ \text{yard} \\ \hline \blacksquare\blacksquare \end{array}$$

Extra Practice for this lesson is provided on page 428.

| like fractions |
| unlike fractions |

Vocabulary Review

Choose a phrase from the list that describes each pair of numbers.

1. $\frac{7}{8}$ and $\frac{5}{8}$ like fractions

2. $\frac{1}{2}$ and $\frac{5}{7}$ unlike fractions

3. $\frac{5}{6}$ and $\frac{3}{16}$ unlike fractions

4. $\frac{2}{9}$ and $\frac{7}{9}$ like fractions

5. Writing Explain why a common denominator is needed to add $\frac{3}{4}$ and $\frac{1}{3}$.   A common denominator is needed so that the same fraction pieces are added.

Chapter Quiz

LESSONS 9·1 to 9·3

Adding and Subtracting Like Fractions and Like Mixed Numbers

Test Tip
Add or subtract the numerators. Keep the same denominator.

Add or subtract.

1. $\frac{5}{6} + \frac{4}{6}$ $1\frac{1}{2}$

2. $\frac{7}{8} - \frac{5}{8}$ $\frac{1}{4}$

3. $\frac{5}{9} - \frac{3}{9}$ $\frac{2}{9}$

4. $\frac{5}{10} + \frac{7}{10}$ $1\frac{1}{5}$

5. $1\frac{2}{6} + 1\frac{5}{6}$ $3\frac{1}{6}$

6. $6\frac{7}{8} - 3\frac{2}{8}$ $3\frac{5}{8}$

7. $3\frac{5}{7} + 9\frac{2}{7}$ 13

8. $7\frac{2}{9} - 5\frac{8}{9}$ $1\frac{1}{3}$

Subtracting from a Whole Number

Subtract.

9. $7 - \frac{5}{6}$ $6\frac{1}{6}$

10. $5 - 3\frac{2}{3}$ $1\frac{1}{3}$

11. $8 - 5\frac{3}{4}$ $2\frac{1}{4}$

12. $12 - \frac{9}{20}$ $11\frac{11}{20}$

Adding and Subtracting Unlike Fractions and Unlike Mixed Numbers

Add or subtract.

13. $\frac{4}{5} + \frac{9}{10}$ $1\frac{7}{10}$

14. $\frac{5}{6} - \frac{2}{3}$ $\frac{1}{6}$

15. $\frac{2}{3} - \frac{2}{5}$ $\frac{4}{15}$

16. $3\frac{1}{6} + 1\frac{3}{4}$ $4\frac{11}{12}$

17. $5\frac{1}{2} - 3\frac{1}{8}$ $2\frac{3}{8}$

18. $7\frac{2}{9} - 1\frac{2}{3}$ $5\frac{5}{9}$

Solving Multi-Part Problems

Solve.

19. Olga bought $3\frac{1}{2}$ yards of red ribbon, $3\frac{3}{4}$ yards of green ribbon, and $2\frac{7}{8}$ yards of fabric. How many more yards of ribbon than fabric did she buy? $4\frac{3}{8}$ yards

20. Hank and his 3 brothers shared $5\frac{1}{3}$ pounds of pecans equally. Of his $\frac{1}{4}$ share, Hank ate $\frac{1}{3}$ pound. How many pounds does he have left?   1 pound

Group Activity See the *Teacher Planning Guide* for a Scoring Rubric for this activity.

With your group, choose 5 stocks to buy. Record the reasons that you would like to buy those stocks. Then, use the Business section of the newspaper to "buy" 100 shares of each stock at the closing prices. Follow the stocks for 5 business days and record the closing prices. Every day, find your profit or loss.

Unit 2 Review

Choose the letter for the correct answer.

Use the table to answer Questions 1 and 2.

Bagels Sold	
Type of Bagel	**Number Sold**
Cinnamon	13
Blueberry	15
Sesame	7
Raisin	5

1. What fraction of all the bagels sold were sesame bagels?
   A. $\frac{5}{7}$ Incorrect; compared raisin to sesame.
   B. $\frac{5}{40}$ Incorrect; compared raisin to total.
   C. $\frac{7}{40}$ Correct.
   D. $\frac{7}{13}$ Incorrect; compared sesame to cinnamon.

2. What fraction of all the bagels sold were raisin bagels?
   A. $\frac{1}{5}$ Incorrect; not reduced correctly.
   B. $\frac{1}{8}$ Correct.
   C. $\frac{3}{8}$ Incorrect; reduced fraction of blueberry to total.
   D. None of the above Incorrect.

3. Which fraction is equivalent to $4\frac{5}{6}$?
   A. $\frac{15}{6}$ Incorrect; added digits not multiplied.
   B. $\frac{26}{6}$ Incorrect; multiplied incorrect digits.
   C. $\frac{29}{6}$ Correct.
   D. $\frac{45}{6}$ Incorrect; used whole number as part of fraction.

4. Michelle bought $3\frac{1}{2}$ dozen bagels. One dozen is 12 bagels. How many bagels did she buy?
   A. 36 Incorrect; multiplied whole number by 12.
   B. 42 Correct.
   C. 84 Incorrect; only multiplied the numerators.
   D. None of the above Incorrect.

5. Find $4 \div \frac{4}{5}$.
   A. $\frac{1}{5}$ Incorrect; divided numerators only.
   B. $3\frac{1}{5}$ Incorrect; multiplied without inverting fraction.
   C. 5 Correct.
   D. None of the above Incorrect.

6. Which sum is greatest?
   A. $\frac{1}{2} + \frac{1}{3}$ Incorrect; $\frac{3}{6} + \frac{2}{6} = \frac{5}{6} < 1$.
   B. $\frac{2}{3} + \frac{1}{10}$ Incorrect; $\cdot\frac{20}{30} + \frac{3}{30} = \frac{23}{30} < 1$.
   C. $\frac{1}{2} + \frac{1}{10}$ Incorrect; $\frac{10}{20} + \frac{2}{20} = \frac{12}{20} < 1$.
   D. $\frac{1}{2} + \frac{2}{3}$ Correct; $\frac{3}{6} + \frac{4}{6} = \frac{7}{6} > 1$.

Critical Thinking
Use the table above. Yoko wants to buy 2 dozen bagels. She needs $\frac{2}{3}$ cinnamon and $\frac{1}{4}$ sesame. Will she have enough for 2 dozen bagels? Why or why not?
CHALLENGE How many more bagels does she need to buy 2 dozen? What could they be?

Critical Thinking
No; she will only have 22 bagels.
Challenge The last 2 bagels can be 2 raisin or 2 blueberry or 1 of each.

198

Chapter 10 Decimals

Chapter 11 Percents

Chapter 12 Ratio and Proportions

Opening the Unit
Have students gather information from newspapers and magazines on environmental issues. Teams can debate the issues using any graphs or charts they may find.

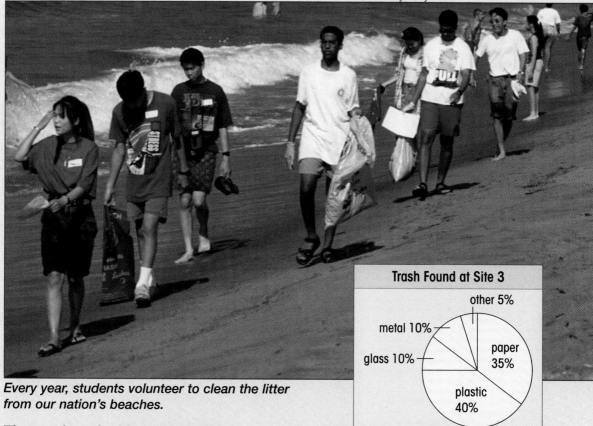

Every year, students volunteer to clean the litter from our nation's beaches.

The graph and table on the right give information about a beach cleanup.

1. Which site had the most volunteers? Site 2

2. How many tons of trash were collected at Site 1? 161.4 tons

3. What percent (%) of the trash at Site 3 was plastic? 40%

Trash Found at Site 3

other 5%
metal 10%
glass 10%
paper 35%
plastic 40%

	Community Beach Cleanup		
Site	Number of Volunteers	Tons of Trash Collected	Pounds per Volunteer
1	6,893	161.4	46.83
2	12,722	199.6	30.89
3	9,789	155.6	31.79
4	8,824	197.3	44.72

These runners are at the end of a close race. Only .01 of a second may separate the winner from the runner in second place! How else are decimals used in sports?

Caption Decimals may also be used in weights, distances, or scores.

Chapter 10 ▷ Decimals

ESL Note In many countries, a comma is used instead of a decimal point.

Words to Know

decimal	a number that names part of a whole
decimal point	the dot in a decimal; a decimal has digits to the right of its decimal point
decimal places	the places to the right of a decimal point
mixed decimal	a number with a whole number and a decimal

Words to Know Point out that the word *decimal* is the basis for all the terms in the chapter.

Decimal Search Project

Look for decimals in different places. Try the newspaper, a magazine, or another textbook. For example, your science or social studies book might contain decimals. Tell the class what is described by the decimals you found. Write two problems using your decimals.

Learning Objectives

- Read and write decimals.
- Compare and order decimals.
- Add, subtract, multiply, and divide decimals.
- Change a decimal to a fraction.
- Change a fraction to a decimal.
- Round decimals.
- Solve problems using decimals.
- Apply knowledge of decimals to banking.

Project The project can be done in small groups or as homework assignments. Have students store the examples they find in folders or envelopes. Students can use these decimals to practice the skills in the chapter.

10-1 ▶ What Is a Decimal?

A **decimal** is a number that names part of a whole. A decimal has a **decimal point** with digits to its right.

▶ **EXAMPLE 1**

The number of digits to the right of the decimal point is the number of **decimal places**.

Number Sense
Write the following decimals on the board:
  6.01   6.10
Ask students how many decimal places there are in each of these decimals.

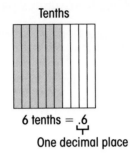

Tenths

6 tenths = .6
One decimal place

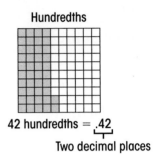

Hundredths

42 hundredths = .42
Two decimal places

▶ **EXAMPLE 2**

2 is a whole number.
.8 is a decimal.

A **mixed decimal** has a whole number part and a decimal part.

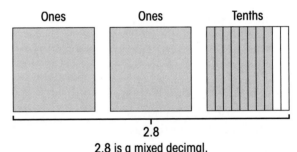

Ones   Ones   Tenths

2.8
2.8 is a mixed decimal.

Avoiding Errors
Make sure that students identify the digits to the right of the decimal point as the decimal part.

Common Error The number of decimal places is incorrect. Be sure that students are counting the zero digits to the right of the decimal point.

Practice

Write the numbers on a separate sheet of paper. Draw a line under each decimal part. Then, tell the number of decimal places.

1. 9.7 1   **2.** 1.25 2   **3.** 4.33 2   **4.** 8.793 3   **5.** .004 3

6. 10.1 1   **7.** 18.2 1   **8.** 6.005 3   **9.** 28.555 3   **10.** 32.4 1

11. 32 0   **12.** 1.00 2   **13.** 100.1 1   **14.** 16.01 2   **15.** 700 0

More practice is provided in Exercise 85 of the *Workbook*.

10·2 ▶ Reading and Writing Decimals

Number Sense

Write the following decimals on the board:

23.504   23.540   23.054

Discuss how zeros are used as placeholders. Ask students to read each of these decimals.

You can show decimals on a place-value chart. From now on, we will use the word *decimal* for both decimals and mixed decimals.

thousands	hundreds	tens	ones	decimal point	tenths	hundredths	thousandths	ten thousandths
		1	5	.	0	6	4	
				.	2	0	3	9
		4	0	.	0	8		

The place-value chart can help you to read decimals.

Read the decimal.   15.064

EXAMPLE 1

Avoiding Errors

Remind students to use the word *and* when writing mixed decimals.

STEP 1	Read the whole number part.	fifteen
STEP 2	Read the decimal point as "and."	and
STEP 3	Read the decimal part.	sixty-four
STEP 4	Read the place value of the last digit.	thousandths

Read 15.064 as "fifteen and sixty-four thousandths."

You can write a decimal from words.

EXAMPLE 2

Write forty and eight hundredths as a decimal.

STEP 1	Write the whole number part.	40
STEP 2	Write a decimal point for "and."	40.
STEP 3	Find the place name of the last digit.	hundredths
STEP 4	Write the decimal part.	40.08

Forty and eight hundredths is 40.08 as a decimal.

Lesson continues on next page.

Common Error Students forget to write the zeros needed as place-holders. Point out the difference between 30.012 and 30.12.

Read aloud the numbers in the chart below. Remember to read the decimal point as "and" if it has a whole number part.

thousands	hundreds	tens	ones	decimal point	tenths	hundredths	thousandths	ten thousandths	
1.				.	7	5	4		seven hundred fifty-four thousandths
2. 1	3	8	2	.	4	3	2		one thousand, three hundred eighty-two and four hundred thirty-two thousandths

Practice B

Write the place name of the last digit in each number below.

3. 32.7
tenths

4. 239.13
hundredths

5. 62.472
thousandths

6. 136.02
hundredths

7. 500.19
hundredths

8. 74.309
thousandths

9. 143.003
thousandths

10. 25.624
thousandths

Practice C

Write each number as a decimal.

11. four tenths .4

12. four hundredths .04

13. two hundred fifty-two thousandths
.252

14. fifty and three thousandths
50.003

Everyday Problem Solving

A newspaper headline can have a decimal in it.

1. Write the number in Headline A as a decimal. 1.4

2. Write the number in Headline B in words.
four hundred thirteen thousandths

3. Look in the newspaper for a decimal. If it is a number, write it in words. If it is in words, write it as a number. Answers may vary. Check student's work to make sure they have written the decimal correctly.

(A) **Local News**
One and Four Tenths Inches
Rain Breaks Record

(B) **Today's Sports**
Ripken's Batting
Average Reaches .413

Extra Practice for this lesson is provided on page 429.

More practice is provided in Exercise 86 of the *Workbook*.

10-3 ▶ Comparing Decimals

Avoiding Errors
Point out that a decimal with the greatest number of digits is not necessarily the greatest in value. For example, $16.014 < 16.14$

Use the pictures to compare the decimals .4 and .04. Notice the different sizes of the shaded parts.

 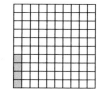

.4 > .04

You can also use what you know about whole numbers to compare decimals.

EXAMPLE 1

> means greater than
< means less than
= means equal

Compare. 327.41 and 325.928

STEP Compare the whole number parts.   327.41 325.928
327 > 325

The number 327.41 is greater than 325.928.

When the whole numbers are the same, compare the decimal parts.

EXAMPLE 2

Number Sense
Ask students to explain why forty hundredths and four tenths have the same value.

Compare. 89.147 and 89.235

STEP 1
Compare the whole number parts.   89.147   89.235
89 = 89

STEP 2
Compare the decimal parts.   89.147   89.235
.147 < .235

The number 89.147 is less than 89.235.

Sometimes decimals may look different, but they have the same value.

.2 = .20

Lesson continues on next page.

You can write a zero to the right of the last decimal place without changing the value.

EXAMPLE 3

Compare.   .147 and .23

STEP 1
Write zeros so that both decimals have the same number of decimal places.

.147   .230
3 places   3 places

STEP 2
Compare the numbers.   .147 < .230

The decimal .147 is less than the decimal .23.
Common Error Students order decimals incorrectly. Remind students to compare decimals first by comparing the whole number part and then by comparing digit by digit to the right of the decimal point.

Practice

Compare each pair of numbers. Use >, <, or = .

1. .3 > .03   **2.** .12 < 1.2   **3.** .009 < .09

4. .502 < .52   **5.** .728 > .71   **6.** .4 < .45

7. 58.07 < 85.07   **8.** 36.5 < 360.5   **9.** 3.01 > 2.98

10. 21.339 < 21.39   **11.** .03 > .005   **12.** 9.99 < 10

Everyday Problem Solving

In a library, books have call numbers on them. The books are put on shelves in order from the smallest to the largest call number. Each shelf is labeled with the call numbers that it holds.

1. If a book is numbered 827.5, which shelf would you find it on? Shelf 1

2. Will a book with the call number 926.16 be on the same shelf as a book with call number 953.16? Why or why not? No, number 926.16 will be on Shelf 2. Number 953.16 will be on Shelf 3.

3. Which book will come first on Shelf 2: 946.17 or 946.62? 946.17

Library Bookshelves	
Shelf	Call Numbers
1	802.1 to 895.5
2	895.6 to 950
3	950.1 to 975.6

Extra Practice for this lesson is provided on page 429.

10-4 Ordering Decimals

Use what you know about comparing decimals to order decimals.

▶ **EXAMPLE**

Number Sense
Write the following on the board:
5.1   5.10   5.100
Ask students to explain how the values of these three decimals compare.

Avoiding Errors
Point out that students should add zeros to the decimals they are ordering so that all the decimals have the same number of decimal places.

Write these decimals in order from greatest to least.
5.091   5.6   5.19

STEP 1
Write zeros so that all the decimals have the same number of decimal places.

5.091	→	5.091
5.6	→	5.600
5.19	→	5.190

Same whole numbers
↓
5.091 ← Smallest
5.600 ← Largest
5.190

STEP 2
Compare the numbers.

The decimals in order are: 5.6   5.19   5.091.

Common Error Students may order the decimals by the number of decimal places. Tell students to add zeros to make the number of digits that follow the decimal equal. Then, compare.

Practice A

Write the decimals in order from largest to smallest.

1. 2.34 2.79
2.05 2.34
2.79 2.05

2. .27 .89
.89 .56
.56 .27

3. 1.83 1.87
1.87 1.84
1.84 1.83

4. 7   7.32
7.32 7.086
7.086 7

Practice B

Write the decimals in order from largest to smallest.

5. .005 .5   .05
.5   .05   .005

6. .72 .95 .53
.95 .72 .53

7. .7 .2 .04
.7 .2 .04

8. .025 .03 .3
.3 .03 .025

9. .65 .32 .1
.65 .32 .1

10. .5 .51 .49
.51 .5 .49

11. 9.75 8.9 9.8
9.8 9.75 8.9

12. 3.82 3.4 3.078
3.82 3.4 3.078

13. 6.407 6.4 6.41
6.41 6.407 6.4

14. 2.5 3 .25
3 2.5 .25

15. 9.99 10 10.01
10.01 10 9.99

16. 8.01 8.1 8.001
8.1 8.01 8.001

Extra Practice for this lesson is provided on page 429.

More practice is provided in Exercise 88 of the *Workbook*.

10·5 Adding Decimals

Number Sense
Use the following example
to show the importance of
aligning the decimal points.

2.3	2.3
5.67	5.67
+ 3	+ 3
5.93	10.97
Incorrect	Correct

You can add decimals. Look at the grids below.

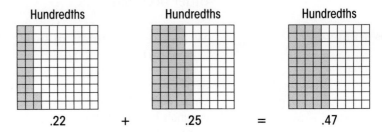

Add decimals the way you add whole numbers. Line
up the decimal points one over the other before you
add. Then, place the decimal point in the sum so that
it lines up with the other decimal points.

▶ EXAMPLE 1

Add.   2.85 + 12.17

Remember:
Vertical means up and down.

STEP 1
Line up the
decimal points.

$$\begin{array}{r} 2.85 \\ + 12.17 \end{array}$$

STEP 2
Add. Place the
decimal point
in the sum.

$$\begin{array}{r} {}^{1\ 1} \\ 2.85 \\ + 12.17 \\ \hline 15.02 \end{array}$$

The sum of 2.85 and 12.17 is 15.02.

Sometimes you must write a decimal point and zeros
so that you can line up the decimal points.

▶ EXAMPLE 2

Add.   6 + 14.85 + 2.5

Avoiding Errors
Point out the difference
between a zero at the end
of a decimal and a zero
within a decimal.
7.20 = 7.2 ≠ 7.02

STEP 1
Line up the
decimal points.

$$\begin{array}{r} 6.00 \\ 14.85 \\ + 2.50 \end{array}$$

STEP 2
Add. Place the
decimal point
in the sum.

$$\begin{array}{r} {}^{1} \\ {}_{1}6.00 \\ 14.85 \\ + 2.50 \\ \hline 23.35 \end{array}$$

The sum of 6 and 14.85 and 2.5 is 23.35.

Practice A

Common Error Digits are not aligned by place value. Have students turn lined paper sideways to help them line up the digits correctly.

Add. The decimal points have been lined up for you.

1.   8.4
       + 1.3
       ———
         9.7

2.   2.37
       + 3.41
       ————
         5.78

3.   5.232
       + .627
       ————
         5.859

4.   5.1
       + 6.8
       ———
        11.9

5. $1.05
         3.96
       + 2.15
       ————
        $7.16

6.   16.155
         4.073
       + 2.009
       ————
        22.237

7. $3.28
         5.00
       + .50
       ———
        $8.78

8.   1.050
         4.000
       + 2.103
       ————
         7.153

Practice B

Add. Remember to line up the decimal points. Write a decimal point and zeros if needed. Show your work in vertical form.

9. 3.4 + 5.1 + 8.2 16.7

10. .112 + .03 .142

11. $159 + $.28 159.28

12. 5.51 + .2 + 8.5 14.21

13. 8 + 9.3 + .502 17.802

14. 65 + 5.1 + .81 70.91

15. 1.7 + .02 + 5.8 7.52

16. $.03 + $3 + $87.50 $90.53

17. .01 + .001 + .0001 .0111

18. 5 + .05 + 5.005 10.055

19. 4 + 42.2 + .08 + .03 46.31

20. $25 + $.15 + $49 $74.15

Everyday Problem Solving

Jen went shopping. Look at the receipt on the right. Some of the information is missing.

1. How much will Jen spend before tax? Add the prices to find the subtotal. $115.13

2. What is the total she needs? Add the sales tax to the subtotal to find out. $123.89

3. Jen has $128.35. Does she have enough money to pay the total you found in question 2? yes

```
CLOTHES PLACE
ITEM          PRICE
SWEATSHIRT   $39.95
JEANS         45.99
DRESS SHIRT   29.79

SUBTOTAL
TAX           8.76
TOTAL
```

Extra Practice for this lesson is provided on page 430.

More practice is provided in Exercise 89 of the *Workbook*.

10·6 Subtracting Decimals

Number Sense
Use the following to show the importance of aligning the decimal points:

$$\begin{array}{r} 2.68 \\ -1.2 \\ \hline 2.56 \end{array} \qquad \begin{array}{r} 2.68 \\ -1.2 \\ \hline 1.48 \end{array}$$

Incorrect   Correct

You can subtract decimals. Look at the grids below.

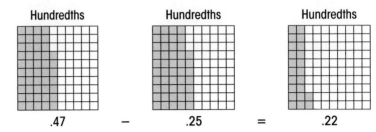

.47   −   .25   =   .22

Subtract decimals the way you subtract whole numbers. Line up the decimal points one over the other before you subtract. Then place the decimal point in the difference so that it lines up with the other decimal points.

► **EXAMPLE 1**

Subtract.   29.34 − 16.52

STEP 1
Line up the decimal points.

$$\begin{array}{r} 29.34 \\ -\ 16.52 \end{array}$$

STEP 2
Subtract. Place the decimal point in the difference.

$$\begin{array}{r} \overset{8\ \ 13}{29.\cancel{3}4} \\ -\ 16.52 \\ \hline 12.82 \end{array}$$

The difference between 29.34 and 16.52 is 12.82.

Sometimes you must write a decimal point and zeros so that you can line up the decimal points.

► **EXAMPLE 2**

Subtract.   87 − 35.83

Avoiding Errors
Point out when it is important to write a decimal point and to add zeros to a decimal.

STEP 1
Line up the decimal points.

$$\begin{array}{r} 87.00 \\ -\ 35.83 \end{array}$$

STEP 2
Subtract. Place the decimal point in the difference.

$$\begin{array}{r} \overset{6\ \ 9\,10}{8\cancel{7}.\cancel{0}\cancel{0}} \\ -\ 35.83 \\ \hline 51.17 \end{array}$$

The difference between 87 and 35.83 is 51.17.

Practice A

Subtract. The decimal points have been lined up for you.

1.	12.5 − 8.3 4.2	**2.**	15.39 − 7.62 7.77	**3.**	4.155 − .706 3.449	**4.**	38.01 − 19.43 18.58
5.	63.47 − 45.28 18.19	**6.**	82.0 − 46.2 35.8	**7.**	467.09 − 18.50 448.59	**8.**	5.293 − .750 4.543

Practice B

Subtract. Remember to line up the decimal points. Write a decimal point and zeros if needed. Show your work in vertical form.

9. 17.8 − 6.5 11.3

10. .321 − .09 .231

11. $28.50 − $12.35 $16.15

12. 37.005 − 8.3 28.705

13. 63.3 − .06 63.24

14. 65 − 5.1 59.9

15. $358.23 − $69.95 $288.28

16. 91.2 − .125 91.075

17. $50 − $.79 $49.21

18. $3.50 − $1.95 $1.55

19. .3 − .003 .297

20. 1 − .001 .999

Everyday Problem Solving

Aaron found this chart in a magazine.

1. Who ran the fastest? The smallest number for time shows the fastest runner. Donovan Baily

2. How much faster was Donovan Baily than Carl Lewis? Subtract to find out.
.08 second

3. How much faster was Carl Lewis than Lindford Christies? .04 second

Olympic 100-Meter Run		
Year	Runner	Time
1988	Carl Lewis, United States	9.92 seconds
1992	Lindford Christies, United States	9.96 seconds
1992	Donovan Baily, Canada	9.84 seconds

More practice is provided in Exercise 90 of the *Workbook*.

10·7 Multiplying Decimals

Remember:
Factors are the numbers multiplied to get a product.

▶ **EXAMPLE 1**

Remember:
A product is the answer to a multiplication problem.

Look at the grid. The green part shows $.3 \times .8$.

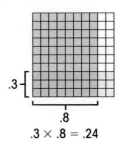

$.3 \times .8 = .24$

Multiply decimals the way you multiply whole numbers. The number of decimal places in the product is equal to the sum of the number of decimal places in the factors.

Multiply. 15.34×4.2

STEP 1
Multiply.

$$\begin{array}{r} 15.34 \\ \times\ \ \ 4.2 \\ \hline 3068 \\ +\ 61360 \\ \hline 64428 \end{array}$$

STEP 2
Count the decimal places.

Place the decimal point.

$$\begin{array}{r} 15.34 \leftarrow \text{2 decimal places} \\ \times\ \ \ 4.2 \leftarrow \text{1 decimal place} \\ \hline 3\ 068 \\ +\ 61\ 360 \\ \hline 64.428 \leftarrow \text{3 decimal places} \end{array}$$

The product of 15.34 and 4.2 is 64.428.

Sometimes, you need to place zeros in the product.

▶ **EXAMPLE 2**

Avoiding Errors
Make sure that students annex zeros to the left of a product and not to the right.
$.3 \times .2 = .06$ $.3 \times .2 \neq .60$

Multiply. $.09 \times .07$

STEP 1
Multiply.

$$\begin{array}{r} .09 \\ \times\ .07 \\ \hline 63 \end{array}$$

STEP 2
Count the decimal places.
Place the decimal point.
Write zeros if needed.

$$\begin{array}{r} .09 \leftarrow \text{2 decimal places} \\ \times\ .07 \leftarrow \text{2 decimal places} \\ \hline .0063 \leftarrow \text{4 decimal places} \end{array}$$

The product of .09 and .07 is .0063.

Practice A

Common Error The decimal point is misplaced in the product. Be sure that students begin counting places on the right.

Copy the multiplication problem. Then, place the decimal point in the product. Write zeros if needed.

1. $\begin{array}{r} 5.82 \\ \times\ \ 2.3 \\ \hline 1\ 3.3\ 8\ 6 \end{array}$

2. $\begin{array}{r} .08 \\ \times\ .06 \\ \hline .0048 \end{array}$

3. $\begin{array}{r} .04 \\ \times\ \ .5 \\ \hline .020 \end{array}$

4. $\begin{array}{r} .2 \\ \times\ .2 \\ \hline .04 \end{array}$

Practice B

Multiply.

5. $\begin{array}{r} 9.65 \\ \times\ \ .12 \\ \hline 1.158 \end{array}$

6. $\begin{array}{r} .18 \\ \times\ .06 \\ \hline .0108 \end{array}$

7. $\begin{array}{r} .24 \\ \times\ \ .5 \\ \hline .12 \end{array}$

8. $\begin{array}{r} 4.23 \\ \times\ \ 1.2 \\ \hline 5.076 \end{array}$

9. $\begin{array}{r} 5.8 \\ \times\ .46 \\ \hline 2.668 \end{array}$

10. $\begin{array}{r} 5.77 \\ \times\ .26 \\ \hline 1.5002 \end{array}$

11. $\begin{array}{r} 627.5 \\ \times\ \ 8.04 \\ \hline 5,045.1 \end{array}$

12. $\begin{array}{r} 5.04 \\ \times\ .67 \\ \hline 3.3768 \end{array}$

13. $3.7 \times .05$ .185

14. 7.003×68 476.204

15. $46.92 \times .01$ .4692

16. $\$65.49 \times 12$ $785.88

17. $\$18.25 \times 30$ $547.50

18. $\$5.99 \times 25$ $149.75

19. $6.9 \times .4$ 2.76

20. $36.4 \times .09$ 3.276

21. $5.59 \times .6$ 3.354

Everyday Problem Solving

Sam saw this advertisement in the newspaper.

1. How much do 4 CDs cost? Multiply to find out. $51.80

2. How much do 3 tapes cost? Multiply to find out. $22.05

3. How much money does Sam need to buy 4 CDs and 3 tapes? $73.85

Extra Practice for this lesson is provided on page 430.

More practice is provided in Exercise 91 of the *Workbook*.

10-8 ▶ Multiplying Decimals by 10, 100, 1,000

Number Sense
Put the following on the board:
4.7 × 10 = 47
4.7 × 100 = 470
Ask the students why it makes sense for the decimal point to move to the right when multiplying.

You can use what you know to learn a shortcut for multiplying decimals by 10, by 100, or by 1,000.

$$\begin{array}{r} .071 \\ \times\ \ 10 \\ \hline .710 \end{array} \qquad \begin{array}{r} .071 \\ \times\ \ 100 \\ \hline 7.100 \end{array} \qquad \begin{array}{r} .071 \\ \times\ \ 1{,}000 \\ \hline 71.000 \end{array}$$

Now look at this:

.071 × 10 = 0.71 = .71
1 zero   1 place to the right

.071 × 100 = 0 7.1 = 7.1
2 zeros   2 places to the right

.071 × 1,000 = 0 7 1. = 71
3 zeros   3 places to the right

Avoiding Errors
Remind students to move the decimal point to the right one place when multiplying by 10, two places when multiplying by 100, and three places when multiplying by 1,000.

To multiply by 10, by 100, or by 1,000, move the decimal point to the right. Write zeros if needed.

▶ **EXAMPLE**

Multiply.   32.5 × 1,000   3 zeros

STEP 1 Count the zeros.   32.5 × 1,000

STEP 2 Move the decimal point.   3 2 5 0 0 = 32,500
Write zeros if needed.

The product of 32.5 and 1,000 is 32,500.

Common Error Students fail to write the necessary zeros in the product. Remind students that they must add zeros to the number if not enough decimal places exist in the original decimal.

Practice

Multiply.

1. .2 × 10 2   **2.** .35 × 10 3.5   **3.** .05 × 10 .5   **4.** 2.97 × 100 297

5. .539 × 100 53.9   **6.** 42.4 × 100 4,240   **7.** 22.8×1,000 22,800   **8.** .457 × 1,000 457

9. .9 × 1,000 900   **10.** 3.38 × 10 33.8   **11.** .07 × 1,000 70   **12.** 463 × 100 46,300

ON-THE-JOB MATH
Bank Teller

Carmen Soleteri works for a bank. She is a bank teller. Carmen helps customers every day. They ask her to cash checks. They also ask her to make deposits and withdrawals. She also counts cash.

This is a good job for Carmen because she likes math and meeting people. She also stays calm under pressure.

To make a deposit, a customer must fill out a deposit slip. Carmen must make sure the total on the slip is correct.

Look at the deposit slips below. Tell whether or not the customer added correctly.

1.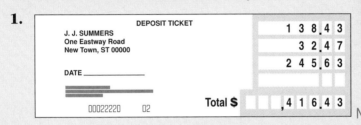

DEPOSIT TICKET

J. J. SUMMERS
One Eastway Road
New Town, ST 00000

DATE _____

00022220   02

	1 3 8 . 4 3
	3 2 . 4 7
	2 4 5 . 6 3
Total $	, 4 1 6 . 4 3

No

2.

	2 3 . 6 4
	6 . 2 8
	5 4 . 7 6
Total $	, 8 4 . 6 8

Yes

3.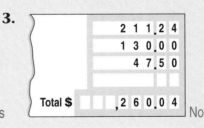

	2 1 1 . 2 4
	1 3 0 . 0 0
	4 7 . 5 0
Total $	, 2 6 0 . 0 4

No

Critical Thinking

What do you think Carmen should say to a customer if the deposit slip is incorrect? Work with a partner to decide what she should say. Share your answer with the class.

Critical Thinking

Assess how well students handle the situation. Behavior should reflect an understanding of how to deal with customers in the workplace.

More practice is provided in Exercise 92 of the *Workbook*.

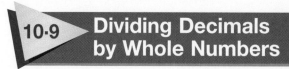

10-9 Dividing Decimals by Whole Numbers

Remember:
A quotient is the answer to a division problem.

Divide decimals the way you divide whole numbers. Place the decimal point in the quotient above the decimal point in the dividend.

$$\begin{array}{r} .08 \leftarrow \text{Quotient} \\ \text{Divisor} \rightarrow 4\overline{).32} \leftarrow \text{Dividend} \end{array}$$

▶ **EXAMPLE 1**

Multiply the quotient by the divisor to check.
$2.68 \times 35 = 93.8$

Number Sense
Ask students to explain why a decimal divided by a whole number results in a number smaller than the dividend.

Divide. $93.8 \div 35$

STEP 1
Place the decimal in the quotient.

$$35\overline{)93.8}$$

STEP 2
Divide. You may need to write zeros on the end of the dividend.

$$\begin{array}{r} 2.68 \\ 35\overline{)93.80} \\ -\ 70 \\ \hline 238 \\ -\ 210 \\ \hline 280 \\ -\ 280 \\ \hline 0 \end{array}$$

The quotient of 93.8 divided by 35 is 2.68.

Sometimes, the decimal quotient will have a repeating pattern. When this happens, the division will never end. To end the division, draw a bar over the repeating pattern.

▶ **EXAMPLE 2**

Avoiding Errors
Point out the importance of lining up the decimal point in the dividend and in the quotient.

Divide. $1.4 \div 33$

STEP 1
Divide until you see a repeating pattern.

$$\begin{array}{r} .04242 \\ 33\overline{)1.40000} \\ -\ 1\ 32 \\ \hline 80 \\ -\ 66 \\ \hline 140 \\ -\ 132 \\ \hline 80 \\ -\ 66 \\ \hline 14 \end{array}$$

STEP 2
Draw a bar over the repeating part of the answer.
$0.04242... \rightarrow .0\overline{42}$

The quotient of 1.4 divided by 33 is $.0\overline{42}$.

Practice A

Common Error A zero was omitted from the quotient. Have students turn lined paper sideways to help them align digits when dividing.

Copy each problem. Then, place the decimal point in the quotient. Write zeros if needed. The first one is done for you.

1. $3)\overline{.27}$ with .09

2. $5)\overline{6.25}$ with 1.25

3. $12)\overline{.048}$ with .004

4. $20)\overline{6.0}$ with .3

Practice B

Divide. Follow the directions from Practice A.

5. $4)\overline{.24}$ .06

6. $5)\overline{.45}$ .09

7. $8)\overline{.56}$ .07

8. $6)\overline{.048}$ .008

9. $58.56 \div 64$ .915

10. $.150 \div 12$ .0125

11. $.526 \div 8$ .06575

12. $12.54 \div 76$ .165

Practice C

Divide. Draw a bar over the repeating part of the quotient.

13. $6)\overline{45.8}$ 7.63

14. $3)\overline{20}$ 6.6

15. $9)\overline{60.4}$ 6.71

16. $11)\overline{640}$ 58.18

17. $9)\overline{4.1}$ .45

18. $27)\overline{95.1}$ 3.52

19. $22)\overline{53.4}$ 2.427

20. $18)\overline{91.4}$ 5.07

Everyday Problem Solving

The information on the right shows the cost of Internet service. You can choose Plan A or Plan B.

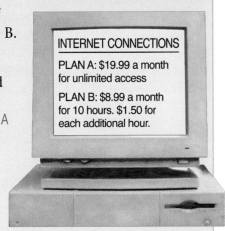

INTERNET CONNECTIONS

PLAN A: $19.99 a month for unlimited access

PLAN B: $8.99 a month for 10 hours. $1.50 for each additional hour.

1. Judy uses the Internet about 24 hours each month. Which plan should she buy? To find the cost of Plan B, you need to multiply 14 hours by $1.50 and then add $8.99. Plan A

2. Li uses the Internet 48 hours each month. Which plan should he buy? Plan A

3. At how many hours of use will Plan A be the better buy? Plan A is the better buy for anything over 17 hr 20 min.

Extra Practice for this lesson is provided on page 431.

More practice is provided in Exercise 93 of the *Workbook*.

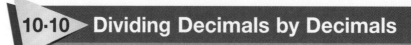

10-10 Dividing Decimals by Decimals

Number Sense
Ask students to explain the difference between how a decimal point moves in a multiplication problem and in a division problem. Then ask them to explain why there is this difference.

Multiplying the divisor and the dividend by 10, by 100, or by 1,000 will not change the quotient.

$$\begin{array}{r} .2 \\ 3\overline{)\,.6} \end{array} \qquad \begin{array}{r} .2 \\ 30\overline{)6.0} \end{array} \qquad \begin{array}{r} .2 \\ 300\overline{)60.0} \end{array} \qquad \begin{array}{r} .2 \\ 3{,}000\overline{)600.0} \end{array}$$

When the divisor is a decimal, multiply the divisor and the dividend by 10, by 100, or by 1,000. This will make your divisor into a whole number.

EXAMPLE 1

When you move the decimal point to the right, you are multiplying by 10, by 100, or by 1,000.

Divide.   2.24 ÷ 3.2

STEP 1
Move the decimal point so that the divisor is a whole number. Place the decimal point in the quotient.

$$3.2.\overline{)2.2.4}$$

STEP 2
Divide.

$$\begin{array}{r} .7 \\ 32\overline{)22.4} \\ -\,22\ 4 \\ \hline 0 \end{array}$$

The quotient of 2.24 divided by 3.2 is .7.

Sometimes, you need to write end zeros for the dividend so that you can move the decimal point to the right.

EXAMPLE 2

Avoiding Errors
Remind students that the decimal point is moved to the right the same number of places in the divisor and dividend and that zeros should be added onto the end of the dividend when necessary.

To check, multiply the quotient by the original decimal divisor.

Divide.   18 ÷ .125   Check your answer.

STEP 1
Move the decimal point. Add zeros if needed.

$$.1\,2\,5.\overline{)18.0\,0\,0.}$$

STEP 2
Divide.

$$\begin{array}{r} 144 \\ 125\overline{)18000} \\ -\,125 \\ \hline 550 \\ -\,500 \\ \hline 500 \\ -\,500 \\ \hline 0 \end{array}$$

The quotient of 18 divided by .125 is 144.

Check: 144 × .125 = 18 ✓

Practice A

Common Error The decimal point is misplaced in the quotient. Have students show the decimal moving in both the divisor and the dividend.

Rewrite each problem to make the divisor a whole number.

1. $.4\overline{)\,.8}$ $4.\overline{)8.}$ **2.** $.15\overline{)\,.45}$ $15.\overline{)45.}$ **3.** $.012\overline{)1.56}$ $12.\overline{)1560.}$ **4.** $.007\overline{)4.921}$ $7.\overline{)4921.}$

Practice B

Divide. Multiply to check your answer.

5. $.4\overline{)\,.8}$ 2   **6.** $.15\overline{)\,.45}$ 3   **7.** $.012\overline{)1.56}$ 130   **8.** $.007\overline{)4.921}$ 703

9. $.6\overline{)72.18}$ 120.3   **10.** $.08\overline{)170.4}$ 2,130   **11.** $.12\overline{)1.56}$ 13   **12.** $6.8\overline{)44.2}$ 6.5

13. $62.7 \div 3.8$ 16.5   **14.** $6.25 \div .25$ 25   **15.** $30 \div .75$ 40   **16.** $\$4.40 \div .55$ 8

Practice C

Divide. The decimal part of some quotients will repeat. Remember to draw a bar over the repeating part.

17. $.06\overline{)5.6}$ $93.\overline{3}$ **18.** $2.3\overline{)\,.92}$ .4   **19.** $.04\overline{)18.8}$ 470   **20.** $.45\overline{)3.9}$ $8.\overline{6}$

21. $55.04 \div 3.2$ 17.2   **22.** $1.825 \div .25$ 7.3   **23.** $3.596 \div 6.2$ .58   **24.** $8.4 \div .012$ 700

25. $2.75 \div .09$ $30.\overline{5}$ **26.** $96 \div 4.8$ 20   **27.** $91 \div .13$ 700   **28.** $2.823 \div .45$ $6.27\overline{3}$

Everyday Problem Solving

Solve each word problem. Remember to divide.

1. Movie tickets cost $5.75 each on Saturday afternoons. On Saturday afternoon, the theater sold $690 worth of tickets. How many tickets were sold? 120

2. The theater club sold $679.50 worth of tickets for the school play. All tickets that were sold were the same price. If 151 people bought tickets, how much did each ticket cost? $4.50

Extra Practice for this lesson is provided on page 431.

10·11 Dividing Decimals by 10, 100, 1,000

Number Sense
Put the following on the board:

2.5 ÷ 10
2.5 ÷ 100

Ask the students why the decimal point moves to the left in the quotient in both examples.

Avoiding Errors
Make sure that students understand that a decimal divided by 10 will be larger than a decimal divided by 100 or 1,000.

You can use what you know to learn a shortcut for dividing decimals by 10, by 100, or by 1,000.

$$\overset{13.23}{10)\overline{132.30}} \qquad \overset{1.323}{100)\overline{132.300}} \qquad \overset{.1323}{1,000)\overline{132.3000}}$$

Now look at this:

$$132.3 \div \underline{10} = 13.2\,3 = 13.23$$
1 zero   1 place to the left

$$132.3 \div \underline{100} = 1.3\,2\,3 = 1.323$$
2 zeros   2 places to the left

$$132.3 \div \underline{1,000} = .1\,3\,2\,3 = .1323$$
3 zeros   3 places to the left

To divide by 10, by 100, or by 1,000, move the decimal point to the left. Write zeros if needed.

► **EXAMPLE**

Remember:
5 = 5.0

Divide.   5 ÷ 1,000   3 zeros

STEP 1   Count the zeros.   5 ÷ 1,000

STEP 2   Move the decimal point 3 places.   .0 0 5 = .005
Write zeros if needed.

The quotient of 5 divided by 1,000 is .005.

Common Error   The decimal point is misplaced in the quotient. Remind students that a number divided by 10, 100, or 1,000 is smaller than the original number.

Practice

Divide.

1. .62 ÷ 10
.062

2. 9.3 ÷ 10
.93

3. 8 ÷ 10
.8

4. 5.74 ÷ 100
.0574

5. .834 ÷ 100
.00834

6. 2 ÷ 100
.02

7. 38.6 ÷ 1,000
.0386

8. .5 ÷ 1,000
.0005

9. 7 ÷ 1,000
.007

10. 12.09 ÷ 100
.1209

11. 38 ÷ 10
3.8

12. 74.5 ÷ 1,000
.0745

USING YOUR CALCULATOR
Number Patterns

You can use a calculator to find a pattern.

Find each sum.

$$29.5 + .5 = \blacksquare$$
$$299.5 + .5 = \blacksquare$$
$$2,999.5 + .5 = \blacksquare$$

DECIMAL POINT
Press to put a decimal
point in a number.

PRESS | 2 | 9 | . | 5 | + | . | 5 | = | 30.

PRESS | C | 0.

PRESS | 2 | 9 | 9 | . | 5 | + | . | 5 | = | 300.

PRESS | C | 0.

PRESS | 2 | 9 | 9 | 9 | . | 5 | + | . | 5 | = | 3000.

Now use the pattern to find $2,999,999.5 + .5 = \blacksquare$.

$$2,999,999.5 + .5 = 3,000,000$$

Guess each missing number. Use a calculator to check.

1. $29,999.5 + .5 = \blacksquare$
30,000

2. $29,999,999.5 + .5 = \blacksquare$
30,000,000

3. $299,999.5 + .5 = \blacksquare$
300,000

Use your calculator to find a pattern in the first row. Then guess each difference in the second row. Use a calculator to check.

4. $60 - .8 = \blacksquare$ 59.2

5. $600 - .8 = \blacksquare$ 599.2

6. $6,000 - .8 = \blacksquare$ 5,999.2

7. $600,000 - .8 = \blacksquare$
599,999.2

8. $60,000 - .8 = \blacksquare$
59,999.2

9. $\blacksquare - .8 = 5,999,999.2$
6,000,000

Use your calculator to find a pattern in the first row. Then guess each quotient in the second row. Use a calculator to check.

10. $9 \div 2 = \blacksquare$ 4.5

11. $9 \div 20 = \blacksquare$ .45

12. $9 \div 200 = \blacksquare$ .045

13. $9 \div 2,000 = \blacksquare$ .0045

14. $9 \div .2 = \blacksquare$ 45

15. $9 \div .02 = \blacksquare$ 450

More practice is provided in Exercise 95 of the *Workbook*.

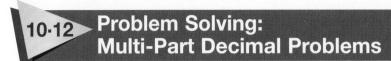

10-12 Problem Solving: Multi-Part Decimal Problems

Some word problems can be solved if you work on one part at a time.

▶ EXAMPLE

Number Sense
Encourage students to estimate the total cost.
3 × $.50 → $1.50
$1.99 → + 2.00
              $3.50

Then estimate the change.
$5 − $3.50 = $1.50

Margaret bought 3 cans of corn. Corn costs $.43 a can. She also bought a bag of potatoes. The potatoes cost $1.99. How much change from $5 did she receive?

STEP 1 **READ   What do you need to find out?**
You need to find the change from $5.
But first you need to find the total cost.

STEP 2 **PLAN   What do you need to do?**
How much does the corn cost?
Multiply to find out.

What is the total cost?
Add to find out.

How much change did she receive?
Subtract to find out.

Avoiding Errors
Be sure that students multiply the number of units by the unit price.

STEP 3 **DO   Follow the plan.**

Multiply	Add	Subtract
$.43	$1.29 Corn	$5.00
× 3	+ 1.99 Potatoes	− 3.28
$1.29 Corn	$3.28 Total cost	$1.72 Change

STEP 4 **CHECK   Does your answer make sense?**
Add $1.72 + $3.28. Does this equal $5?

$1.72 Change
+ 3.28 Total cost
$5.00 ✓

Margaret received $1.72 as change.

Problem Solving

READ the problem. Answer the questions under PLAN.
DO the plan to solve the problem.

1. Al bought 5 pounds of apples. The apples were $.39 a pound. He also bought a bag of grapes. The grapes were $2.58. How much change from $10 did he receive?

   DO
   5 × $.39 = $1.95
   $1.95 + $2.58 = $4.53
   $10 − $4.53 = $5.47

   PLAN $1.95
   How much did the apples cost? What was the total cost? How much change did he receive? $5.47
   $4.53

2. Helen bought 1 ear of corn and cabbage. Ten ears of corn cost $3.50. The cabbage was $.99. How much change from $2 did she receive?

   DO
   $3.50 ÷ 10 = $.35
   $.35 + $.99 = $1.34
   $2 − $1.34 = $.66

   PLAN $.35
   How much did 1 ear of corn cost? What was the total cost? How much change did she receive? $.66
   $1.34

3. Bill bought 2 pounds of butter. Butter costs $1.78 a pound. He also bought 1 roll. Rolls cost $4.80 for 12 rolls. What was the total cost?

   DO
   2 × $1.78 = $3.56
   $4.80 ÷ 12 = $.40
   $3.56 + $.40 = $3.96

   PLAN $3.56
   How much did the butter cost? How much did the roll cost? What was the total cost? $3.96
   $.40

Problem Solving Strategy

Often, problems can be solved by working backward.

Cathy bought tomatoes for $3.50. She also bought lettuce. Cathy gave the store clerk $5.00. Her change was $1.00. How much did the lettuce cost?

Fill in the blanks below to find the cost of the lettuce.

$1.00 Change $3.50 Tomatoes
$4.00 + ▨ Total cost $.50 + ▨ Lettuce
$5.00 $4.00 ▨ Total cost

Extra Practice for this lesson is provided on page 431.

10·13 ▶ Renaming Decimals as Fractions

Number Sense
Write the following two decimals on the board:
  .56   .560
Ask the students to rename these decimals as fractions. What do they notice?

You can use place value to help you change decimals to fractions.

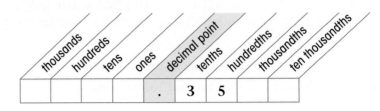

▶ **EXAMPLE**

Avoiding Errors
Remind students that they must reduce fractions to lowest terms.

Rename the decimal .35 as a fraction.

STEP 1 Use the decimal digits as the numerator.

$$.35 = \frac{35}{}$$

Hundredths
↓

STEP 2 Use the last place value as the denominator.

$$.35 = \frac{35}{100}$$

STEP 3 Reduce the fraction to lowest terms.

$$\frac{35}{100} = \frac{35 \div 5}{100 \div 5} = \frac{7}{20}$$

.35 written as a fraction in lowest terms is $\frac{7}{20}$.

Common Error The named fraction is off by a factor of 10. Have students write the decimal in a place-value chart before renaming it as a fraction.

Practice

Rename each decimal as a fraction. Reduce to lowest terms.

1. .5
$$\frac{5}{10} = \frac{1}{2}$$

2. .05
$$\frac{5}{100} = \frac{1}{20}$$

3. .005
$$\frac{5}{1000} = \frac{1}{200}$$

4. .076
$$\frac{76}{1000} = \frac{19}{250}$$

5. .76
$$\frac{76}{100} = \frac{19}{25}$$

6. .845
$$\frac{845}{1000} = \frac{169}{200}$$

7. .682
$$\frac{682}{1000} = \frac{341}{500}$$

8. .98
$$\frac{98}{100} = \frac{49}{50}$$

9. .328
$$\frac{328}{1000} = \frac{41}{125}$$

10. .455
$$\frac{455}{1000} = \frac{91}{200}$$

11. .873
$$\frac{873}{1000}$$

12. .605
$$\frac{605}{1000} = \frac{121}{200}$$

13. .4
$$\frac{4}{10} = \frac{2}{5}$$

14. .40
$$\frac{40}{100} = \frac{2}{5}$$

15. .32
$$\frac{32}{100} = \frac{8}{25}$$

16. .8
$$\frac{8}{10} = \frac{4}{5}$$

17. .375
$$\frac{375}{1000} = \frac{3}{8}$$

18. .75
$$\frac{75}{100} = \frac{3}{4}$$

19. .10
$$\frac{10}{100} = \frac{1}{10}$$

20. .28
$$\frac{28}{100} = \frac{7}{25}$$

Extra Practice for this lesson is provided on page 432.

More practice is provided in Exercise 97 of the *Workbook*.

10-14 ▶ Renaming Fractions as Decimals

You can change a fraction to a decimal. Divide the numerator by the denominator.

▶ **EXAMPLE**

Rename the fraction $\frac{7}{20}$ as a decimal.

STEP 1 Write the fraction as a division problem.

$$\frac{7}{20} \rightarrow 20\overline{)7}$$

Number Sense
Have students solve this word problem: Seven inches of rope are cut into 20 equal pieces. How long is each piece?

STEP 2 Divide.

$$
\begin{array}{r}
.35 \\
20\overline{)7.00} \\
-\,6\,0 \\
\hline
1\,00 \\
-\,1\,00 \\
\hline
0
\end{array}
$$

Avoiding Errors
Remind students that they must add a decimal point and zeros to the end of the dividend before dividing.

$\frac{7}{20}$ written as a decimal is .35.

Practice A

Write each fraction as a division problem.

1. $\frac{3}{5}$ $5\overline{)3}$ **2.** $\frac{1}{2}$ $2\overline{)1}$ **3.** $\frac{11}{20}$ $20\overline{)11}$ **4.** $\frac{3}{25}$ $25\overline{)3}$ **5.** $\frac{27}{50}$ $50\overline{)27}$

Practice B

Common Error The decimal point is misplaced in the quotient. Have students use graphing paper to align digits in the proper columns.

Rename each fraction as a decimal by using division.

6. $\frac{3}{5}$ .6   **7.** $\frac{1}{2}$ .5   **8.** $\frac{11}{20}$ .55   **9.** $\frac{3}{25}$ .12   **10.** $\frac{1}{4}$ .25

11. $\frac{11}{200}$ .055   **12.** $\frac{19}{500}$ .038   **13.** $\frac{31}{250}$ .124   **14.** $\frac{101}{125}$ .808   **15.** $\frac{39}{40}$ .975

16. $\frac{4}{5}$ .8   **17.** $\frac{3}{20}$ .15   **18.** $\frac{53}{20}$ 2.65   **19.** $\frac{39}{50}$ .78   **20.** $\frac{47}{50}$ .94

21. $\frac{9}{20}$ .45   **22.** $\frac{87}{125}$ .696   **23.** $\frac{7}{250}$ .028   **24.** $\frac{23}{40}$ .575   **25.** $\frac{27}{50}$ .54

Extra Practice for this lesson is provided on page 432.

More practice is provided in Exercise 98 of the *Workbook*.

10·15 ▶ Rounding Decimals

A number line can help you round decimals. Round the decimal 3.482 to the nearest hundredth.

3.482 is closer to 3.48 than to 3.49.
3.482 rounds to 3.48.

You can also follow steps to round decimals.

▶ **EXAMPLE 1**

Round the decimal 3.482 to the nearest hundredth.

STEP 1   Underline the rounding place.   3.48<u>2</u>
            Look at the digit to its right.

STEP 2   Compare the digit to 5.
            2 is smaller than 5.

STEP 3   Round as you would   Leave 8 alone.
            whole numbers.

STEP 4   Drop all digits to the right   3.48
            of the rounding place.

3.482 rounded to the nearest hundredth is 3.48.

Sometimes, you have to change the numbers in two places.

▶ **EXAMPLE 2**

Round the decimal 2.963 to the nearest tenth.

STEP 1   Underline the rounding place.   2.<u>9</u>63
            Look at the digit to its right.

STEP 2   Compare the digit to 5.   6 is larger than 5.

STEP 3   Round as you would   Add 1 to 9 tenths.
            whole numbers. $2.9 + .1 = 3.0$

STEP 4   Drop all digits to the right   2.963 becomes 3.0.
            of the rounding place.

Practice A

Common Error A decimal like 9.95 is incorrectly rounded to 9.100. The student rounded the 9 to 10 but did not understand the meaning of the 10. Help the student see how this process is similar to the carrying they do in addition.

Write the name of the underlined place value.

1. 3.2<u>9</u>8
hundredths

2. .<u>3</u>52
tenths

3. 1.0<u>1</u>5
hundredths

4. 78.09<u>9</u>
thousandths

5. .2<u>9</u>1
hundredths

6. 2.1<u>5</u>2
hundredths

7. 4.<u>6</u>21
tenths

8. 15.2<u>2</u>8
hundredths

Practice B

Round each decimal to the nearest hundredth or cent.

9. .375 .38

10. $1.496 $1.50

11. 2.8724 2.87

12. 23.059 23.06

13. .913 .91

14. 67.305 67.31

15. $105.995 $106

16. 48.994 48.99

17. 3.534 3.53

18. 2.299 2.30

19. .864 .86

20. 10.775 10.78

Practice C

Round each decimal to the nearest tenth.

21. 3.298 3.3

22. 54.351 54.4

23. 32.446 32.4

24. 99.321 99.3

25. .15 .2

26. 26.547 26.5

27. 8.95 9

28. 5.09 5.1

29. 30.736 30.7

30. 15.792 15.8

31. 9.56 9.6

32. 1.309 1.3

Everyday Problem Solving

1. Jannie has $25. Does she have enough money to buy the items on the receipt on the right? Round up the prices to the nearest dollar. Then, find the total.
$5 + $9 + $7 = $21; yes, she has enough money.

2. Why is it better to round prices up when you want to see if you have enough money?
Rounding up gives you a greater total than you actually need. So if you have that amount or more, you will know that you have enough for the purchase.

AL'S TAKE-OUT

CHEESEBURGER	$4.58
FOOT-LONG SUB	$8.02
CHEF'S SALAD	$6.84

| decimal |
| decimal places |
| decimal point |
| mixed decimal |

Vocabulary Review
Complete each sentence with a word from the list.

1. A ___?___ is the dot in a decimal. decimal point

2. A number that names part of a whole number
   is a ___?___. decimal

3. A ___?___ contains a whole number and a decimal. mixed decim

4. ___?___ are to the right of the decimal point. decimal places

5. **Writing** Show that you understand these words.
   Write a sentence for each word. Do not use the
   sentences above. Answers will vary. Check students' sentences.

Chapter Quiz

LESSONS 10·1 to 10·4

Test Tip
When comparing decimals,
first compare the whole
number parts.

Writing, Comparing, and Ordering Decimals
Write each number as a decimal.

1. three hundredths .03

2. seven and five tenths 7.5

3. twenty-two thousandths .022

4. fifty and five hundredths 50.05

Compare each pair of numbers. Use >, <, or =.

5. 15.03   9.03 >   6. 1.52   1.63 <

7. 8.6   8.61 <   8. 7.23   7.203 >

9. 6.3   6.25 >   10. 45.03   45.03 =

LESSONS 10·5 and 10·6

Test Tip
Line up the decimal points
when adding or subtracting
decimals.

Adding and Subtracting Decimals
Add or subtract.

11. 8.65 + 9.37 18.02   12. 5.8 + 26.98 32.78

13. 16.25 − 9.7 6.55   14. 6 + 4.59 + .729 11.319

15. 14.05 − 8.59 5.46   16. 7 − 3.075 3.925

Multiplying and Dividing Decimals
Multiply. Show your work in vertical form.

17. 1.2×4 4.8

18. $.7 \times .06$ .042

19. $2.5 \times .5$ 1.25

20. 8.09×1.7 13.753

21. $38.5 \times .29$ 11.165

22. 478×6.05 2,891.9

Divide.

23. $36.4 \div 24$ $1.51\overline{6}$

24. $448.7 \div 35$ 12.82

25. $6 \div 12$ .5

26. $37.95 \div 4.6$ 8.25

27. $5 \div .09$ $55.\overline{5}$

28. $.453 \div .15$ 3.02

Solving Problems with Decimals
Solve each problem.

29. Greg buys 3 pounds of cheese at $1.29 a pound and bread for $2.29. How much change from $10 does he receive? $3.84

30. Janine has $20. Does she have enough money to buy socks for $2.99 and a T-shirt for $12.95? yes

Changing Decimals and Fractions
Rename each decimal as a fraction.

31. $.2$ $\frac{1}{5}$

32. $.25$ $\frac{1}{4}$

33. $.03$ $\frac{3}{100}$

Rename each fraction as a decimal.

34. $\frac{3}{5}$ .6

35. $\frac{5}{8}$ .625

36. $\frac{3}{4}$ .75

Group Activity See the *Teacher Planning Guide* for a Scoring Rubric for this activity.
With your group, use a grocery store flyer to shop for a family of three for a week. You have $125 to spend. Make a list of the items you want to buy and the cost. Decide on the items to purchase and explain your choices.

Group Activity Be sure students spend less than $125.

From the water's surface, you only see the tip of an iceberg. This is only 11% of the entire iceberg. The rest is hidden underwater. If an iceberg weighs 1,550,000 tons, what percent of its weight is above the surface? Multiply 11% times the weight. Subtract to find how much is hidden below the water.

Caption 170,500 tons is above the water. 1,379,500 tons is below the water.

Chapter 11 ▷ Percents

ESL Note *Percent* comes from the Latin words *per centum*, which means "of 100." Have students think of other English words that come from the same Latin root, such as *cent, century,* and *centimeter.*

Words to Know

percent	a part of a whole divided into 100 parts
sales tax	a tax that is a percentage of the price of an item
discount	amount that a price is reduced
sale price	price of an item after the discount is subtracted
commission	payment based on a percent of sales
base salary	salary before adding commission
gross salary	commission plus the base salary
percent increase	percent more than an original number
percent decrease	percent less than an original number

Words to Know Discuss in what fields of work some of these words are used.

Nutrition Facts Project

Nutrition facts are listed on all foods. They are given as a percentage of the "recommended daily allowance" (RDA). Collect several nutrition facts labels and record in your journal the name of the product and the %RDA of total fat, sodium, carbohydrates, and protein. Find out how many servings you would need to eat to get 100% of any nutrient.

Project The question asked cannot be answered until Lesson 11.3 is completed. However, students can collect and organize their data and can compare the fat, sodium, carbohydrate, and protein contents in the various foods before doing Lesson 11.3.

Learning Objectives

- Write percents.
- Change among percents, decimals, and fractions.
- Find the part, the percent, and the whole in a problem.
- Find sales tax, discount, and commission.
- Find the percent increase or decrease and the original number.
- Solve problems about percents.
- Apply percents to find a tip.

More practice is provided in Exercise 99 of the *Workbook*.

11-1 ▶ What Is a Percent?

A **percent** is a part of a whole that is divided into 100 equal parts. The sign for percent is %.

▶ **EXAMPLE**

What part of the whole is shaded?

Number Sense
Discuss the difference between the whole number 3 and 3%. Since percent is out of 100, 3% is 3 out of 100. The number 3 is 3 wholes, or 300%.

STEP 1 Count the number of shaded squares.   48 out of 100

STEP 2 Write the number and percent sign.   48%

48% of the whole is shaded.

Avoiding Errors
Remind students that they can use decimal grids. Each model grid equals 100 squares, and one column equals 10 squares.

A percent more than 100% is more than one whole.

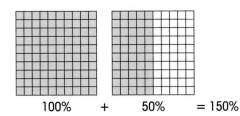

100%   +   50%   = 150%

Practice

Common Error Answers do not have percent signs. Emphasize that the percent sign is needed after a number so that the reader knows that it is out of 100 equal parts.

Write the percent for the part shaded in each model.

1. 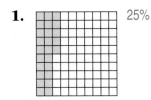 25%

2. 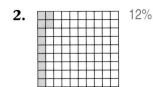 12%

3.  65%

Extra Practice for this lesson is provided on page 433.

More practice is provided in Exercise 100 of the *Workbook*.

11·2 Changing Percents to Decimals

Percent means per hundred. You can write a percent as a decimal. The hundredths place is two places to the right of the decimal point.

▶ EXAMPLE 1

Number Sense
Encourage students to use 100% as a reference point. Percents under 100% are decimals less than 1. Percents over 100% are decimals greater than 1.

Change 36% to a decimal.

STEP 1	Drop the percent sign. Place a decimal point to the right of the last digit.	36% becomes 36.
STEP 2	Move the decimal point two places to the left.	.36

36% written as a decimal is .36.

Sometimes a percent is a mixed number.

▶ EXAMPLE 2

Avoiding Errors
Focus attention on the decimal places. Thus, 10% is .10, while 1% is .01.

Change $4\frac{1}{2}$% to a decimal.

STEP 1	Change the mixed number to a decimal.	$4\frac{1}{2}\% = 4.5\%$
STEP 2	Drop the percent sign. Move the decimal point two places to the left. Fill any extra places with zeros.	$4.5\% = .045$

$4\frac{1}{2}$% written as a decimal is .045.

Common Error The decimal point is moved two places in the wrong direction. Remind students that dropping the percent sign means moving left.

Practice

Change each percent to a decimal.

1. 15% .15 **2.** 12% .12 **3.** 85% .85 **4.** 27% .27 **5.** 8% .08

6. 80% .8 **7.** 5% .05 **8.** $5\frac{1}{2}$% .055 **9.** $3\frac{1}{2}$% .035 **10.** 3.5% .035

11. 3% .03 **12.** 1% .01 **13.** 10% .1 **14.** 138% 1.38 **15.** 250% 2.5

Extra Practice for this lesson
is provided on page 433.

More practice is provided in Exercise 101 of the *Workbook*.

11·3 Finding the Part

A percent problem consists of three numbers: the percent, the whole, and the part.

25% of 100 is 25
↑   ↑   ↑
Percent Whole Part

You can find the part if you are given the percent and the whole. This problem can be asked in two ways.

Find 25% of 100.
What is 25% of 100?

► **EXAMPLE 1**

Remember that the clue word
of means to multiply.

Find 35% of 80.

STEP 1 Change the percent to a decimal.

$35\% = .35$

STEP 2 Multiply the decimal by the number that comes after the word *of.* Write the decimal point in the correct place in the product.

$$
\begin{array}{r}
80 \quad \leftarrow \text{Whole} \\
\times \quad .35 \quad \leftarrow \text{Percent} \\
\hline
4\,00 \\
24\,00 \\
\hline
28.00 \quad \leftarrow \text{Part}
\end{array}
$$

35% of 80 is 28.

► **EXAMPLE 2**

What is 125% of 40?

STEP 1 Change the percent to a decimal.

$125\% = 1.25$

STEP 2 Multiply the decimal by the number that comes after the word *of.* Write the decimal point in the correct place in the product.

$$
\begin{array}{r}
1.25 \quad \leftarrow \text{Percent} \\
\times \quad 40 \quad \leftarrow \text{Whole} \\
\hline
50.00 \quad \leftarrow \text{Part}
\end{array}
$$

50 is 125% of 40.

Practice A

Find the part.

1. 10% of 60 is ▒ 6

2. 12% of 100 is ▒ 12

3. 15% of 40 is ▒ 6

4. 25% of 80 is ▒ 20

5. 10% of 85 is ▒ 8.5

6. 50% of 75 is ▒ 37.5

7. 55% of 60 is ▒ 33

8. 75% of 96 is ▒ 72

9. 34% of 100 is ▒ 34

10. 27% of 800 is ▒ 216

11. 7% of 650 is ▒ 45.5

12. 49% of 1,000 is ▒ 490

Practice B

Answer each question.

13. What is 15% of 36? 5.4

14. What is 40% of 80? 32

15. What is 75% of 90? 67.5

16. What is 23% of 200? 46

17. What is 2% of 500? 10

18. What is 68% of 50? 34

19. What is 10% of 505? 50.5

20. What is 99% of 200? 198

21. What is 150% of 350? 525

22. What is 254% of 100? 254

Everyday Problem Solving

The student counselor made a chart of after-school jobs.

1. How many girls work at supermarkets?
Find 65% of 60. 39 girls

2. How many boys work at supermarkets?
21 boys

3. How many girls work at video stores?
9 girls

4. How many boys work at video stores?
Explain. 36 boys; subtract the number of girls from the total number, or find 80% of 45.

After-School Jobs

Supermarkets
60 Students
65% GIRLS
35% BOYS

Video Stores
45 Students
20% GIRLS
? BOYS

Extra Practice for this lesson is provided on page 433.

More practice is provided in Exercise 102 of the *Workbook*.

11·4 Sales Tax

Many states charge **sales tax** on items you buy. The sales tax is a percent of the cost of the item. Finding the sales tax is a percent problem. It has the same three parts.

8% of $10 is $.80

↑   ↑   ↑

Tax rate   Cost   Sales tax
Percent   Whole   Part

EXAMPLE 1

Remember:
Part = Percent × Whole

A book costs $7.00. The sales tax is 6%. How much sales tax is charged?

STEP 1	Change the percent to a decimal.	6% = .06
STEP 2	Multiply the decimal by the cost of the item. This is the amount of sales tax.	.06 × $7 = $.42

The sales tax on the book is $.42.

To find the total cost, add the cost of the item to the sales tax.

EXAMPLE 2

A book costs $8.50. The rate of the sales tax is 8%. What is the total cost of the book, including the sales tax?

STEP 1	Change the percent to a decimal.	8% = .08
STEP 2	Multiply the decimal by the cost of the item. This is the amount of sales tax.	.08 × $8.50 = $.68
STEP 3	Add the sales tax to the cost of the book.	$8.50 + $.68 = $9.18

The total cost of the book with sales tax is $9.18.

Common Error Students confuse the amount of sales tax with the rate of sales tax. The amount is in dollars and cents, whereas the rate is a percent.

Copy the chart below. Find the sales tax for each item. Then find the total cost.

	Sales Tax	Cost of Item	Amount of Sales Tax	Total Cost
1.	5%	$65	? $3.25	? $68.25
2.	7%	$35	? $2.45	? $37.45
3.	9%	$120	? $10.80	? $130.80
4.	12%	$555	? $66.60	? $621.60

Practice B

Solve.

5. The sales tax is 4%. The cost of lunch is $6.50. What is the amount of the sales tax? $.26

6. The sales tax is 5%. The cost of a camera is $40. What is the amount of the sales tax? $2

7. A small television costs $150. If the sales tax is 6%, what is the total cost of the television? $159

8. The sales tax is 8%. A VCR costs $205. What is the amount of the sales tax? $16.40

9. A bike light costs $15. If the sales tax is 6%, what is the total cost of the light? $15.90

10. Computer software costs $36. The sales tax is $7\frac{1}{2}$%. What is the total cost of the software? $38.70

Extra Practice for this lesson is provided on page 434.

More practice is provided in Exercise 103 of the *Workbook*.

11·5 ▸ Discounts

Number Sense
A discount and a sales tax are both parts of a whole that you find by using percent. With a discount, you pay less than the original price; with sales tax, you pay more.

Stores often put items on sale. During a sale, the regular price of an item is reduced. The amount the price is reduced is the **discount**. Finding a discount is a percent problem. It has the same three parts.

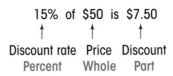

15% of $50 is $7.50

Discount rate Price Discount
Percent   Whole   Part

▶ **EXAMPLE 1**

A shirt costs $35. It is on sale at 20% off. What is the discount?

Remember:
Part = Percent × Whole

STEP 1 Change the percent to a decimal.

20% = .20

STEP 2 Multiply the decimal by the price. This is the discount.

.20 × $35 = $7

The discount is $7.

To find the **sale price** of an item, you need to subtract the discount from the regular price.

▶ **EXAMPLE 2**

A pair of sneakers costs $55. They are on sale at 20% off. What is the sale price?

Avoiding Errors
Emphasize that to find the sale price, you subtract the discount from the original price.

STEP 1 Change the percent to a decimal.

20% = .20

STEP 2 Multiply the decimal by the price. This is the discount.

.20 × $55 = $11

STEP 3 Subtract the discount from the regular price. This is the sale price.

$55 − $11 = $44

The sale price of the sneakers is $44.

Practice A

Common Error Students confuse the discount with the rate of discount. The rate is a percent, whereas the discount is a dollar amount.

Copy the chart below. Find the discount for each item. Then find the sale price.

	Discount Rate	Price of Item	Discount	Sale Price
1.	5%	$35	? $1.75	? $33.25
2.	8%	$150	? $12.00	? $138.00
3.	15%	$62	? $9.30	? $52.70
4.	25%	$250	? $62.50	? $187.50

Practice B

Solve.

5. A pair of pants cost $40. They are on sale at 30% off. What is the discount? $12

6. What is the sale price of the pants in Question 5? $28

7. A shirt costs $18. It is on sale at 15% off. What is the sale price? $15.30

8. A key chain costs $7.50. It is on sale at 20% off. What is the discount? $1.50

9. Kevin gets an 8% discount on all videos. What does he pay for a $23 video? $21.16

10. A suit costs $350. It is on sale at 23% off. What is the sale price of the suit? $269.50

More practice is provided in Exercise 104 of the *Workbook*.

11-6 ▶ Commissions

Number Sense
Discuss why both the commission and the sales are important.
  20% of $50 is $10.
  10% of $100 is $10.
A lower rate may not mean a lower commission!

A **commission** is payment based on a percent of sales. Finding a commission is a percent problem.

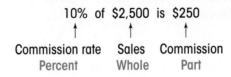

10% of $2,500 is $250

Commission rate — Percent
Sales — Whole
Commission — Part

▶ **EXAMPLE 1**

Remember:
Part = Percent × Whole

Mr. Barnes sold $3,500 of pet food. As a salesperson, his commission is 9% of his sales. What is the amount of his commission?

STEP 1 Change the percent to a decimal.

$9\% = .09$

STEP 2 Multiply the decimal by the total sales. This is the commission.

$.09 \times \$3,500 = \$315$

Mr. Barnes's commission is $315.

The **base salary** is how much you get paid before adding in the commission. To find the **gross salary**, you add the commission to the base salary.

▶ **EXAMPLE 2**

Avoiding Errors
Point out that finding the commission is similar to finding the part in a percent problem.

Robin's base salary is $200 per week. Last week, her sales totaled $26,000. If her commission is 4%, what was her gross salary for the week?

STEP 1 Change the percent to a decimal.

$4\% = .04$

STEP 2 Multiply the decimal by the total sales. This is the commission.

$.04 \times \$26,000 = \$1,040$

STEP 3 Add the commission to the base salary. This is the gross salary.

```
  $1,040  ← Commission
+    200  ← Base salary
  $1,240  ← Gross salary
```

Robin's gross salary for the week was $1,240.

Common Error The commission rate is multiplied by the base salary instead of by the total sales. Explain to students that the base salary is the salary earned even if no sales are made.

Copy the chart below. Find the commission and gross salary for each salesperson.

Name	Base Salary	Total Sales	Commission Rate	Commission	Gross Salary
1. Manny	$158	$7,800	6%	? $468	? $626
2. Charles	$215	$4,200	5%	? $210	? $425
3. Anne	$225	$3,000	4%	? $120	? $345
4. Katerina	$175	$5,500	7%	? $385	? $560

Practice B

Solve.

5. Harry's sales are $480. His commission is 6% of sales. What is the amount of his commission? $28.80

6. Mr. Lee earns a 5% commission on sales. Last month, his sales were $7,100. What was the amount of his commission? $355

7. Margo's total sales were $38,920 last month. She is paid 7% commission. What was the amount of her commission? $2,724.40

8. Amy's base salary is $150 per week. Her sales this week total $3,500. If her commission is 20%, what is her gross salary for the week? $850

9. Ray's base salary is $300 per month. His commission is 5% of sales. If he sells $28,000 this month, what is his gross salary? $1,700

10. Sol's base salary is $950 per month. His commission is $8\frac{1}{2}$% of sales. If he sells $10,500 this month, what is his gross salary? $1,842.50

Extra Practice for this lesson is provided on page 435.

MATH IN YOUR LIFE
Tipping

Mario's special birthday dinner at Fiesta Restaurant costs $39.54. He plans to leave a 15% tip. Here is an easy way to find the dollar amount of a 15% tip.

Round up the cost to the nearest dollar.

$39.54 rounds to $40.

Find **10%** of the cost. Move the decimal point one place to the left.

10% × $40 = $4.0

Find half that amount to get **5%**.

$4 ÷ 2 = $2

Add the 10% and 5% amounts.

$4 + $2 = $6

The tip is about $6. Mario adds the tip to his bill. His total cost is $39.54 + $6 = $45.54.

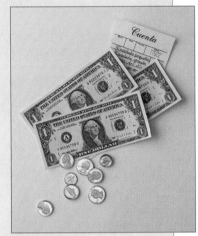

Another time, Mario spent $25.70 on lunch. He left $3.90 as a tip. Did he leave enough? Yes

Solve.

1. The tip for a banquet is 15%. The banquet total is $597. About how much will the tip be? $90

2. The cost of a family dinner was $58.25. Wesley tipped the waitress 15%. About how much was the tip? About what was the total cost? tip $9; total cost $67.25

Critical Thinking

At a different restaurant the service was extra special. Mario wanted to leave a 20% tip. How could he change his quick method to find 20%?

Critical Thinking

You can move the decimal point to get 10% and then double this amount.

More practice is provided in Exercise 105 of the *Workbook*.

11-7 Changing Decimals to Percents

Percent means per hundred or hundredth. You can write a decimal as a percent.

▶ **EXAMPLE 1**

Number Sense
Discuss the meaning of percent. Students should "see" two places after the decimal point. Tell them to add a zero to help change the decimal to a percent:
.4 = .40, which is 40%
.1 = .10, which is 10%

Change .36 to a percent.

STEP 1 Move the decimal point two places to the right.　　.36 becomes 36.

STEP 2 Since 36. is equal to 36, drop the decimal point. Write the percent sign.　　36%

.36 written as a percent is 36%.

Sometimes, the decimal has more than two places to the right of the decimal point.

▶ **EXAMPLE 2**

Avoiding Errors
Decimals such as .045 may be written incorrectly as 45%. Emphasize moving the decimal point only two places, including zeros.

Change .045 to a percent.

STEP 1 Move the decimal point two places to the right.　　.045 becomes 04.5

STEP 2 Drop the zero to the left of the number. Write the percent sign.　　4.5%

.045 written as a percent is 4.5%.

Common Error Students may simply affix a % sign to a whole number (3 = 3%). Have them show the step for moving the decimal point.

Practice

Change each decimal to a percent.

1. .89 89%
2. .07 7%
3. 1.5 150%

4. .173 17.3%
5. 2 200%
6. .5 50%

7. .25 25%
8. .13 13%
9. .7 70%

10. .225 22.5%
11. .305 30.5%
12. 62.3 6,230%

Extra Practice for this lesson is provided on page 435.

11·8 Changing Fractions to Percents

Number Sense
Compare relative sizes of fractions and percents.
$\frac{1}{5} < \frac{2}{5} < \frac{3}{5}$
20% < 40% < 60%

A fraction can be written as a division problem.

$$\frac{\text{numerator}}{\text{denominator}} \rightarrow \text{denominator)}\overline{\text{numerator}}$$

Use this idea to change a fraction to a percent.

▶ **EXAMPLE**

Change $\frac{3}{4}$ to a percent.

Remember:
Write a decimal point and zeros in the dividend. Stop writing zeros when the quotient stops or repeats.

STEP 1 Write the fraction as a division problem in which the numerator is divided by the denominator.

$\frac{3}{4} \rightarrow 4)\overline{3}$

STEP 2 Divide. The quotient will be a decimal.

$$\begin{array}{r} .75 \\ 4)\overline{3.00} \\ -2\,8 \\ \hline 20 \\ -20 \\ \hline 0 \end{array}$$

Avoiding Errors
Students may need to be reminded to insert a decimal point and zeros in division, such as:
4)3.00 .

STEP 3 Write the decimal as a percent. Move the decimal point two spaces to the right. Write the percent sign.

75. = 75%

Common Error Decimal answers are not converted to percents. Remind students to move the decimal point before writing the percent symbol.

Practice

Change each fraction to a percent.

1. $\frac{1}{4}$ 25% **2.** $\frac{3}{5}$ 60% **3.** $\frac{3}{10}$ 30% **4.** $\frac{1}{2}$ 50% **5.** $\frac{1}{5}$ 20%

6. $\frac{5}{8}$ 62.5% **7.** $\frac{4}{5}$ 80% **8.** $\frac{7}{10}$ 70% **9.** $\frac{1}{8}$ 12.5% **10.** $\frac{1}{100}$ 1%

11. $\frac{1}{20}$ 5% **12.** $\frac{3}{8}$ 37.5% **13.** $\frac{2}{5}$ 40% **14.** $\frac{1}{25}$ 4% **15.** $\frac{1}{200}$ .5%

Extra Practice for this lesson is provided on page 435.

USING YOUR CALCULATOR
The Percent Key

You can use a calculator to do percent problems. Most calculators have a special percent (%) key that helps solve percent problems.

Find 30% of 60.

Of is a clue word for multiplication. Multiply 30% by 60.

PRESS [3] [0] [%] $\boxed{\qquad 0.3}$

The percent (%) key changed 30% into a decimal automatically.

PRESS [×] [6] [0] [=] $\boxed{\qquad 18.}$

The display shows that 30% of 60 is 18.

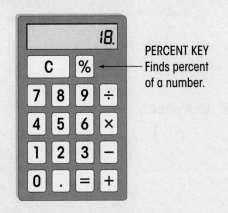

PERCENT KEY
Finds percent of a number.

Calculator Tip

The % key may not work the same on all calculators. Sometimes, 30% of 60 must be entered as 60 × 30%. Here you do not need to press = to get the answer.

Solve each problem using a calculator. Use the percent (%) key.

1. 25% of 88 22
2. 20% of 590 118
3. 75% of 240 180
4. 19% of 100 19
5. 50% of 98 49
6. 60% of 150 90
7. 150% of 400 600
8. 240% of 60 144
9. 175% of 360 630
10. 23% of 90 20.7

Solve each problem using a calculator. Compare the answers. What do you notice? Both answers are the same.

11. 20% of 35 and 35% of 20 7; 7
12. 10% of 90 and 90% of 10 9; 9

11·9 Finding the Percent

You can find the percent if you are given the whole
and the part.

25% of 100 is 25
↑ ↑ ↑
Percent Whole Part

▶ **EXAMPLE 1**

What percent of 50 is 10?

STEP 1 Write a fraction. The denominator
is the whole. It is the number after
the word *of*. The numerator is the
part.

$\dfrac{10}{50}$ ← Part
← Whole

STEP 2 Divide the numerator by the
denominator.

$$\begin{array}{r} .2 \\ 50\overline{)10.0} \\ -10\,0 \\ \hline 0 \end{array}$$

STEP 3 Change the decimal to a percent.

$.2 = 20. = 20\%$

10 is 20% of 50.

Be careful. Sometimes the percent is greater than 100%.
Then the part will be greater than the whole. You will
start with an improper fraction.

▶ **EXAMPLE 2**

42 is what percent of 35?

STEP 1 Write a fraction. The denominator
is the whole. It is the number after
the word *of*. The numerator is the
part.

$\dfrac{42}{35}$ ← Part
← Whole

STEP 2 Divide the numerator by the
denominator.

$$\begin{array}{r} 1.2 \\ 35\overline{)42.0} \\ -35 \\ \hline 7\,0 \\ -7\,0 \\ \hline 0 \end{array}$$

STEP 3 Change the decimal to a percent.

$1.2 = 120. = 120\%$

42 is 120% of 35.

Practice

Common Error The quotient is used as the percent. Remind students that after dividing, the decimal point must be moved two places to the right to change to a percent.

Find the percent in each problem.

1. What percent of 24 is 12? 50%

2. What percent of 100 is 5? 5%

3. 24 is what percent of 96? 25%

4. 6 is what percent of 60? 10%

5. 36 is what percent of 300? 12%

6. 36 is what percent of 100? 36%

7. What percent of 4 is 12? 300%

8. What percent of 125 is 9? 7.2%

9. 20 is what percent of 200? 10%

10. 19 is what percent of 38? 50%

11. What percent of 75 is 25? 33.3%

12. What percent of 40 is 5? 12.5%

13. 12 is what percent of 6? 200%

14. 105 is what percent of 60? 175%

Everyday Problem Solving

Soccer is a popular sport all year. Use the chart to answer the questions.

1. How many games did the Tornadoes play? 12 games

2. What percent of their games did the Tornadoes win? What percent of their games did they lose? 75%, 25%

3. How many games did the Blue Sox play? What percent of their games did they win? 10 games; 80%

4. What percent of their games did the Red Birds win? 66.6%

5. A prize is given to the team with the highest percent of wins. Which team gets the prize? Blue Sox

THE WEEK IN SPORTS

TEAM	GAMES WON	GAMES LOST	GAMES TIED	TOTAL GAMES PLAYED
RED BIRDS	10	5	0	?
BLUE SOX	8	2	0	?
TORNADOES	9	3	0	?

Extra Practice for this lesson is provided on page 436.

More practice is provided in Exercise 108 of the *Workbook*.

11·10 Finding the Percent Increase/Decrease

If an original number is made larger, you can find the **percent increase**. If an original number is made smaller, you can find the **percent decrease**.

EXAMPLE 1

Number Sense
Percent increase implies that an original number is made larger. Percent decrease implies that an original number is made smaller. In both cases, the percent is a percent of the original number.

The number 20 has been increased to 22. What is the percent increase?

STEP 1 Find the amount of increase. Subtract the original number from the new number.

$$\begin{array}{r} 22 \\ -\ 20 \\ \hline 2 \end{array} \leftarrow \text{Increase}$$

STEP 2 Write a fraction that compares the increase with the original number.

$\dfrac{2}{20}$

STEP 3 Change the fraction to a percent.

$20\overline{)2} = .1 = 10\%$

The percent increase is 10%.

Notice that the fraction compares 2 with the original number, 20.

EXAMPLE 2

Avoiding Errors
The numerator of the fraction is a difference, the amount of increase or decrease. The denominator of the fraction is the original number, not the new number.

The number 48 has been decreased to 12. What is the percent decrease?

STEP 1 Find the amount of decrease. Subtract the new number from the original number.

$$\begin{array}{r} 48 \\ -\ 12 \\ \hline 36 \end{array} \leftarrow \text{Decrease}$$

STEP 2 Write a fraction that compares this decrease with the original number.

$\dfrac{36}{48}$

STEP 3 Change the fraction to a percent.

$48\overline{)36} = .75 = 75\%$

The percent decrease is 75%.

Practice A

Common Error If two prices are given, students may compare the increase (or decrease) with the new price. Emphasize that we want to find the percent increase/decrease from the <u>original</u> price.

Copy the chart below. Find the percent increase or decrease for each stereo model.

Model Name	Price in June	Price in July	Percent Increase or Decrease
1. Hi Sound	$120	$126	? 5% increase
2. Boomer	$80	$72	? 10% decrease
3. XKE	$90	$180	? 100% increase
4. 10Z	$75	$60	? 20% decrease

Practice B

Solve to find the percent increase or decrease.

5. Lia's total sales were $1,200 last month. This month her sales are $1,500. What is the percent increase? 25%

6. A baseball card is worth $55 now. Last year it was worth $50. What is the percent increase? 10%

7. Your $200 printer now costs $140. What is the percent decrease? 30%

8. A used skateboard sells for $66. Originally, it cost $100. What is the percent increase or decrease? 34% decrease

9. Your $150 CD player now sells for $210. What is the percent increase? 40%

10. Last year, Ms. Cahill had 35 students in her class. This year she has 28 students. What is the percent decrease? 20%

Extra Practice for this lesson is provided on page 436.

More practice is provided in Exercise 109 of the *Workbook*.

 **Finding the Whole**

You know the three numbers in a percent problem.

25% of 100 is 25.

↑   ↑   ↑

Percent   Whole   Part

You can find the whole if you are given the percent and the part.

► **EXAMPLE 1**

20% of ■ is 5.

Remember:
Whole = Part ÷ Percent

STEP 1 Change the percent to a decimal.

20% = .20

STEP 2 Divide the part by the percent. The quotient is the whole.

$$\begin{array}{r} 25 \leftarrow \text{Whole} \\ \text{Percent} \rightarrow 20\overline{)500,} \leftarrow \text{Part} \\ \underline{-40} \\ 100 \\ \underline{-100} \\ 0 \end{array}$$

Number Sense
Show why multiplication yields an unreasonable answer. For example:
50% of what number is 10?
Incorrect: .5 × 10 = 5
Help students realize that a number greater than 10 is needed for 50% of it to be 10.

20% of 25 is 5.

When the percent is greater than 100%, the part will be greater than the whole.

► **EXAMPLE 2**

80 is 160% of what number?

STEP 1 Change the percent to a decimal.

160% = 1.60

Avoiding Errors
Remind students to place the decimal point in the quotient directly above the decimal point in the dividend when dividing. Refer students to Lesson 10.10.

STEP 2 Divide the part by the percent. The quotient is the whole.

$$\begin{array}{r} 50 \leftarrow \text{Whole} \\ \text{Percent} \rightarrow 160\overline{)8000,} \leftarrow \text{Part} \\ \underline{-800} \\ 0 \end{array}$$

80 is 160% of 50.

Notice that the part is 80. The whole is 50. The part is greater than the whole.

Practice A

Common Error The divisor and dividend are interchanged, so that the quotient is incorrect. Stress to students that the divisor is always the percent, which has been changed to a decimal.

Find the whole in each problem.

1. 10% of ▨ is 8 80

2. 50% of ▨ is 250 500

3. 5% of ▨ is 50 1,000

4. 9% of ▨ is 18 200

5. 12% of ▨ is 78 650

6. 20% of ▨ is 32 160

7. 74% of ▨ is 407 550

8. 66% of ▨ is 165 250

9. 24% of ▨ is 18 75

10. 60% of ▨ is 84 140

11. 15% of ▨ is 45 300

12. 49% of ▨ is 196 400

Practice B

Solve to find the whole in each problem.

13. 35 is 50% of what number? 70

14. 63 is 18% of what number? 350

15. 60% of what number is 72? 120

16. 75% of what number is 12? 16

17. 36 is 30% of what number? 120

18. 60 is 15% of what number? 400

19. 225% of what number is 54? 24

20. 110% of what number is 121? 110

Everyday Problem Solving

A bank pays money (called interest) to each person with a savings account. The interest rate times the savings (called the principal) equals the interest.

1. How much interest does Will get? $60

2. How much interest does Angela get? $60

3. Find Mr. Smythe's interest. $200

4. What is Mrs. Smythe's principal? (Hint: 5% of what number is $300?) $6,000

Annual Interest			
Name	Interest Rate	Interest	Principal
Mr. Smythe	4%	?	$5,000
Mrs. Smythe	5%	$300	?
Will	6%	?	$1,000
Angela	8%	?	$750

Extra Practice for this lesson is provided on page 436.

More practice is provided in Exercise 110 of the *Workbook*.

11·12 ▶ Finding the Original Price

Number Sense
In Example 1, show students that 75 with a 20% decrease is 60. The 20% is off the original (unknown) price.

Suppose a price is changed by a percent. If you are given the percent and the new price, you can find the original price.

80% of $75 is $60
↑   ↑   ↑
Percent Original New
price   price
Percent Whole   Part

▶ **EXAMPLE 1**

The original price of a pair of hiking boots was decreased by 20%. The boots now cost $60. What was the original price?

Remember:
Make the decimal divisor a whole number. Move the decimal point to the right.

$$80.\overline{)6000.}$$

STEP 1 Find what percent the new price is of the original price. Subtract the percent decrease from 100.	100% − 20% = 80%
STEP 2 Solve the percent problem. Find the whole. Divide the part by the percent.	80% of ? is 60. 60 ÷ .80 is $75.

The original price was $75. Notice that it was the original price that had a 20% decrease.

▶ **EXAMPLE 2**

A ski trip now costs $260. This is a 30% increase from the original price. What was the original price?

Remember:
Whole = Part ÷ Percent

STEP 1 Find what percent the new price is of the original price. Add the percent increase to 100.	100% + 30% = 130%
STEP 2 Solve the percent problem. Find the whole. Divide the part by the percent.	130% of ? is 260. 260 ÷ 1.30 is $200.

Avoiding Errors
20% off the original price means that the new price is 80% of the original. 30% added to the original price means that the new price is 130% of the original.

The original price was $200. The original price had a 30% increase.

Practice A

Common Error Percent increase/decrease is used to solve the problem. Tell students to see if the answer makes sense. If there was a decrease, original should be more than new. If there was an increase, original should be less than new.

Copy the chart below. Find the original price for each item.

Item	Percent Increase or Decrease	New Price	Original Price
1. Printer	50% decrease	$125	? $250
2. Magazine subscription	30% decrease	$42	? $60
3. Club membership	10% increase	$88	? $80
4. Season tickets	20% increase	$75	? $62.50

Practice B

Solve to find the original cost in each problem.

5. A shirt is on sale for $10. This is 50% off the original price. What was the original price? $20

6. Rosa's new bracelet costs $12. All bracelets are 60% off the original price. What was the original price? $30

7. Kevin's skateboard is 20% off the original price. If he pays $80, what was the original price? $100

8. A stamp album has increased in value 25%. It is now worth $4,500. What was its original value? $3,600

Extra Practice for this lesson is provided on page 437.

More practice is provided in Exercise 111 of the *Workbook*.

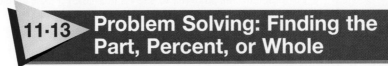

11·13 Problem Solving: Finding the Part, Percent, or Whole

To solve a percent word problem, you need to know what you are given and what you need to find. Look for the three parts of the percent problem.

▶ **EXAMPLE**

At the Global Tire Factory, 25% of the employees ride to work by bus. There are 215 employees who ride the bus. How many employees work at the factory?

STEP 1   READ   What do you need to find out?
You need to find the total number of employees at the factory.

STEP 2   PLAN   What do you need to do?
Identify the percent problem you need to solve. Look at what you are given. What do you need to find?

25% of **?** is 215
↑   ↑   ↑
Percent Whole Part

You need to find the whole.

STEP 3   DO   Follow the plan.
25% of what number is 215?
Divide the part by the percent.
215 ÷ .25 = 860 employees

STEP 4   CHECK   Does your answer make sense?
25% of 860 employees should be 215.
.25 × 860 = 215 ✓

There are 860 employees at Global Tire Factory.

Number Sense
Encourage students to decide if the answer should be a larger number or a smaller number than that in the word problem. This will help them decide which type of percent problem they need to solve.

Remember:
Whole = Part ÷ Percent
Part = Percent × Whole
Percent = Part ÷ Whole × 100

Avoiding Errors
Remind students to refer back to Lessons 11.3, 11.9, and 11.11. These lessons show the steps involved in solving this particular kind of percent problem.

Problem Solving

READ each problem. Answer the questions under PLAN.
DO the plan to solve each problem.

1. At a tire store yesterday, 20% of the day's customers bought premium tires. The salesman sold premium tires to 60 customers. How many total customers bought tires yesterday? 300 customers

   PLAN
   What are you given? the percent, the part
   What do you need to find? the whole

   DO
   Part ÷ Percent = Whole
   60 ÷ .20 = 300

2. There are 900 tires manufactured at the Global Tire Factory every day. Today, 62% of them are shipped to stores out of state. How many tires were shipped out of state? 558 tires

   PLAN
   What are you given? the percent, the whole
   What do you need to find? the part

   DO
   Percent × Whole = Part
   .62 × 900 = 558

3. There were 500 people at the company picnic. Of the total, 125 people work in the shipping department. What percent of the people at the picnic work in the shipping department? 25%

   PLAN
   What are you given? the part, the whole
   What do you need to find? the percent

   DO
   $\frac{\text{Part}}{\text{Whole}} = \frac{125}{500} = \text{Percent}$
   125 ÷ 500 = .25 = 25%

Problem-Solving Strategy

Sometimes a sentence diagram can help you plan. Write ✓ next to what you know. Write ? to show what to find.

Sentence Diagram

▊% of $▊ is $▊
↑   ↑   ↑
Percent Whole Part

Eric earns $2,000 ✓each month at Global Tire. His rent is 28% ✓of his salary. How much is his rent? $560
?

Extra Practice for this lesson is provided on page 437.

Vocabulary Review

Choose a words or words from the list to complete each sentence.

base salary
commission
discount
gross salary
percent
percent decrease
percent increase
sale price
sales tax

1. The __?__ will make an original number larger. percent increase

2. A store will add __?__ to the price of an item. sales tax

3. Payment based on the percent of sales is called __?__. commission

4. A __?__ tells how many of 100 parts are in a whole. percent

5. A price can be reduced by a __?__. discount

6. You get the __?__ of an item after subtracting the discount. sale price

7. The sum of the __?__ and the commission is the __?__. base salary; gross salary

8. The __?__ will make an original number smaller. percent decrease

9. **Writing** Write a paragraph entitled "Percents in Everyday Life." Use at least five words from the list above. Underline the words as you use them. Answers will vary.

Chapter Quiz

LESSONS 11·1, 11·2, 11·7, and 11·8

Test Tip
Change between percents and decimals by moving the decimal point 2 places left or right. Remember that percent is out of 100 parts.

Changing Fractions, Decimals, and Percents
Copy the chart. Fill in the missing numbers.

	Percent	Fraction	Decimal
1.	7%	? $\frac{7}{100}$	? .07
2.	? 75%	$\frac{3}{4}$	? .75
3.	? 120%	? $\frac{6}{5}$ or $1\frac{1}{5}$	1.2
4.	16%	? $\frac{4}{25}$	? .16
5.	? 80%	$\frac{4}{5}$	? .8

Finding the Part, Percent, or Whole

Solve.

6. What number is 36% of 58? 20.88

7. What percent of 96 is 24? 25%

8. 16 is 40% of what number? 40

9. Candy costs $3.75. The sales tax is 4%. What is the total cost of the candy? $3.90

10. A CD costs $15. It's on sale for 10% off. What is the discount? $1.50

11. Ed sold $2,400 in computer parts. His commission is 8%. How much did he make in commission? $192

Solving Three Kinds of Percent Problems

Solve.

12. Dinner for two totaled $56.00. A 15% tip is required. What is the amount of the tip? $9

13. A briefcase was originally priced at $95. It now sells for $76. What is the percent decrease? 20%

14. A shirt is on sale for $18. This is 25% off the original price. What is the original price? $24

15. Dana sold 45 tickets to the dance. This is 18% of all the tickets that were sold. How many tickets were sold? 250 tickets

Group Activity See the *Teacher Planning Guide* for a Scoring Rubric for this activity.
Work with your group to find an advertisement that uses percents. Pretend to purchase three items from the ad. For each item, find and record the percent of discount, its original price, and the sale price. Decide which store has the fairest advertisement. Explain your reasoning.

Builders use models to show what a building should look like. Every model has a scale. You can use the scale to find the actual size of something in the model. Suppose a wall in a model is 6 inches long. The scale for the model is 1 inch = 2 feet. How long is the actual wall? Multiply the scale by the measurement of the wall in the model.

Caption The actual wall is 12 feet long.

Chapter 12 ▷ Ratios and Proportions

ESL Note Ask students for different meanings they may know for the word *scale* (such as a scale used to weigh objects, fish scales, and a "sliding scale" for doctor's fees). Explain this new meaning of scale and ask for examples.

Words to Know

ratio	a comparison of one amount with another
proportion	a statement that two ratios are equal
cross products	the results of cross multiplying
rate	a comparison of two amounts with different units of measure
multiple unit pricing	the cost of a set of items
scale drawing	a picture that shows the proportional size of actual objects
scale	a ratio that compares the size of a drawing with the size of the original object

Words to Know Have students discuss the difference between the terms *ratio* and *proportion*. Give examples of each.

Scale Drawing Project

Make a scale drawing of your bedroom. Measure the length and width of the room. Measure the length and width of each piece of furniture. Choose a scale so that your drawing will fit on a sheet of graph paper. An example of a scale is 1 inch in your drawing = 2 feet in your room. Label the actual measurements on your drawing.

Project Encourage students to be neat and exact with their drawings, as if they were making a blueprint. Have them label objects in the room, label the measurements, and write the scale on their drawing.

Learning Objectives

• Write ratios.

• Solve proportions.

• Find multiple unit prices.

• Use scale drawings to find actual sizes.

• Solve problems using proportions.

• Apply using map scales to find distances.

More Practice is provided in Exercise 112 of the *Workbook*.

12·1   What Is a Ratio?

A **ratio** is a comparison of one amount with another. You can write a ratio to compare the number of blue squares with all squares in the picture.

The ratio of blue squares to all squares is three to five. There are three ways to write this ratio.

In words	With a ratio sign	As a fraction
3 to 5	3:5	$\frac{3}{5}$

If the ratio is an improper fraction, do not change it to a whole or mixed number.

EXAMPLE 1

Number Sense
Review with students how to reduce fractions. Also, review what each part of a fraction represents. This will lead the discussion into "parts out of," which will lead into "number of parts to number of parts," which is a ratio.

Write the ratio of yellow squares to blue squares.

STEP 1   Count the yellow squares.   3 Yellow
Count the blue squares.   4 Blue

STEP 2   Write the ratio as a fraction.
The order of the numbers is $\frac{3}{4}$ ← Yellow
important.   ← Blue

The ratio of yellow squares to blue squares is
3 to 4, 3:4, or $\frac{3}{4}$.

Ratios are written in lowest terms.

> **EXAMPLE 2**

Remember:

$\frac{2}{6} = \frac{2 \div 2}{6 \div 2} = \frac{1}{3}$

Avoiding Errors
Explain that the first quantity named is written first when using the ratio sign, and it is written on top when writing a fraction.

Write the ratio of vowels to the total number of letters in the word GRAPES.

STEP 1 Count the number of vowels in the word.

GRAPES ← 2 vowels

Count the total number of letters in the word.

GRAPES ← 6 letters

STEP 2 Write the ratio. Be sure it is in lowest tems.

$\frac{2}{6} = \frac{1}{3}$

The ratio of vowels to the total number of letters in GRAPES is 1 to 3, 1:3, or $\frac{1}{3}$.

Common Error Students put quantities in the wrong places. After they write the ratio with numbers, have them write the ratio again using words to describe what the numbers represent.

Practice

Write each ratio with a ratio sign or as a fraction.

1. blue circles to all circles 5:5, $\frac{5}{5}$

2. blue circles to yellow circles 3:2, $\frac{3}{2}$

3. total number of letters to vowels in the word HOUSE 5:3, $\frac{5}{3}$

4. vowels to total number of letters in the word FLAVOR 1:3, $\frac{1}{3}$

Everyday Problem Solving

Eric uses the recipe shown to make punch.

1. What is the ratio of pineapple juice to orange juice? 4:1, $\frac{4}{1}$

2. What is the ratio of lemon juice to ginger ale? 1:18, $\frac{1}{18}$

3. What is the ratio of orange juice to lemon juice? 3:1, $\frac{3}{1}$

Party Punch

Mix the following ingredients:

12 cups pineapple juice

1 cup lemon juice

3 cups orange juice

18 cups ginger ale

Extra Practice for this lesson is provided on page 438.

More Practice is provided in Exercise 113 of the *Workbook*.

12·2 What Is a Proportion?

Number Sense
Show students that to change a picture of the ratio $\frac{3}{4}$ to $\frac{6}{8}$, just draw two lines through the parts in either direction.

A **proportion** shows two equal ratios. Look at the squares below. Each ratio compares the blue parts to all parts. The ratios are equal and form a proportion.

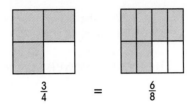

$$\frac{3}{4} \quad = \quad \frac{6}{8}$$

This proportion above is read:
Three is to four as six is to eight.

▶ **EXAMPLE 1**

Write a ratio of the blue parts to all parts for each rectangle. Do the ratios form a proportion?

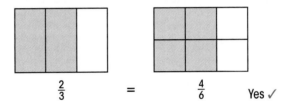

$$\frac{2}{3} \quad = \quad \frac{4}{6} \qquad \text{Yes } \checkmark$$

Thus, $\frac{2}{3}$ and $\frac{4}{6}$ do form a proportion.

You can tell if two ratios form a proportion by cross multiplying. The results are the **cross products**. If the cross products are equal, the ratios do form a proportion.

▶ **EXAMPLE 2**

Avoiding Errors
If the cross products are not calculated correctly, the answer may be wrong.

Do $\frac{3}{4}$ and $\frac{12}{16}$ form a proportion?

STEP 1 Find the cross products.

$$\frac{3}{4} \bowtie \frac{12}{16}$$

Cross products:
$3 \times 16 = 48$
$4 \times 12 = 48$

STEP 2 Compare the cross products. If the cross products are equal, the ratios form a proportion.

$48 = 48 \checkmark$

The ratios $\frac{3}{4}$ and $\frac{12}{16}$ do form a proportion.

Practice A

Write a ratio of the blue parts to all parts for each figure.
Do the ratios form a proportion? Write *Yes* or *No*.

1. 1:2, 2:4; yes

2. 1:2, 1:3; no

3. 1:3, 3:9; yes

4. 2;5, 4:10; yes

5. 2:6, 3:8; no

6. 1:2, 3:6; yes

Practice B

Decide if each pair of ratios forms a proportion. Write *Yes* or *No*.

7. $\frac{3}{4}$ $\frac{18}{24}$ yes

8. $\frac{2}{7}$ $\frac{9}{10}$ no

9. $\frac{5}{9}$ $\frac{15}{27}$ yes

10. $\frac{10}{15}$ $\frac{12}{18}$ yes

11. $\frac{5}{8}$ $\frac{4}{5}$ no

12. $\frac{4}{5}$ $\frac{5}{7}$ no

13. $\frac{2}{9}$ $\frac{4}{18}$ yes

14. $\frac{5}{8}$ $\frac{6}{7}$ no

15. $\frac{9}{24}$ $\frac{6}{16}$ yes

16. $\frac{1}{7}$ $\frac{3}{20}$ no

17. $\frac{4}{10}$ $\frac{12}{30}$ yes

18. $\frac{14}{16}$ $\frac{18}{24}$ no

12-3 ▶ Solving Proportions

You can find a missing number in a proportion.

▶ **EXAMPLE**

Find the missing number in the proportion.

$$\frac{2}{3} = \frac{?}{21}$$

Number Sense
Draw 3 large circles on the board and shade 2 of them. Repeat the drawing six more times and show that 14 circles are shaded out of 21 circles. Explain that the proportion $\frac{2}{3} = \frac{14}{21}$ is true.

STEP 1 Find the cross product.

$$\frac{2}{3} \diagdown \frac{?}{21}$$
$$2 \times 21 = 42$$

STEP 2 Divide the cross product by the remaining number in the proportion. The quotient is the missing number.

$$42 \div 3 = 14$$
$$? = 14$$

Avoiding Errors
Explain that the missing number in a proportion can be found in any one of four places. Emphasize that the same technique is used for solving all proportions.

STEP 3 Check the cross products to be sure that they are equal.

$$\frac{2}{3} \diagup\!\!\!\!\diagdown \frac{14}{21}$$
$$2 \times 21 = 3 \times 14$$
$$42 = 42 \checkmark$$

The missing number is 14.

Common Error Students multiply the top numbers of the ratios. Encourage students to draw a large "X" within each proportion to show which numbers are multiplied.

Practice

Find the missing number in each proportion.

1. $\frac{?}{12} = \frac{5}{10}$ 6

2. $\frac{3}{?} = \frac{7}{21}$ 9

3. $\frac{8}{32} = \frac{?}{16}$ 4

4. $\frac{3}{18} = \frac{4}{?}$ 24

5. $\frac{4}{8} = \frac{?}{2}$ 1

6. $\frac{11}{?} = \frac{2}{4}$ 22

7. $\frac{4}{7} = \frac{?}{14}$ 8

8. $\frac{9}{12} = \frac{3}{?}$ 4

9. $\frac{5}{?} = \frac{50}{70}$ 7

10. $\frac{8}{9} = \frac{16}{?}$ 18

11. $\frac{?}{35} = \frac{3}{5}$ 21

12. $\frac{15}{60} = \frac{1}{?}$ 4

Extra Practice for this lesson is provided on page 438.

USING YOUR CALCULATOR
Solving Proportions

You can solve proportions with your calculator.
Find the missing number in the proportion.

$\dfrac{3}{4} = \dfrac{?}{28}$

Multiply to find the cross product.

PRESS $\boxed{3}$ $\boxed{\times}$ $\boxed{2}$ $\boxed{8}$ *Do not press the equal sign.*

Divide by the remaining number.

PRESS $\boxed{\div}$ $\boxed{4}$ $\boxed{=}$ | 21. |

The missing number is 21.

$\dfrac{3}{4} = \dfrac{21}{28}$

Now, check the proportion. First, find the cross products. Write them down on your paper. Check to see if the cross products are equal.

PRESS $\boxed{3}$ $\boxed{\times}$ $\boxed{2}$ $\boxed{8}$ $\boxed{=}$ | 84. |

PRESS $\boxed{4}$ $\boxed{\times}$ $\boxed{2}$ $\boxed{1}$ $\boxed{=}$ | 84. |

$84 = 84$ ✓

The ratios form a proportion. The missing number is 21.

> **Calculator Tip**
> Some calculators display the product of the numbers after pressing the division key. This will not affect the answer.

Find the missing number in each proportion. Then, check each proportion.

1. $\dfrac{50}{120} = \dfrac{5}{?}$ 12

2. $\dfrac{?}{500} = \dfrac{9}{10}$ 450

3. $\dfrac{11}{?} = \dfrac{55}{775}$ 155

4. $\dfrac{36}{250} = \dfrac{144}{?}$ 1,000

5. $\dfrac{160}{200} = \dfrac{?}{340}$ 272

6. $\dfrac{50}{?} = \dfrac{400}{640}$ 80

7. $\dfrac{?}{375} = \dfrac{96}{2250}$ 16

8. $\dfrac{24}{360} = \dfrac{3}{?}$ 45

9. $\dfrac{2}{38} = \dfrac{?}{475}$ 25

More Practice is provided in Exercise 115 of the *Workbook*.

12·4 Multiple Unit Pricing

Number Sense
Have students solve the following: If one pencil costs 20¢, what is the cost of 6 pencils? Then solve this problem using the following proportion:
$\frac{1}{20¢} = \frac{6}{?}$

A **rate** is a comparison of two amounts with different units of measure. An example of a rate is **multiple unit pricing**. Multiple unit pricing is the cost of a set of items. For example, suppose that 4 cans of cat food sell for $2. This can be written as

$$\frac{4 \text{ cans}}{\$2} \quad \text{or} \quad \frac{\$2}{4 \text{ cans}}$$

If you know the rate, you can use a proportion to find the price of any number of the same item.

▶ **EXAMPLE 1**

The price of workout shorts is $24.50 for 5 pairs. What is the price of 3 pairs of shorts?

STEP 1 Set up a proportion with a missing number.

$$\frac{\$24.50}{5 \text{ shorts}} \diagdown \frac{\$?}{3 \text{ shorts}}$$

STEP 2 Find the cross product.

$$\$24.50 \times 3 = \$73.50$$

STEP 3 Divide the cross product by the remaining number.

$$\$73.50 \div 5 = \$14.70$$

STEP 4 Check the ratios to see if they form a proportion.

$$\frac{\$24.50}{5 \text{ shorts}} \diagup \frac{\$14.70}{3 \text{ shorts}}$$

The cross products are equal.
The ratios form a proportion.
The answer is correct.

$$\$24.50 \times 3 = \$14.70 \times 5$$
$$\$73.50 = \$73.50 \checkmark$$

The price of 3 pairs of workout shorts is $14.70.

You can use a proportion to find how many items you can buy for a certain amount of money.

The price of workout shorts is $24.50 for 5 pairs. How many shorts can you buy for $9.80?

STEP 1 Set up a proportion with a missing number.

$$\frac{\$24.50}{5 \text{ shorts}} \nearrow \frac{\$9.80}{? \text{ shorts}}$$

STEP 2 Find the cross product.

$5 \times \$9.80 = \$49$

STEP 3 Divide the cross product by the remaining number.

$\$49 \div \$24.50 = 2$

STEP 4 Check the ratios to see if they form a proportion.

$$\frac{\$24.50}{5 \text{ shorts}} \diagdown\diagup \frac{\$9.80}{2 \text{ shorts}}$$

The cross products are equal.
The ratios form a proportion.
The answer is correct.

$\$24.50 \times 2 = \$9.80 \times 5$
$\$49 = \$49 \checkmark$

You can buy 2 pairs of shorts for $9.80.

Common Errors Students may not assign the proper unit value to the answer. Tell them to write the units in the proportion, even next to the question mark.

Practice

Solve each problem using a proportion.

1. If 4 cans of soup cost $3.00, how much do 6 cans cost? $4.50

2. If 20 golf balls sell for $25.00, how much do 3 golf balls cost? $3.75

3. The Grand Prix Raceway charges $6.75 to make 5 laps around the track. How much would it cost to make 15 laps? $20.25

4. A bead store sells 200 crystal beads for $8.00. How many beads could you buy with $10.00? 250 beads

5. Goetz Landscape charges $18.50 for 25 pounds of sand. How much would 80 pounds of sand cost? $59.20

6. A long-distance phone call to Ling's grandmother costs $4.35 for 3 minutes. How much would a 20-minute phone call cost? $29.00

Extra Practice for this lesson is provided on page 438.

More Practice is provided in Exercise 116 of the *Workbook*.

12-5 ▶ **Scale Drawings**

Number Sense
Draw a square on an overhead projector. Then, move the projector to make the square larger or smaller. Explain that the scale used to compare the two squares is being changed.

Length = Larger wall
Width = Shorter wall

A **scale drawing** shows an object that is either larger or smaller than actual size. The **scale** is the ratio of the size of the picture to the size of the original object.

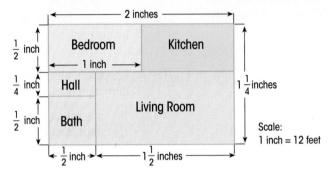

▶ **EXAMPLE**

Remember:
To multiply by a mixed number, change it to an improper fraction.

$$12 \times 1\frac{1}{2}$$

$$= \frac{12}{1} \times \frac{3}{2} = \frac{36}{2} = 18$$

Avoiding Errors
Students may be confused by the use of the equal sign. For the scale 1 inch = 12 feet, the equal sign really means "stands for," as in "1 inch stands for 12 feet."

Find the actual length of the living room.

STEP 1 Set up a proportion with a missing number.

Scale $\dfrac{1 \text{ in.}}{12 \text{ ft}}$ ⤢ $\dfrac{1\frac{1}{2}}{? \text{ ft}}$

STEP 2 Find the cross product.

$$12 \times 1\frac{1}{2} = 18$$

STEP 3 Divide the cross product by the remaining number in the proportion.

$$18 \div 1 = 18$$

STEP 4 Check your answer.

$\dfrac{1 \text{ in.}}{12 \text{ ft}}$ ⤢ $\dfrac{1\frac{1}{2} \text{ in.}}{18 \text{ ft}}$

$$1 \times 18 = 12 \times 1\frac{1}{2}$$

$$18 = 18 \checkmark$$

The length of the living room is 18 feet.

Common Error Students arrange the proportion incorrectly. Remind them to label the units and position numbers in the proportion according to the units.

Practice

Use the scale drawing from the top of the page to find the actual size.

1. the width of the living room 9 feet

2. the length of the kitchen 12 feet

3. the length of the bedroom 12 feet

4. the width of the bedroom 6 feet

Extra Practice for this Lesson is provided on page 438.

ON-THE-JOB MATH
Courier

Chris is a courier. He delivers packages to homes and businesses.

He uses the map scale to find distances from one location to another.

Use the scale from the map to find the distances Chris needs to ride to deliver packages.

1. Chris delivers the first package to Power Records. How far will he ride from the Courier's Office? 3 miles

2. The next package is delivered to Hair Art. How far will Chris ride from Power Records? 7 miles

3. From Hair Art, Chris rides to Eagle Carpet for a delivery. How far will he ride? 2.5 miles

4. From Eagle Carpet, Chris rides to the Sub Zone for lunch. Then, he rides to Colony Cleaners. How far will he ride? 5.5 miles

Critical Thinking
Chris uses the map to find distances between deliveries. How else does the map help him in his job?

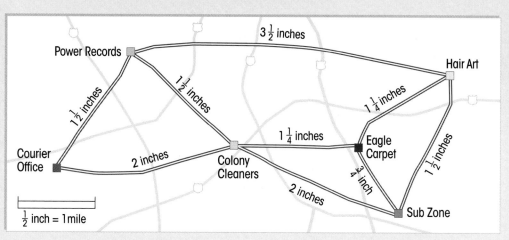

Power Records — $3\frac{1}{2}$ inches — Hair Art

$1\frac{3}{4}$ inches
$1\frac{1}{2}$ inches
$1\frac{1}{4}$ inches

Courier Office — 2 inches — Colony Cleaners — $1\frac{1}{4}$ inches — Eagle Carpet

$\frac{3}{4}$ inch
$1\frac{1}{2}$ inches

2 inches — Sub Zone

$\frac{1}{2}$ inch = 1 mile

Critical Thinking The map helps Chris to find his way from place to place.

More Practice is provided in Exercise 117 of the *Workbook*.

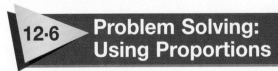

12·6 ▶ Problem Solving: Using Proportions

Proportions can be used to solve word problems. You can use ratios or rates to compare amounts.

▶ **EXAMPLE**

Josh can mow 4 lawns in 3 hours. How long will it take him to mow 12 lawns?

Number Sense
Provide examples of proportion problems that students may find useful or interesting. For example: if it takes you 1 hour to do a page of homework, how long will it take you to work on 3 pages?

STEP 1   READ   What do you need to find out?
You need to find out how long it will take Josh to mow 12 lawns.

STEP 2   PLAN   What do you need to do?
Set up a proportion and solve.

$$\frac{4 \text{ lawns}}{3 \text{ hours}} = \frac{12 \text{ lawns}}{? \text{ hours}}$$

STEP 3   DO   Follow the plan.
Solve the proportion.

$$\frac{4}{3} \not\nearrow \frac{12}{?}$$

Multiply the cross product.
$3 \times 12 = 36$

Divide by the remaining number.
$36 \div 4 = 9$

Avoiding Errors
Before students give the final answer to a word problem, be sure they check their proportions. Ask them to show all work.

STEP 4   CHECK   Does your answer make sense?
Do the ratios form a proportion?
Check the cross products.

$$\frac{4}{3} \diagdown\!\!\!\!\diagup \frac{12}{9}$$

$4 \times 9 = 36$

$3 \times 12 = 36$

$36 = 36 \checkmark$

It will take Josh 9 hours to mow 12 lawns.

Problem Solving

READ the problem. Answer the question under PLAN. DO the plan to solve the problem.

1. Ali can deliver 12 pizzas in 30 minutes. How many pizzas can she deliver in 45 minutes? 18 pizzas

   PLAN
   What proportion should you write?
   $\dfrac{12 \text{ pizzas}}{30 \text{ minutes}} = \dfrac{? \text{ pizzas}}{45 \text{ minutes}}$

   DO
   $12 \times 45 = 540$
   $540 \div 30 = 18$

2. Mary can deliver 8 pizzas in 20 minutes. How long will it take her to deliver 10 pizzas? 25 minutes

   PLAN
   What proportion should you write?
   $\dfrac{8 \text{ pizzas}}{20 \text{ minutes}} = \dfrac{10 \text{ pizzas}}{? \text{ minutes}}$

   DO
   $20 \times 10 = 200$
   $200 \div 8 = 25$

3. Sam can read 3 pages in 10 minutes. How long will it take him to read 15 pages? 50 minutes

   PLAN
   What proportion should you write?
   $\dfrac{3 \text{ pages}}{10 \text{ minutes}} = \dfrac{15 \text{ pages}}{? \text{ minutes}}$

   DO
   $15 \times 10 = 150$
   $150 \div 3 = 50$

Problem Solving Strategy

Drawing a picture can help you solve a problem.

Ann uses 2 bales of hay to feed 6 horses. How many horses can she feed with 3 bales of hay? 9 horses

Draw a picture of 2 bales of hay and 6 horses. Each bale of hay feeds 3 horses. Now draw 1 more bale of hay with another 3 horses. Count all the horses.

Extra Practice for this Lesson is provided on page 438.

cross products

multiple unit pricing

proportion

rate

ratio

scale

scale drawing

Vocabulary Review

Complete each sentence with a word from the list.

1. A __?__ is a comparison of two quantities. ratio

2. A __?__ is made up of two equal ratios. proportion

3. To check if two ratios are equal, compare the __?__. cross products

4. A __?__ is a comparison of two amounts with different units of measure. rate

5. Four cans of soup for $5 is an example of __?__. multiple unit pricing

6. A drawing that shows an object and is either larger or smaller than its actual size is called a __?__. scale drawing

7. The ratio of the size of the picture to the size of the original object is called the __?__. scale

8. **Writing** Give examples of a ratio, a proportion, and a cross product. Explain the relationship among the three terms. Answers will vary. Check students' work.

Chapter Quiz

LESSON 12·1

Test Tip
To write a ratio, remember that the first amount named is written as the top number in a fraction.

Writing Ratios

Write each ratio using a ratio sign and a fraction.

1. all letters to vowels in ELEPHANT 8/3, 8:3

2. vowels to all letters in SOCCER 1/3; 1:3

LESSON 12·2

Test Tip
If cross products are equal, then the ratios form a proportion.

Identifying Proportions

Decide if each pair of ratios forms a proportion. Write *Yes* or *No*.

3. $\frac{4}{5}$ $\frac{8}{12}$ no

4. $\frac{14}{16}$ $\frac{28}{32}$ yes

5. $\frac{5}{10}$ $\frac{6}{12}$ yes

6. $\frac{3}{4}$ $\frac{6}{7}$ no

Solving Proportions

Find the missing number in each proportion.

7. $\dfrac{12}{8} = \dfrac{30}{?}$ 20

8. $\dfrac{60}{80} = \dfrac{?}{36}$ 27

9. $\dfrac{63}{3} = \dfrac{?}{2}$ 42

10. $\dfrac{25}{75} = \dfrac{4}{?}$ 12

Test Tip
To solve a proportion, find the cross product and divide by the remaining number.

Finding Multiple Unit Prices

Find the price or the number of items.

11. If 3 bars of soap cost $2, how much will 12 bars of soap cost? $8

12. Tennis balls cost 3 for $5. How many tennis balls can be bought with $20? 12 tennis balls

Test Tip
Be sure to write the prices in the same place for each ratio.

Using Scale Drawings

Use a proportion to solve each problem.

13. The scale on a map is 1 inch = 15 miles. A line on the map is 2 inches. How many miles does the line represent? 30 miles

Test Tip
Write the scale as a ratio. Then, write another ratio using the units in the first ratio. Solve the proportion.

Solving Problems with Proportions

Solve each problem. Use a proportion.

14. If 18 trees are needed to cover 3 acres, how many trees are needed to cover 60 acres? 360 trees

Test Tip
Look for words that indicate a ratio, such as **5 to 4** or **3 out of every 24**. Then, write a proportion to solve the problem.

Group Activity See the *Teacher Planning Guide* for a Scoring Rubric for this activity.
Work in a small group. Visit a supermarket or use newspaper ads to find items and their multiple unit prices. Record the item, the number of items, and the price. First, find the cost of five items. Second, find the number of items you could buy for $10. Write and solve a proportion for each part of this activity.

Unit 3 Review

Choose the letter for the correct answer.

Use the table to answer Questions 1–3.

Jo's Grocery	
Item	**Cost**
Beans	$.79 can
Tomatoes	$1.19 pound
Apples	5 for $1.20

1. Bruce wants to buy 5 cans of beans. He has $5. What can you conclude?

  A. He has exactly the money he needs. Incorrect; used exact amounts

  B. He does not have enough money. Incorrect; used prices of tomatoes

  C. He will receive change. Correct;

  D. The beans are too expensive. Incorrect

2. Sally bought 5 apples and 1 pound of tomatoes. Sales tax is 6%. What is her total cost?

  A. $2.39 Incorrect; not include sales tax

  B. $2.54 Correct

  C. $6.36 Incorrect; found 5 x 1.20 + $.36

  D. $7.63 Incorrect; multiplied 5 x 1.20, added tomatoes, then added tax

3. How much do 8 apples cost?

  A. $1.92 Correct

  B. $2.00 Incorrect; calculated each apple at $.25

  C. $3.60 Incorrect; multiplied 3 x $1.20

  D. $9.60 Incorrect; multiplied 8 x $1.20

4. Sue buys 3 pears and 9 apples. What percent of the fruit are apples?

  A. 9% Incorrect; changed 3 apples to 3%

  B. 25% Incorrect; used 9 pears as total fruit

  C. 75% Correct

  D. $133\frac{1}{3}$% Incorrect; changed 9/3 to a percent

5. 25% of Doug's order is for vegetables. His total cost is $12. How much does he spend on vegetables?

  A. $3 Correct

  B. $6 Incorrect; confused 25% with 50%

  C. $9 Incorrect; found amount *not* spent

  D. $15 Incorrect; found 25% and added it to total

6. 30% of Lori's order is for meat. She spends $12 on meat. What is the total cost of her order?

  A. $3.60 Incorrect; multiplied 30% x $12

  B. $15.60 Incorrect; added 30% of $12 to $12

  C. $20.40 Incorrect; found 70%, added it to $12

  D. $40.00 Correct

Critical Thinking

What can you buy for $10? Choose items from the table above. List the number of items, the cost, and the total cost.

CHALLENGE When you choose the items to buy, come as close to $10 as you can.

Possible challenge answer: 35 apples and 2 cans of beans cost $9.98.

Unit ▶ 4 ◀ Measurement and Geometry

Opening the Unit Have each student write the name of an animal with an estimate of the height and weight using customary units. After completing Lesson 14.3, have students review reasonableness estimates.

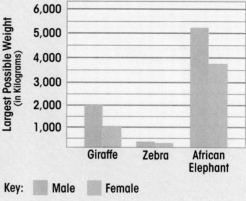

Key: ▮ Male ▮ Female

Animal	Height in Feet	Height in Meters
Giraffe	18	5.50
Zebra	4	1.22
African Elephant	10	3.05

On the African plains, there are many kinds of animals living together. Each type of animal has a different shape and color to protect it from its predators. The sizes of these animals are also very different. Giraffes can grow to be 18 feet tall. A typical zebra is 4 feet tall at the shoulders. The African Elephant is about 10 feet tall at the shoulders.

The graph and table above give information about the heights and weights of three different animals that live in Africa.

1. Which animal weighs more: the male giraffe or the female giraffe? male giraffe

2. A zebra is about 4 feet tall. What is this height in meters? 1.22 meters

3. Is the heaviest male animal also the tallest animal? No

275

The scrap tires in this picture can no longer be used on cars. Each year about 250 million tires are scrapped. These tires are being recycled in different ways. For example, one tire can be recycled into about 2.5 gallons of oil. If every scrap tire from last year was recycled into oil, about how many gallons would be produced?

Caption 625,000,000 gallons of oil

Chapter 13 ▷ Graphs and Statistics

ESL Note Discuss the words describing types of graphs. Provide visual examples of each.

Words to Know

data	information gathered from surveys or experiments
graph	a visual display that shows data in different ways; includes bar, line, and circle graphs
pictograph	a graph that uses pictures to represent data
mean	sum of the data divided by the number of data; also called *average*
median	middle number when data are ordered from least to greatest
mode	number or numbers that appear most often in a set of data
histogram	a graph that shows how many times an event occurred
probability	the chance that an event will occur

Words to Know Compare and contrast the words *mean*, *median*, and *mode*.

Survey Graph Project

Write a survey question that can be answered by your classmates. For example, "What is your favorite flavor of ice cream?" List five possible answer choices. Post your question in the classoom. Have each student initial a choice. Then, use the data to make a graph. Display your results.

Learning Objectives

- Read and make pictographs, bar graphs, and line graphs.
- Read circle graphs and histograms.
- Find the mean, median, and mode of a set of data.
- Find simple probability.
- Solve problems about choosing a scale.
- Apply circle graphs to budgets.

Project Students may poll a second group for more data or to make a double bar graph. Have students adjust the scales on graphs after completing Lesson 13.6.

More Practice is provided in Exercise 118 of the *Workbook*.

13·1 ▶ Pictographs

Number Sense
Review rounding numbers to the nearest 100, 1,000, and 100,000.

Data is information gathered from surveys. A **graph** is a visual display of data. A **pictograph** uses pictures to show the data in the graph.

▶ **EXAMPLE**

Avoiding Errors
Point out that the numbers in the table can be rounded before deciding how much each symbol represents.

Make a pictograph of the data in the table.

Corporate Contributions	
Name	**Contribution**
Maco, Inc.	$467,565
SpaceLab	$630,241
Tobias Co.	$342,882
LMB Industries	$486,037

STEP 1 Choose a picture to represent the information. Assign a number to the picture. This is the key.

Key ▭ = $100,000

STEP 2 Round data to match the key.
Round to the nearest $100,000.

STEP 3 Draw the graph. Be sure to give your graph a title.

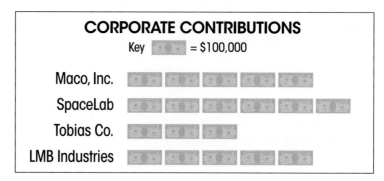

CORPORATE CONTRIBUTIONS
Key ▭ = $100,000

Maco, Inc.
SpaceLab
Tobias Co.
LMB Industries

Practice

Make a pictograph of the data in each table.

1. Round to the nearest hundred.

Summer Camp Attendance	
Name of Camp	**Attendance**
Voyagers	454
Camp White Water	638
Riding Camp	594
Safari Camp	719
Computer Camp	276

Summer Camp Attendance
Key ♀ = 100 campers

2. Round to the nearest thousand.

Automobile Sales	
Automobile	**Number Sold**
Subcompacts	5,014
Compacts	7,832
Midsized automobiles	4,910
Luxury automobiles	2,071

Automobile Sales
Key 🚗 = 1,000 cars

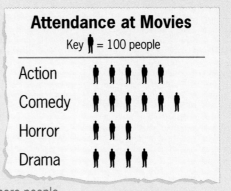

Everyday Problem Solving

Michael found this pictograph in the entertainment section of the newspaper.

1. Which type of movie do most people go to see? comedy

2. Which type of movie do the fewest number of people go to see? How do you know?
horror; it has the least number of stick figures.

3. About how many more people go to see comedies than dramas? about 200 more people

Attendance at Movies
Key ♀ = 100 people

Action ♂ ♂ ♂ ♂ ♂
Comedy ♂ ♂ ♂ ♂ ♂ ♂
Horror ♂ ♂ ♂
Drama ♂ ♂ ♂ ♂

Extra Practice for this lesson is provided on page 439.

13·2 Single Bar Graphs

A bar graph is a graph that uses bars to display data. The bars can be horizontal or vertical. Each bar stands for an item. The length of the bar shows the number of items you have.

EXAMPLE

Number Sense
Discuss the advantages of displaying data in a bar graph. Be sure students realize that the lengths of the bars visually show the size of the data.

Make a horizontal bar graph of the data in the table.

Cars in the Parking Lot	
Type of Car	Number
Honda	115
Chevrolet	90
Toyota	100
GM	65
Ford	80

STEP 1 Choose a scale. You need to show numbers from 65 to 115. Use intervals of 20.

Avoiding Errors
Discuss with students how to choose the appropriate range and interval size for the scale. Point out that 65 is halfway between 60 and 70 on the scale.

STEP 2 Write the names of the cars along the side. Write the intervals along the bottom.

STEP 3 Draw the bars to show the number of cars for each type.

STEP 4 Write a title for the graph and labels.

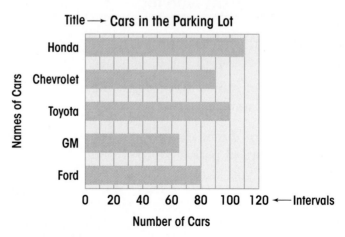

Practice

Common Error Students do not use equal intervals for the scale. Have students <u>skip count</u> the numbers for the intervals to verify the accuracy of the scale.

Make horizontal bar graphs of the data in each table.

1.

Speed of Pitches (miles per hour)	
Pitcher	Speed of Pitch
Oakley	75
Garcia	88
Wu	92
Vanderhoot	69
Turner	97

2.

School Enrollment	
School	Students
Franklin	150
Washington	250
Lincoln	375
Kennedy	225
Lee	100
Roosevelt	75

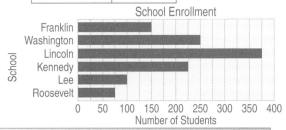

Everyday Problem Solving

Members of the Columbia School Science Club tested model rockets. They recorded the height of each rocket. This vertical bar graph displays their results.

1. How high did Rob's rocket go? 550 feet

2. How high did Deb's rocket go? 350 feet

3. Whose rocket reached a height of 325 feet? Ann's rocket

4. Whose rocket went the highest?
Sue's rocket

5. How much higher did Rob's rocket go than Tom's rocket? 150 feet

6. How much higher did Deb's rocket go than Ann's rocket? 25 feet

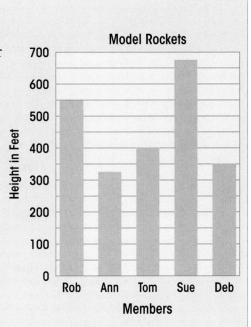

Extra Practice for this lesson
is provided on page 439.

More Practice is provided in Exercise 120 of the *Workbook*.

13·3 ▶ Double Bar Graphs

You can use a double bar graph to compare two different sets of data about the same thing.

▶ **EXAMPLE**

Make a horizontal double bar graph of the data below.

Number Sense
Have students bring in examples of double bar graphs found in newspapers and magazines. Display around the room.

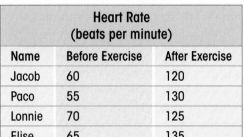

Heart Rate (beats per minute)		
Name	Before Exercise	After Exercise
Jacob	60	120
Paco	55	130
Lonnie	70	125
Elise	65	135

STEP 1 Choose a scale. You need to show numbers from 55 to 135. Use intervals of 25.

Avoiding Errors
Discuss how the size and range of data values affect the units and intervals used on the scale.

STEP 2 Write the names of the people along the side. Write the intervals along the bottom.

STEP 3 In one color, draw bars to show the heart rate before exercise. In another color, draw bars next to the first ones to show the heart rate after exercise.

STEP 4 Write a title for the graph and a key for the bars.

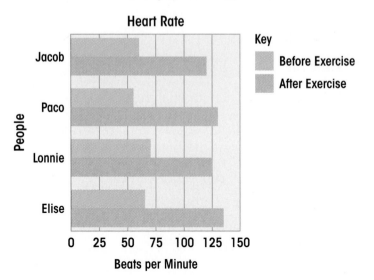

Common Error Students confuse columns. Have students copy the chart. Then, shade each column the way the data will be represented on the graph.

Make horizontal double bar graphs to display the data in each table.

1.

Baseball Games Won		
Team	1998	1999
Tigers	8	12
Sharks	10	14
Bulls	7	5
Volcanoes	9	9
Green Sox	15	11

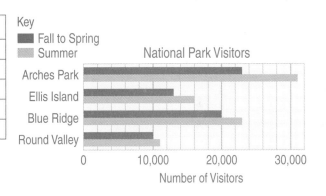

2.

National Park Visitors		
Location	Fall to Spring	Summer
Arches Park	23,000	31,000
Ellis Island	13,000	16,000
Blue Ridge	20,000	23,000
Round Valley	10,000	11,000

Everyday Problem Solving

The cinema shows three different movies.

1. How many tickets were sold for the 7:00 show of movie 1? 150 tickets

2. How many tickets were sold for the 5:00 show of movie 2? 175 tickets

3. For which movie were the most tickets sold? movie 3 at 7:00

Extra Practice for this lesson is provided on page 439.

More Practice is provided in Exercise 121 of the *Workbook*.

13-4 ▶ Single Line Graphs

Line graphs are used to show change, usually over a period of time. Data are plotted on the graph with dots. The dots are then connected by line segments.

▶ **EXAMPLE**

Make a line graph of the data in the table.

Rainfall	
Month	Inches of Rain
January	4.5
March	5.5
May	2.5
July	2.0
September	3.5
December	4.0

Number Sense

Bring in examples of line graphs from newspapers or magazines. Show the graphs to students, and discuss the components of a line graph and how to interpret the data shown by the graph.

STEP 1 Choose a scale. You need to show numbers from 2.0 to 5.5. Start at 0. Use intervals of 1.

STEP 2 Write the months along the bottom. Write the intervals along the side.

STEP 3 Put a dot above each month to show the inches of rain that fell that month.

Avoiding Errors

Encourage students to use graph paper to help align vertical and horizontal axes.

STEP 4 Connect the dots from left to right with a line.

STEP 5 Label the intervals. Write a title for the graph.

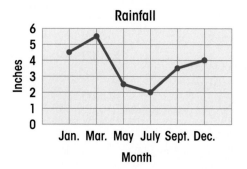

Practice

Common Error Students connect the points of the graph incorrectly. Be sure that students connect the points in order from left to right.

Make line graphs of the data in each table.

1.

Number of Songs Recorded	
Month	**Number**
January–February	175
March–April	250
May–June	200
July–August	150
September–October	300
November–December	100

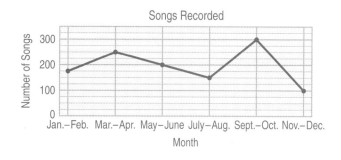

2.

Corn Prices	
Year	**Price (per Bushel)**
1983	$2.75
1986	$4.50
1989	$1.90
1992	$2.25
1995	$3.00
1998	$4.90

Everyday Problem Solving

The town of Centerville displayed this graph at its last parade.

1. When was the population greatest?
1994 and 1998

2. What was the population in 1992?
15,000 people

3. Between which years did the population decrease? How do you know?
1994 to 1996; the line goes down.

4. Between which years did the town have the greatest increase in population?
1992 to 1994

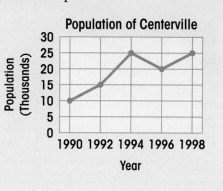

Extra Practice for this lesson is provided on page 440.

13-5 ▶ Double Line Graphs

A double line graph can be used to compare sets of related data.

▶ **EXAMPLE**

Number Sense
Discuss reasons to use a double line graph. Elicit examples.

Make a double line graph of the data in the table.

Population of the Twin Cities (Rounded Numbers)		
Year	St. Paul	Minneapolis
1960	75,000	125,000
1970	100,000	180,000
1980	110,000	240,000
1990	150,000	310,000

STEP 1 Choose a scale. You need to show numbers from 75,000 to 310,000. Use intervals of 50,000.

STEP 2 Write the years along the bottom. Write the intervals along the side.

Avoiding Errors
Make sure that students graph only one set of data points at a time. Remind them to connect the points for one set of data before plotting the second set of data.

STEP 3 In one color, put a dot above each year to show the population in St. Paul. In another color, put a dot to show the population in Minneapolis.

STEP 4 Connect the dots for each set of data. Be sure that there is a different color line for each city.

STEP 5 Write a title for the graph. Write a key for the lines.

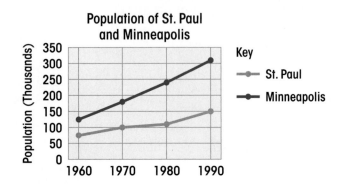

Practice

Common Error Students may not use the same color for one set of data. Have students shade each column with the same color they choose for the line representing the data.

Make double line graphs of the data in each table.

1.

Communication Requests		
Month	Phone	Fax
January	175	75
February	150	125
March	125	125
April	150	175
May	100	250

2.

Temperature		
Time of Day	Indoors	Outdoors
7:00 A.M.	55°	30°
10:00 A.M.	70°	35°
1:00 P.M.	70°	45°
4:00 P.M.	65°	40°

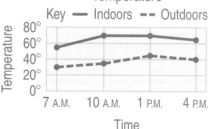

Everyday Problem Solving

Ray's Sport Shop sells snowboards and surfboards. This is a graph of the store's sales.

1. In which month are the most surfboards sold? June

2. In which month are the fewest snowboards sold? June

3. When are snowboard sales and surfboard sales about the same? March

4. How could a retail store that sells both items use this information? to decide how many of each item to order each month

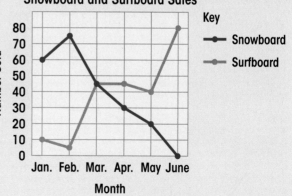

Extra Practice for this lesson is provided on page 440.

More Practice is provided in Exercise 123 of the *Workbook*.

13·6 Problem Solving: Choosing a Scale

EXAMPLE

Number Sense
Name situations in which a
person or company might use
a graph to influence people's
decisions.

Graphs can be drawn to present different messages.

Sports Palace wants to show that it sells more skates
than the competition. Which graph should it use
and why?

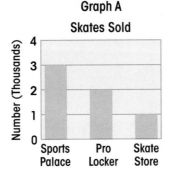

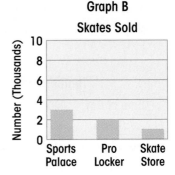

STEP 1   READ   What do you need to find out?
Which graph is better for Sports Palace?

STEP 2   PLAN   What do you need to do?
Look at each graph. Compare the lengh of the
bars in each graph.

Avoiding Errors
Point out the intervals used
for the scale of a graph.

STEP 3   DO   Follow the plan.
Look at Graph A. The number of skates Sports
Palace sold looks greater because the difference
between the lengths of the bars is greater.

STEP 4   CHECK   Does your answer make sense?
The scale in Graph A makes it appear as if the
sales are better.✓

Sports Palace should use Graph A.

Practice

READ the problems about the graphs shown. Make a PLAN.
DO the plan to solve the problems.

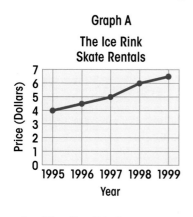

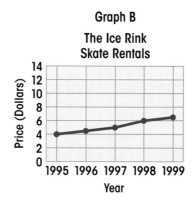

1. The Ice Rink wants to show customers that prices have
    not increased very much over five years. Which graph
    should it use and why? Graph B; scale is larger, so differences between prices look less.

2. The Ice Rink wants to show the owners that prices have
    increased a lot over 5 years. Which graph should it
    use and why? Graph A; scale is smaller, so differences between prices look greater.

Problem Solving Strategy

Graphs may be used to solve
multipart problems.

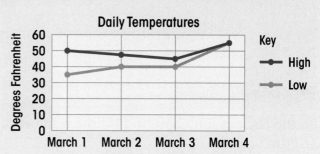

    What is the greatest
    difference between high
    and low temperatures
    shown in the graph?

Find the date with the greatest
temperature change. March 1
Subtract the low from the high temperature. $50° - 35° = 15°$

13·7 Circle Graphs

Number Sense
Bring in circle graphs from newspapers and magazines to compare and display around the classroom.

▶ **EXAMPLE**

Avoiding Errors
Remind students to move the decimal point two places to the left when changing a percent to a decimal.

Circle graphs are used to show how the total amount (100%) of something is divided into parts. You can compare amounts by comparing the sizes of the parts of the graph.

How many runners were 9 to 12 years old?

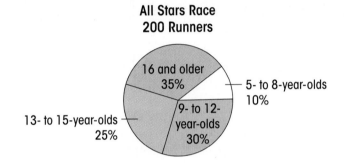

All Stars Race
200 Runners

16 and older 35%
5- to 8-year-olds 10%
13- to 15-year-olds 25%
9- to 12-year-olds 30%

STEP 1 Find out how much the whole circle represents.

200 runners

STEP 2 Find the percent of runners who were 9- to 12-year-olds.

30%

STEP 3 Multiply the percent of 9- to 12-year-olds by the total number of runners.

30% × 200 = .30 × 200
= 60

There were 60 runners that were 9 to 12 years old.

Common Error Students multiply the percent by the total without changing the percent to a decimal. Encourage students to make sure that their answers are reasonable.

Practice

Use the circle graph above to find the number of runners in each age group.

1. 5- to 8-year-olds 20 runners **2.** 13- to 15-year-olds 50 runners **3.** 16 and older 70 runners

4. A total of how many people are 13 and older? 120 runners

Extra Practice for this lesson is provided on page 441.

MATH IN YOUR LIFE
Making a Budget

The Browns' total monthly income is $2,000. The Browns made a monthly budget of what they spend.

They want to make a circle graph to show their budget. They need to find what percent each cost is of the total monthly income.

Part ÷ Whole × 100 = Percent

$240 ÷ $2,000 × 100 = 12%

↑ ↑
Utilities   Income

The yellow part of the circle graph is marked to show Utilities 12%.

Find the percents for each cost in the Browns' budget. Copy the circle graph. Label the circle graph with the costs and percents.

1. Housing 25%

2. Food 20%

3. Transportation 15%

4. Savings 5%

5. Recreation 10%

6. Other 13%

> **BROWNS' MONTHLY BUDGET OF $2,000**
>
> | | |
> |---|---|
> | Housing | $500 |
> | Food | $400 |
> | Transportation | $300 |
> | Utilities | $240 |
> | Recreation | $200 |
> | Other | $260 |
> | Savings | $100 |

Browns' Monthly Budget

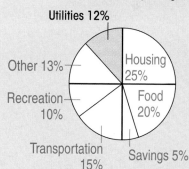

Utilities 12%
Other 13%
Recreation 10%
Transportation 15%
Housing 25%
Food 20%
Savings 5%

Critical Thinking

Next year, the Browns want to take a family vacation. They want to put more money in savings each month. How might they change their budget to save for vacation? Make a new graph that shows the new budget.

Critical Thinking

Answers may vary but should demonstrate an understanding that savings can be increased by decreasing another expense, preferably an unfixed cost, such as Recreation or Other.

More Practice is provided in Exercise 125 of the *Workbook*.

13·8 ▶ Mean (Average)

The **mean** is an average. The average is one way to describe the middle of a set.

To find the mean of a set of numbers, first add the numbers. Then, divide the sum by the number of numbers in the set.

$$\text{Mean} = \frac{\text{Sum of the numbers}}{\text{Number of numbers}}$$

The mean does not have to be a number in the set.

▶ **EXAMPLE 1**

Cindy's test grades in mathematics are 72, 85, 78, and 90. What is her mean test grade?

STEP 1 Find the sum of the numbers.

$72 + 85 + 78 + 90 = 325$

STEP 2 Count the number of numbers.

4 tests

STEP 3 Divide the sum by the number of numbers.

$\frac{325}{4} = 325 \div 4$
$= 81.25 \leftarrow$ Mean

Cindy's mean test grade is 81.25.

▶ **EXAMPLE 2**

Prices of CDs at Music Land are $8.50, $10.25, and $15. What is the mean price of the CDs?

STEP 1 Find the sum of the numbers.

$\$8.50 + \$10.25 + \$15.00 = \$33.75$

STEP 2 Count the number of numbers.

3 prices

STEP 3 Divide the sum by the number of numbers.

$\frac{33.75}{3} = 33.75 \div 3$
$= \$11.25 \leftarrow$ Mean

Music Land's mean CD price is $11.25.

Practice

Common Error Students divide by the wrong number. Encourage students to check the number of addends by recounting.

Find the mean of each set of numbers.

1. 4, 11, 23, 40 19.5

2. 54, 67, 110, 124, 145 100

3. 110, 110, 114, 130 116

4. 1, 3, 4, 5, 7, 8, 11, 12, 12 7

5. 54, 782, 1003 613

6. 78, 3, 47, 102, 78, 34 57

7. 12, 10, 8.5, 17.5 12

8. 60, 20, 24, 38, 56 39.6

9. 34, 40, 21, 52, 47 38.8

10. $1\frac{1}{2}$, 2, $3\frac{1}{2}$, 5 3

11. 125, 350, 275, 300, 225 255

12. $18.50, $25, $48.30, $42 $33.45

Everyday Problem Solving

Usef is shopping for a stereo set. He recorded these prices from his favorite stores.

1. What is the mean price? $94.50

2. Usef finds a new store where the stereo is $130. Will this new price increase or decrease the mean? increase

3. Next month, each store will have a sale. All the stereos will be half price. Will the mean price be half price? yes

4. Usef decides to buy the stereo at Wayne's Electronics. How much money is he saving by not buying at Stereo City? $18

STORE	PRICE
Sounds and More	$90
Wayne's Electronics	$87
Stereo City	$105
The Right Music	$96

Extra Practice for this lesson is provided on page 441.

More Practice is provided in Exercise 126 of the *Workbook*.

13-9 ▶ Median and Mode

Number Sense
Give students a visual reference for a median. Refer to the divider in the middle of a highway or road. Explain that a median refers to something that is in the middle.

The **median** is the middle number when a set of numbers is ordered from least to greatest.

3   5   8   10   14   16   19

↑
Median

If there is an even number of numbers, the median is the *average* of the two middle numbers.

▶ **EXAMPLE 1**

Remember
$\frac{23}{2} = 23 \div 2$

Find the median.   12   11   16   9   13   11

STEP 1 Arrange the numbers from least to greatest. Find the two middle numbers.

9   11   <u>11   12</u>   13   16
middle numbers

STEP 2 Find the average of the two middle numbers.

$\frac{11 + 12}{2} = \frac{23}{2} = 11.5$

The median is 11.5.

The **mode** is the number that occurs most often.

▶ **EXAMPLE 2**

Avoiding Errors
Remind students to put the numbers in order before finding the median and mode.

Find the mode.   4   3   1   7   7   1   7

STEP Find the number that occurs most often.

4   3   1   7   7   1   7

The mode is 7.

Sometimes, there is no mode.

12, 18, 25, 36, 48   ← There is no mode.

Sometimes, there is more than one mode.

2, 5, 5, 8, 9, 9, 10   ← There are two modes.

Practice A

Find the median of each set of numbers. Remember to put the numbers in order first.

1. 55, 43, 17, 73, 29 43

2. 171, 89, 138, 211, 146 146

3. 30, 20, 26, 24 25

4. 674, 592, 460, 630, 525 592

5. 106, 95, 100, 86 97.5

6. 4, 8, 9, 3, 2, 10, 7, 8, 5 7

7. 1.7, 6.5, 7.4, 9.9, 1.2 6.5

8. 11.6, 17.5, 18.9, 12.5 15

Practice B

Find the mode of each set of numbers. If there is not a mode, write *none*.

9. 19, 32, 7, 12, 19, 11 19

10. 24, 23, 23, 22, 24, 25, 21 23 and 24

11. 450, 402, 452, 405 none

12. 1.5, 2.5, 1.4, 3.7, 1.6, 3.7 3.7

Everyday Problem Solving

Mr. Jones saw this graph on the weather channel.

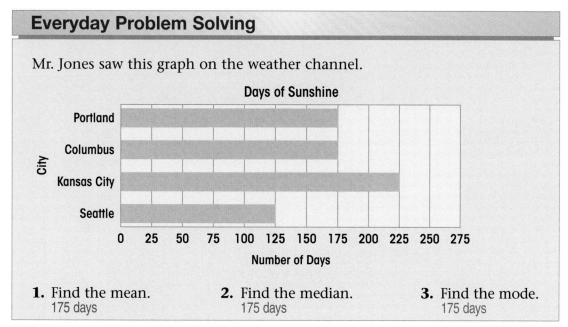

1. Find the mean.
175 days

2. Find the median.
175 days

3. Find the mode.
175 days

Extra Practice for this lesson is provided on page 441.

More Practice is provided in Exercise 127 of the *Workbook*.

 **Histograms**

A **histogram** is a graph that shows how many items occur between two numbers.

▶ **EXAMPLE**

Number Sense
Discuss the meaning and use of *interval*. Have students create intervals to show time ranges, money in a bank, and scores on a test.

Avoiding Errors
Point out that reading a histogram is similar to reading a bar graph.

A teacher asked 60 students how much time was spent doing homework last week. The histogram below is a graph of the data. How many students spent between 10 and 12 hours doing homework last week?

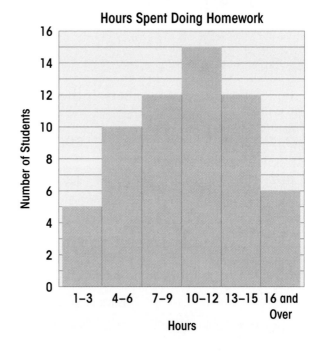

STEP 1 Find "10–12 hours" at the bottom of the graph.

STEP 2 The top of the bar shows the number of students who spent 10–12 hours doing homework.

STEP 3 Read the scale on the left.

Of the 60 students, 15 students spent between 10 and 12 hours doing homework last week.

Practice

Use the histogram below to answer Questions 1–5.

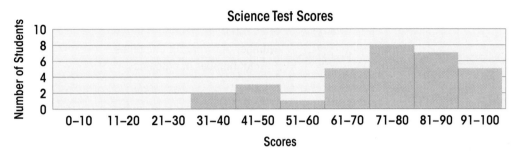

1. What does the histogram show? number of students receiving certain scores on a science test

2. How many students received a score between 81 and 90? 7 students

3. How many students received a score of 50 or below? 5 students

4. What scores were received most frequently? 71–80

Use the histogram below to answer Questions 6–10.

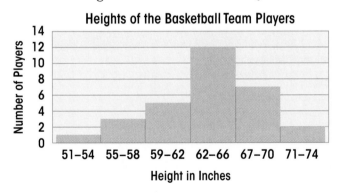

5. What does the histogram show? heights of the players on the basketball team

6. How many players are between 55 and 58 inches tall? 3 players

7. How many players are over 62 inches tall? 21 players

8. What is the total number of players on the basketball team? 30 players

Extra Practice for this lesson
is provided on page 442.

More Practice is provided in Exercise 128 of the *Workbook*.

13-11 ▶ Probability

Probability is the chance that something will happen. Probability is often written as a fraction.

$$\text{Probability} = \frac{\text{Number of favorable outcomes}}{\text{Total number of outcomes}}$$

▶ **EXAMPLE**

Number Sense
Discuss the probability of tossing a coin. You can toss either heads or tails. The probability of tossing heads is 1 out of 2 or $\frac{1}{2}$.

Avoiding Errors
Students should understand that the probability of an event can never be less than zero or greater than 1.

Dave spins a spinner. What is the probability that he will land on yellow?

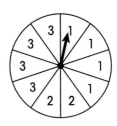

STEP 1 Count the number of yellow sections.   4 yellow sections

STEP 2 Count all the sections.   12 sections

STEP 3 Write the probability as a fraction. Reduce to lowest terms. $\frac{4}{12} = \frac{1}{3}$

The probability that Dave will spin yellow is $\frac{1}{3}$.

Common Error Students find the probability as the number of favorable outcomes divided by the number of unfavorable outcomes. Emphasize that the probability of an event is found by dividing by the total number of possible outcomes.

Practice

Find the probability of each outcome.
Be sure fractions are in lowest terms.

1. the probability of spinning a 1 $\frac{2}{5}$

2. the probability of spinning a 2 $\frac{1}{5}$

3. the probability of spinning a 3 $\frac{2}{5}$

4. the probability of spinning an odd number $\frac{4}{5}$

5. the probability of spinning an even number $\frac{1}{5}$

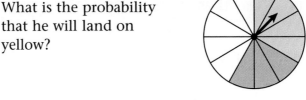

Extra Practice for this lesson is provided on page 442.

USING YOUR CALCULATOR
Showing Probability as a Decimal and a Percent

You can use a calculator to show the probability of an event as a decimal or a percent.

Max's school is selling raffle tickets for two CD players. Only 2 people can win. Exactly 80 tickets were sold. What is the probability of winning a CD player if someone buys one ticket?

$$\text{Probability} = \frac{\text{Number of winning tickets}}{\text{Total number of tickets sold}} = \frac{2}{80}$$

> **Calculator Tip**
> Remember not to clear the display after you find the decimal.

Show the probability of winning as a decimal.

PRESS $\boxed{2}$ $\boxed{\div}$ $\boxed{8}$ $\boxed{0}$ $\boxed{=}$ ⸺ 0.025

DO NOT clear the display.

A person who bought one raffle ticket has a .025 chance of winning a CD player.

Show the probability of winning as a percent.

PRESS $\boxed{\times}$ $\boxed{1}$ $\boxed{0}$ $\boxed{0}$ $\boxed{=}$ ⸺ 2.5

A person who bought one raffle ticket has a 2.5% chance of winning a CD player.

Show the probability of each event as a decimal and as a percent.

1. choosing a red marble 0.1, 10%

2. choosing a green marble 0.4, 40%

3. choosing a blue marble 0.25, 25%

4. choosing a white marble 0.2, 20%

5. choosing a yellow marble 0.05, 5%

data
graphs
histogram
mean
median
mode
pictograph
probability

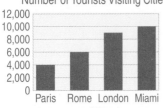

Number of Tourists Visiting Cities

LESSONS 13·1 to 13·5

Test Tip
To find the number of symbols in a pictograph row, divide the amount by the number represented by one symbol.

Vocabulary Review

Complete each sentence with a word from the list.

1. __?__ can be information from a survey. Data

2. The __?__ is the middle number in a set of numbers. median

3. The __?__ is found by adding the numbers and dividing by the number of numbers in the set. mean

4. __?__ is the chance that an event will occur. Probability

5. The __?__ is the number or numbers that occur most often in a set of numbers. mode

6. A __?__ and a __?__ are two types of __?__. pictograph, histogram, graphs

7. **Writing** What kind of graph will best display data showing the 10 longest rivers in the world? Explain.
   Possible Answer: bar graph

Chapter Quiz

Reading and Making Pictographs, Bar Graphs, and Line Graphs

1. In a pictograph,

   🧍 = 1,000 tourists.

   How many symbols are needed to show each amount in the table?
   Paris 4, Rome 6, London 9, Miami 10

City	Tourists
Paris	4,000
Rome	6,000
London	9,000
Miami	10,000

2. Make a bar graph using data from the table above.
   Answer in left margin above.

3. Make a line graph using the following data about weekly museum tourists: Answer in left margin.

Monday	400	Friday	600
Tuesday	300	Saturday	1,000
Wednesday	0	Sunday	0
Thursday	550		

LESSON 13·7

Test Tip
For circle graphs, change the percents to decimals and multiply by the total number.

Reading Circle Graphs
Use the graph to answer each question.

4. How many members are in the Football Club?

5. How many total members are in the Hockey and Baseball Clubs?

4. 60 members   **5.** 62 members

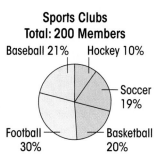

Sports Clubs
Total: 200 Members

Baseball 21%   Hockey 10%

Soccer 19%

Football 30%   Basketball 20%

LESSONS 13·8 and 13·9

Test Tip
Put a set of numbers in order before finding mean, median, or mode.

Finding Mean, Median, and Mode
Find the mean, median, and mode of each set of numbers.

6. 2, 6, 4, 5, 3, 7, 2, 6, 6, 8, 10, 12, 7

7. 12, 23, 33, 41, 12, 22, 22, 38, 40

6. mean = 6, median = 6, mode = 6

7. mean = 27, median = 23, mode = 22, 12

LESSON 13·11

Test Tip
Always reduce probability answers to lowest terms.

Finding Probability
Find the probability of each event.

8. choosing a yellow golf ball $\frac{1}{12}$

9. choosing a white golf ball $\frac{1}{3}$

10. choosing a pink golf ball $\frac{1}{4}$

11. choosing a green golf ball $\frac{1}{3}$

Group Activity   See the *Teacher Planning Guide* for a Scoring Rubric for this activity.

With your group, conduct a survey on a school issue. Interview friends, teachers, neighbors, and family. After the data have been recorded, organize them into one chart. Find the mean, median, and mode of the data. Then, display the data in a graph.

The Great Wall of China is the longest man-made object on Earth. Tourists can walk along the top of the wall. In some places, it is 25 feet high and 12 feet wide on top. The towers are 40 feet high. How much taller are the towers than the wall?

Caption 40 − 25 = 15 feet. The towers are 15 feet taller than the wall.

Chapter 14 ▷ Customary Measurement

ESL Note Because many foreign students have never studied this system of measurement, extra time will be needed to reinforce the vocabulary and basic facts that are common knowledge to most American students.

Words to Know

length	how long an object is
Customary System of Measurement	measurement units used in the United States
weight	how heavy an object is
capacity	how much space is in a container
elapsed time	the amount of time that has passed between two given times
degrees (°)	units used to measure temperature

Words to Know Give examples (16 feet, 25 pounds, 5 gallons, etc.), and ask students to quickly tell you if the measurement is an example of length, weight, or capacity.

Million Project

Work with a partner. Choose one of the questions below. Explain how you will find the answer.

- How long (in days) would it take to count to a million if you say one number each second?

- How much water (in gallons) is in a million drops?

- How much would a million pennies weigh (in pounds)?

Learning Objectives

- Change units of length, weight, capacity, and time.
- Find elapsed time.
- Find changes in temperature.
- Solve problems using customary measurements.
- Apply measurement to framing.

Project Provide necessary measuring tools, such as measuring cups, droppers, and an ounce scale. Let students use calculators, and have them clearly explain on their poster each step they took to reach their result. Have students make up their own "millions" question to solve.

More Practice is provided in Exercise 129 of the *Workbook*.

14·1 Length

The **length** of an object is how long it is. In the United States, objects are measured in the **Customary System of Measurement**. The customary units for length from smallest to largest are inch, foot, yard, and mile.

Useful Facts	
1 foot (ft)	= 12 inches (in.)
1 yard (yd)	= 36 inches
1 yard	= 3 feet
1 mile (mi)	= 5,280 feet

Smallest — in.
ft
yd
Largest — mi

Number Sense
Use manipulatives to show how to determine whether you should multiply or divide when changing between different measurement units.

You may need to change from one unit of measure to another in your daily life. To change a larger unit to a smaller unit, multiply.

EXAMPLE 1

Change $2\frac{1}{2}$ feet to inches.

Remember:
$2\frac{1}{2} = \frac{5}{2}$

STEP 1	Choose the fact you need.	1 foot = 12 inches
STEP 2	Decide whether to multiply or divide.	$2\frac{1}{2}$ feet to ■ inches larger to smaller: multiply
STEP 3	Multiply.	$2\frac{1}{2} \times 12 = \frac{5}{2} \times 12$ = 30

There are 30 inches in $2\frac{1}{2}$ feet.

To change a smaller unit to a larger unit, divide.

EXAMPLE 2

Change 5 feet to yards.

Avoiding Errors
Have students think of reference measures that are about 1 inch (length of a postage stamp), 1 foot (length of a shoebox), and 1 yard (width of a doorway) in length.

STEP 1	Choose the fact you need.	1 yard = 3 feet
STEP 2	Decide whether to multiply or divide.	5 feet to ■ yards smaller to larger: divide
STEP 3	Divide.	$5 \div 3 = 1\frac{2}{3}$

There are $1\frac{2}{3}$ yards in 5 feet.

Practice A

Multiply to change each measurement.

1. 2 feet = ■ inches 24

2. 5 yards = ■ feet 15

3. 2 yards = ■ inches 72

4. $2\frac{1}{2}$ miles = ■ feet 13,200

5. 8 feet = ■ inches 96

6. $9\frac{2}{3}$ yards = ■ feet 29

Divide to change each measurement.

7. 6 feet = ■ yards 2

8. 108 inches = ■ yards 3

9. 144 inches = ■ feet 12

10. 10,560 feet = ■ miles 2

11. 180 inches = ■ yards 5

12. 17 feet = ■ yards $5\frac{2}{3}$

Practice B

Change each measurement. First, decide whether to multiply or divide.

13. 12 yards = ■ feet multiply, 36

14. 100 inches = ■ feet divide, $8\frac{1}{3}$

15. 1,760 feet = ■ mile divide, $\frac{1}{3}$

16. 10 feet = ■ inches multiply, 120

17. 32 feet = ■ yards divide, $10\frac{2}{3}$

18. $3\frac{1}{2}$ yards = ■ inches multiply, 126

Everyday Problem Solving

Choose the best unit from the box to measure each object.

1. a pencil inches

2. a soccer field yards

3. a car feet

4. a highway miles

Unit Choices
inches
yards
feet
miles

Extra Practice for this lesson is provided on page 443.

More Practice is provided in Exercise 130 of the *Workbook*.

14·2 Weight

The **weight** of an object tells how heavy it is. The customary units of weight from smallest to largest are ounce, pound, and ton.

Number Sense
Use manipulatives to show the relationship between pounds and ounces. Discuss how to decide whether to multiply or divide when changing to larger or smaller units.

Useful Facts
1 pound (lb) = 16 ounces (oz)
1 ton (tn) = 2,000 pounds

Smallest   oz
lb
Largest   tn

To change a larger unit to a smaller unit, multiply.

EXAMPLE 1

Change 2.5 pounds to ounces.

STEP 1	Choose the fact you need.	1 pound = 16 ounces
STEP 2	Decide whether to multiply or divide.	2.5 pounds to ■ ounces larger to smaller: multiply
STEP 3	Multiply.	2.5 × 16 = 40

There are 40 ounces in 2.5 pounds.

To change a smaller unit to a larger unit, divide.

EXAMPLE 2

Change 3,000 pounds to tons.

Avoiding Errors
Have students think of reference measures that weigh about 1 ounce (a strawberry), 1 pound (football), and 1 ton (a small car).

STEP 1	Choose the fact you need.	1 ton = 2,000 pounds
STEP 2	Decide whether to multiply or divide.	3,000 pounds to ■ tons smaller to larger: divide
STEP 3	Divide.	3,000 ÷ 2,000 = 1.5

There are 1.5, or $1\frac{1}{2}$, tons in 3,000 pounds.

Practice A

Multiply to change each measurement.

1. 2 pounds = ■ ounces 32

2. 2 tons = ■ pounds 4,000

3. $4\frac{1}{2}$ pounds = ■ ounces 72

4. $3\frac{1}{2}$ tons = ■ pounds 7,000

5. 5.3 pounds = ■ ounces 84.8

6. 6.8 tons = ■ pounds 13,600

Divide to change each measurement.

7. 48 ounces = ■ pounds 3

8. 8,000 pounds = ■ tons 4

9. 104 ounces = ■ pounds 6.5

10. 6,400 pounds = ■ tons 3.2

11. 328 ounces = ■ pounds 20.5

12. 19,600 pounds = ■ tons 9.8

Practice B

Change each measurement. First, decide whether to multiply or divide.

13. 64 ounces = ■ pounds divide, 4

14. 3 tons = ■ pounds multiply, 6,000

15. 9 pounds = ■ ounces multiply,144

16. 12,000 pounds = ■ tons divide, 6

17. 160 ounces = ■ pounds divide, 10

18. 7.5 tons = ■ pounds multiply, 15,000

19. $\frac{5}{8}$ pound = ■ ounces multiply, 10

20. 1,000 pounds = ■ ton divide, $\frac{1}{2}$

Everyday Problem Solving

Choose the best unit from the box to measure each object.

1. small truck tons

2. bunch of strawberries ounces

3. chair pounds

4. raccoon pounds

Unit Choices
ounces
tons
pounds

Extra Practice for this lesson is provided on page 443.

More Practice is provided in Exercise 131 of the *Workbook.*

14·3 Capacity (Liquid Measure)

Capacity is the amount of space inside a container. Often, it is a measure for liquids. The customary units of liquid measure from smallest to largest are fluid ounce, pint, quart, and gallon.

Number Sense
Use manipulatives to illustrate the relationship between gallons, quarts, and pints. Show students how to determine whether they should multiply or divide when changing between different units.

Useful Facts	
1 pint (pt)	= 16 fluid ounces (fl oz)
1 quart (qt)	= 32 fluid ounces
1 quart	= 2 pints (pt)
1 gallon (gal)	= 4 quarts

Smallest → fl oz
pt
qt
Largest → gal

To change a larger unit to a smaller unit, multiply.

► EXAMPLE 1

Change $1\frac{1}{2}$ gallons to quarts.

Avoiding Errors
Have students think of reference measures that are about 1 fluid ounce (capacity of 2 tablespoons), 1 pint (small carton of milk), 1 quart (can of motor oil), and 1 gallon (large can of paint).

STEP 1 Choose the fact you need.   1 gallon = 4 quarts

STEP 2 Decide whether to multiply $1\frac{1}{2}$ gallons to ■ quarts
or divide.   larger to smaller: multiply

STEP 3 Multiply. $1\frac{1}{2} \times 4 = \frac{3}{2} = \frac{4}{1} = 6$

There are 6 quarts in $1\frac{1}{2}$ gallons.

To change a smaller unit to a larger unit, divide.

► EXAMPLE 2

Change 6 pints to quarts.

STEP 1 Choose the fact you need.   1 quart = 2 pints

STEP 2 Decide whether to multiply   6 pints to ■ quarts
or divide.   smaller to larger: divide

STEP 3 Divide. $6 \div 2 = 3$

There are 3 quarts in 6 pints.

Practice A

Common Error Students do not know whether to multiply or divide. Show students empty containers for a pint, a quart, and a gallon. This will help them understand the relative sizes of the units.

Multiply to change each measurement.

1. 4 quarts = ■ pints 8

2. 2 quarts = ■ fluid ounces 64

3. 3 pints = ■ fluid ounces 48

4. 5 gallons = ■ quarts 20

5. $4\frac{1}{2}$ quarts = ■ pints 9

6. $2\frac{1}{2}$ pints = ■ fluid ounces 40

Divide to change each measurement.

7. 12 quarts = ■ gallons 3

8. 10 pints = ■ quarts 5

9. 96 fluid ounces = ■ quarts 3

10. 11 pints = ■ quarts 5.5

11. 2 quarts = ■ gallon $\frac{1}{2}$

12. 12 fluid ounces = ■ pint $\frac{3}{4}$

Practice B

Change each measurement. First, decide whether to multiply or divide.

13. 4 pints = ■ quarts divide, 2

14. 16 quarts = ■ gallons divide, 4

15. 7 pints = ■ fluid ounces multiply, 112

16. 9 quarts = ■ pints multiply, 18

17. 80 fluid ounces = ■ quarts divide, 2.5

18. 24 fluid ounces = ■ pints divide,1.5

Everyday Problem Solving

Choose the best unit from the box to measure each object.

1. bathtub water gallons

2. large carton of milk quarts

3. juice glass fluid ounces

4. carton of cream pints

Unit Choices
fluid ounces
pints
quarts
gallons

Extra Practice for this lesson is provided on page 444.

14-4 ▶ Time

Number Sense
Give students a feeling for a second and a minute. Use a stopwatch to time each unit.

Remember:
To change a larger unit to a smaller unit, multiply. To change a smaller unit to a larger unit, divide.

Time is how long it takes for something to happen. You can measure time with a clock, a stopwatch, or a calendar. The units of time from smallest to largest are shown below.

Useful Facts	Smallest	sec
60 seconds (sec) = 1 minute (min)		min
60 minutes = 1 hour (hr)		hr
24 hours = 1 day		d
7 days (d) = 1 week (wk)		wk
52 weeks = 1 year (yr)		mo
12 months (mo) = 1 year	Largest	yr

▶ **EXAMPLE**

Avoiding Errors
Emphasize that the same rules of larger to smaller, multiply, and smaller to larger, divide, still hold true for the units of time.

Change $1\frac{1}{4}$ hours to minutes.

STEP 1 Choose the fact you need.   1 hour = 60 minutes

STEP 2 Decide whether to multiply or divide. $1\frac{1}{4}$ hours to ■ minutes
larger to smaller: multiply

STEP 3 Multiply. $1\frac{1}{4} \times 60 = \frac{5}{4} \times \frac{60}{1} = 75$

There are 75 minutes in $1\frac{1}{4}$ hours.

Common Error Students choose an incorrect fact to change the measurement. Have students write the facts on index cards for easy reference.

Practice

Change each measurement. First, decide whether to multiply or divide.

1. 3 days = ■ hours multiply, 72

2. 4 years = ■ months multiply, 48

3. 104 weeks = ■ years divide, 2

4. 360 minutes = ■ hours divide, 6

5. 49 days = ■ weeks divide, 7

6. 78 weeks = ■ years divide, $1\frac{1}{2}$

7. 90 seconds = ■ minutes divide, $1\frac{1}{2}$

8. 36 months = ■ years divide, 3

Extra Practice for this lesson is provided on page 444.

USING YOUR CALCULATOR
How Old Are You?

The question above can be answered in several ways.
A newborn baby might be 300 minutes old. A toddler
can be 380 days old.

Suppose that Rachel is 15 years, 3 months, and 12 days old.
About how old is she in days?

Remember that to change a larger unit to smaller
units, multiply.

Change 15 years to days.

PRESS   1 5 × 3 6 5 =   5,475

Change 3 months to days. Use 30 days = 1 month
to find about how many days.

PRESS   3 × 3 0 =   90

Add the extra 12 days.

PRESS   5 4 7 5 + 9 0 + 1 2 =   5,577

Rachel is 5,577 days old.

Use a calculator to solve each problem.

1. Jenna is 10 years, 2 months, and 5
   days old. How old is she in days?   3,715 days

2. Preston is 20 years, 7 months, and 10
   days old. How old is he in days?   7,520 days

3. How old are you in days?   Answers will vary.

> **Calculator Tip**
> After pressing
> equals, remember
> to write down the
> total and then
> clear the display.

More Practice is provided in Exercise 133 of the *Workbook*.

14-5 ▶ Problem Solving: Working with Units of Measure

Sometimes you need to regroup units of measure when you add or subtract quantities.

▶ **EXAMPLE**

Number Sense
Show students large and small containers. Discuss how many of a smaller container they think will fill a larger. Ask students to explain ways they might find out.

Avoiding Errors
Be sure that students change the quarts into gallons by dividing by 4.

Remember:
4 quarts = 1 gallon

Vince is using the recipe on the right to make punch for a party. Can he use a punch bowl that holds 2 gallons for his punch?

> **Party Punch**
> 3 quarts apple juice
> 3 quarts cherry juice
> 2 quarts white grape juice
> 1 quart club soda

STEP 1   READ   What do you need to find out?
You need to find out how much punch Vince is making.

STEP 2   PLAN   What do you need to do?
Add to find the total number of quarts. **Change** the quarts to gallons. To do this, divide by 4. Will the punch fit in the bowl? **Compare** the total to 2 gallons.

STEP 3   DO   Follow the plan.

Add.

$$\begin{array}{r} 3 \text{ quarts} \\ 3 \text{ quarts} \\ 2 \text{ quarts} \\ + 1 \text{ quart} \\ \hline 9 \text{ quarts} \end{array}$$

Divide.

$9 \text{ quarts} \div 4 = 2\frac{1}{4} \text{ gallons}$

Compare.

$2\frac{1}{4} > 2$

STEP 4   CHECK   Does your answer make sense?
No, 8 quarts is the same as 2 gallons, so 9 quarts is more than 2 gallons. ✓

Vince needs a punch bowl that holds more than 2 gallons of punch.

Common Error Students do not complete the entire problem. Encourage students to use their answer in the problem to check that it makes sense.

READ the problem. Answer the questions under PLAN. DO the plan to solve the problem.

1. Leroy made 2 gallons of chili on Saturday. He made 2 more gallons on Sunday, and 1 gallon on Monday. He wants to can the chili. He has 24 one-quart jars. Does he have enough jars to can all the chili? yes

   PLAN
   How many gallons of chili did Leroy make? 5 gallons
   How many quarts of chili did he make? 20 quarts

   DO
   2 gallons
   2 gallons
   + 1 gallon
   5 gallons

   5 gallons × 4 =
   20 quarts

2. A group of climbers were climbing 2 miles to the top of a mountain. On the first day, they climbed 1,650 feet. On the second day, they climbed 2,725 feet. On the third day, they climbed 5,750 feet. Did they reach the top of the mountain on the third day? no

   PLAN
   How many feet did they climb in 3 days? 10,125 feet
   How many feet to the top of the mountain? 10,560 feet

   DO
   1,650 feet
   2,725 feet
   + 5,750 feet
   10,125 feet

   2 × 5,280 =
   10,560 feet

Problem Solving Strategy

Sometimes, a picture helps you find the information you need.

Jane wants to frame a picture that is $1\frac{1}{2}$ feet wide and 2 feet long. Framing costs $3 per foot. How much will the framing cost? Fill in the blanks.

Draw a picture.

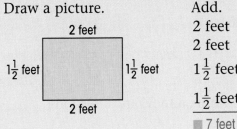

Add.
2 feet
2 feet
$1\frac{1}{2}$ feet
$1\frac{1}{2}$ feet
_____
■ 7 feet

Multiply.
$3
× ■ 7 feet
■ $21

The framing will cost ■. $21

More Practice is provided in Exercise 134 of the *Workbook*.

14·6 Elapsed Time

Elapsed time is the amount of time that has passed from one given time to another. To solve problems involving elapsed time, you subtract.

Sometimes, you will need to rename 1 hour (hr) to 60 minutes (min) in order to subtract.

▶ **EXAMPLE 1**

Jamal's math class starts at 9:40 A.M. and ends at 11:10 A.M. How long is he in math class?

Number Sense
Use the following example to show the necessity of changing between A.M. and P.M.:
From 11:00 A.M. to 1:00 P.M.
Incorrect: 11 − 1 = 10 hours
Correct: (1 + 12) − 11 = 2 hours

STEP 1 Set up a subtraction problem with hours and minutes. Write the later time first.

$$\begin{array}{r} 11 \text{ hr } 10 \text{ min} \\ -\ 9 \text{ hr } 40 \text{ min} \\ \hline \end{array}$$

STEP 2 Rename for more minutes. Subtract.

$$\begin{array}{r} \overset{10}{\cancel{11}} \text{ hr } \overset{70}{\cancel{10}} \text{ min} \\ -\ 9 \text{ hr } 40 \text{ min} \\ \hline 1 \text{ hr } 30 \text{ min} \end{array}$$

Jamal is in math class for 1 hour and 30 minutes.

Sometimes, the later time is after 12 noon or after 12 midnight. You will need to add 12 to the later time so that you can subtract.

▶ **EXAMPLE 2**

The Senior Prom begins at 8:00 P.M. and ends at 1:30 A.M. How long is the prom?

Avoiding Errors
Remind students that renaming can be done in two ways: 60 minutes for 1 hour, or adding 12 hours to change between A.M. and P.M.

STEP 1 Set up a subtraction problem. Write the later time first.

$$\begin{array}{r} 1\!:\!30 \text{ A.M.} \\ -\ 8\!:\!00 \text{ P.M.} \\ \hline \end{array}$$

STEP 2 Add 12 to the 1. Subtract.

$$\begin{array}{r} \overset{13}{\cancel{1}}\!:\!30 \text{ A.M.} \\ -\ 8\!:\!00 \text{ P.M.} \\ \hline 5\!:\!30 \end{array}$$

The prom is 5 hours and 30 minutes long.

Practice

Common Error The later time is subtracted from the earlier time. Emphasize that elapsed time is found by subtracting the earlier time from the later time.

Find the elapsed time.

1. 2:40 A.M. to 5:50 A.M.
3 hours 10 minutes

2. 7:20 A.M. to 8:35 A.M.
1 hour 15 minutes

3. 2:20 P.M. to 6:05 P.M.
3 hours 45 minutes

4. 3:48 P.M. to 7:12 P.M.
3 hours 24 minutes

5. 9:15 A.M. to 11:09 A.M.
1 hour 54 minutes

6. 5:29 P.M. to 8:03 P.M.
2 hours 34 minutes

7. 7:15 P.M. to 1:40 A.M.
6 hours 25 minutes

8. 9:18 P.M. to 3:45 A.M.
6 hours 27 minutes

9. 11:17 A.M. to 4:50 P.M.
5 hours 33 minutes

10. 1:11 A.M. to 6:30 A.M.
5 hours 19 minutes

11. 5:17 A.M. to 2:34 P.M.
9 hours 17 minutes

12. 11:25 P.M. to 3:05 A.M.
3 hours 40 minutes

Everyday Problem Solving

We use elapsed time every day.

1. How much time has elapsed from the time shown on Clock A to the time shown on Clock B? 6 hours 25 minutes

2. Paul put a roast in the oven at the time shown. The roast needs to be in the oven for 2 hours 20 minutes. When should Paul take the roast out of the oven? 5:20 P.M.

3. The plane departed from Denver. It arrived in Chicago at the time shown. The flight lasted 3 hours and 10 minutes. What time was it in Chicago when the plane departed? 10:10 A.M.

4. Luke went to sleep at the time shown. He awoke at 6:30 A.M. How long did he sleep? 8 hours 10 minutes

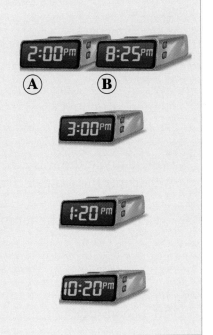

Extra Practice for this lesson is provided on page 445.

More Practice is provided in Exercise 135 of the *Workbook*.

14-7 ▶ Temperature

Number Sense
Using a real or paper thermometer, show students how to find the temperature. Temperature fell 18° from 82°. Temperature rose 12° from 45°.

Temperature is measured on a thermometer in degrees. A temperature of 43 degrees is written as 43°. The symbol for degree is °. A **rise** in temperature means an increase. You need to **add**. A **fall** in temperature means a decrease. You need to **subtract**.

▶ **EXAMPLE**

Avoiding Errors
Review basic facts for addition and subtraction.

The temperature was 59° in the morning. It rose 15° by afternoon. What was the temperature in the afternoon?

STEP 1 Decide whether to add or subtract.

It rose 15° means to add.

STEP 2 Add.

$$\begin{array}{r} 59° \\ + 15° \\ \hline 74° \end{array}$$

The temperature in the afternoon was 74°.

Common Error Students use the wrong operation in calculating the new temperature. Emphasize the clue words *rose, increased, fell, decreased,* or *dropped*. These words often tell whether to add or subtract.

Practice

Add or subtract to find the new temperature. To decide, look for the clue words *rise* and *fall*.

1. By noon, the temperature was 98°. By late afternoon, the temperature had <u>risen</u> 6°. What was the temperature in the late afternoon? 104°

2. The temperature was 22°. It <u>fell</u> 17° during the night. What was the temperature at the end of the night? 5°

3. In the morning, the temperature was 57°. It <u>rose</u> 10° four hours later. What was the temperature four hours later? 67°

4. In the morning, the temperature was 23°. In the afternoon, the temperature rose to 38°. How many degrees did it change? It rose 15°.

Extra Practice for this lesson is provided on page 445.

ON-THE-JOB MATH
Picture Framer

Pedro Lopez is a picture framer. He cuts, fits, and builds picture frames. Pedro enjoys his job, because he works with his hands to create something new from plain wood. He is always proud of his work.

First, he measures to find the length and width of the frame. Then, he adds to find how much wood he needs to buy altogether. Wood comes in feet, so he needs to change inches to feet.

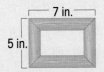

7 inches + 7 inches + 5 inches + 5 inches = 24 inches
24 inches ÷ 12 inches per feet = 2 feet

Pedro needs to buy 2 feet of wood.

Find the total amount of wood in feet for each frame.

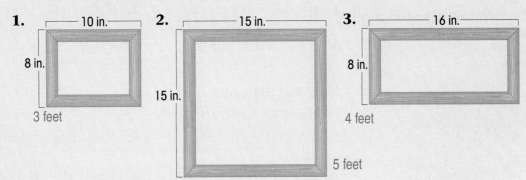

1. 10 in. / 8 in. / 3 feet

2. 15 in. / 15 in. / 5 feet

3. 16 in. / 8 in. / 4 feet

Critical Thinking

Pedro has a frame that is 14 inches long and 8 inches wide. He can only buy wood in whole-foot measurements. How much wood should he buy? Why?

Critical Thinking

He must buy 4 feet of wood so that he has enough for 44 inches of framing. There will be 4 inches left over.

capacity

Customary System of Measurement

degrees

elapsed time

length

weight

Vocabulary Review

Complete each sentence with a word from the list.

1. The temperature 14° means 14 __?__ . degrees

2. The __?__ of an object is a measure of how heavy it is. weight

3. The __?__ of an object is a measure of how long it is. length

4. In the United States, we use the __?__ . Customary System of Measurement

5. The amount that a cup can hold is called its __?__ . capacity

6. The __?__ from 7:00 A.M. to 9:00 A.M. is 2 hours. elapsed time

7. **Writing** Write a paragraph using all of the vocabulary words.

Chapter Quiz

LESSONS 14·1 to 14·3

Test Tip
To change a larger unit to a smaller unit, multiply. To change a smaller unit to a larger unit, divide.

Changing Lengths

Change each measurement.

1. 6 yards = ▦ feet
   18

2. 60 inches = ▦ feet
   5

3. 2,640 feet = ▦ mile
   $\frac{1}{2}$

4. 3 feet = ▦ inches
   36

Changing Weights

Change each measurement.

5. 1.6 tons = ▦ pounds
   3,200

6. 40 ounces = ▦ pounds
   2.5

7. 6,000 pounds = ▦ tons
   3

8. 3 pounds = ▦ ounces
   48

Changing Capacity

Change each measurment.

9. 3 pints = ▦ fluid ounces
   48

10. 6 pints = ▦ quarts
    3

11. 12 quarts = ▦ gallons
    3

12. 6 gallons = ▦ quarts
    24

Changing Time
Change each measurement.

13. 360 seconds = ■ minutes
6

14. 12 hours = ■ day
$\frac{1}{2}$

15. 7 weeks = ■ days
49

16. 3 years = ■ months
36

Solving Problems with Measurements
Solve.

17. Sharon left the house early to run some errands on her way to work. She spent $\frac{1}{2}$ hour in the bakery, 20 minutes at the dry cleaners, and 50 minutes driving to work. How long did it take her to get to work? 1 hour 40 minutes

Finding Elapsed Time
Find the elapsed time.

18. 2:38 P.M. to 3:55 P.M.
1 hour 17 minutes

19. 6:38 A.M. to 10:19 A.M.
3 hours 41 minutes

Finding Temperature
Find the change in temperature.

20. The temperature this morning was 65°. It rose 16° by the end of the day. What was the temperature at the end of the day? 81°

Group Activity
See the *Teacher Planning Guide* for a Scoring Rubric for this activity.

Plan a class picnic with your group. Use a grocery store ad from a newspaper to decide what foods to serve. Decide how much of each item you need. List the items and amounts using weight or capacity. Find the total weight or capacity of the picnic food.

Photo Provide the following speed limits (mixed up and out of order) in mph and km/hr. Tell students that 1 mile is about 1.6 kilometer. Challenge them to match up the pairs to make accurate "Think Metric" signs.

25 mph = 40 km/hr   55 mph = 88 km/hr   30 mph = 48 km/hr   65 mph = 104 km/hr

Measurements can be found all around you. This sign is showing the speed limit on a bridge in both customary and metric units. Speed limits are measured in miles per hour or in kilometers per hour. Which measurement on the sign is the metric measurement?

Caption The metric measurement is 70 km/hr.

Chapter 15 ▷ Metric Measurement

ESL Note Students may be more comfortable with the metric system than with the customary system. Review the meaning of the terms and relate them to their customary system counterparts.

Words to Know

metric system	the system of measurement based on the number 10 that is used in most countries
meter	the basic unit used to measure length
gram	the basic unit used to measure weight
liter	the basic unit used to measure liquid capacity
unit price	the cost of one item or one unit measure of an item

Words to Know Compare meter, gram, and liter with foot, pound, and gallon as basic units of measurement.

Metric Search Project

Look for metric measurements in different places. Try magazine and newspaper ads. Collect food labels that have both customary and metric units on them. Tell the class what types of items have metric units for measurements. Describe how the customary measurements compare with the metric. Write the items and measurements you find in your journal.

Project The project can be done in small groups or as a homework assignment. Have students store their examples in folders or in their journals. Students will be able to compare and estimate measurements after completing Lesson 15.5.

Learning Objectives

- Identify prefixes used in the metric system.
- Change metric units of length, mass, and liquid capacity.
- Compare metric and customary units of measurement.
- Solve problems using metric measurements.
- Apply metric measurements to finding the better buy.

More Practice is provided in Exercise 136 of the *Workbook*.

15·1 ▶ What Is the Metric System?

Number Sense
Review place values from 1,000 to .001.

The **metric system** is the system of measurement used by most countries. It is an easy system to use, because it is based on the number 10. There are three basic units. A **meter** is used to measure length. A **gram** is used to measure weight. A **liter** is used to measure capacity. Prefixes in front of a base tell you how many units there are.

Prefix	Value	Example	
kilo-	1,000	1 kilometer	= 1,000 meters
hecto-	100	1 hectometer =	100 meters
deka-	10	1 dekameter =	10 meters
deci-	.1	1 decimeter =	.1 meter
centi-	.01	1 centimeter =	.01 meter
milli-	.001	1 millimeter =	.001 meter

You can use the same prefixes for liters and grams.

▶ **EXAMPLE**

How many liters are in a kiloliter?

Avoiding Errors
To help students remember the order of the prefixes, create a sentence using the first letter of each prefix.

STEP 1 Find the prefix.   kiloliter

STEP 2 Determine the value of the prefix.   *Kilo* means 1,000.

There are 1,000 liters in a kiloliter.

Practice

Common Error The wrong power of 10 is chosen. Be sure that students use a ruler to help find the correct prefixes in the chart.

Answer each question. Use the chart above to help you.

1. How many grams in a kilogram? 1,000 grams

2. How many meters in a hectometer? 100 meters

3. How much of a meter is a centimeter? .01 meter

4. How much of a liter is a milliliter? .001 liter

MATH IN YOUR LIFE
Better Buy

Erica sees her favorite shampoo on sale. There are two different sizes. She wants to choose the size that will cost less per unit.

Erica needs to find the **unit price** of each bottle. The unit price is the price for 1 gram of shampoo. To find the price of 1 gram, she divides the price of the bottle by the number of units in the bottle.

Unit Price for Medium-size Bottle
$4.00 ÷ 400 grams = $.01 per gram
$.01 × 100 = 1¢ per gram

Unit Price for Large Bottle
$7.20 ÷ 600 grams = $.012 per gram
$.012 × 100 = 1.2¢ per gram

$4.00 $7.20

Erica chooses the medium-size bottle, because 1¢ per gram is less than 1.2¢ per gram.

Tell which item is the better buy.

1.

4 L for	3 L for
$2.90	$2.15

71.6¢ per liter;
3 liters for $2.15

2.

200 g for	100 g for
$1.00	$.55

.5¢ per gram;
200 grams for $1.00

3.

5 kg for	12 kg for
$3.80	$9.00

75¢ per kilogram;
12 kilograms for $9.00

Critical Thinking
Many supermarkets display the unit price of each item on the shelf label. How would this help Erica choose her purchases?

Critical Thinking
Erica could compare the unit prices shown and choose the better buy.

More Practice is provided in Exercise 137 of the *Workbook*.

15·2 ▶ Length

In the metric system, the meter is used to measure length. All other measures of length are based on the meter.

Useful Facts		
1 kilometer (km)	= 1,000 meters (m)	**Largest** km
1 hectometer (hm)	= 100 meters	hm
1 dekameter (dam)	= 10 meters	dam
1 meter	= 1 meter	m
10 decimeters (dm)	= 1 meter	dm
100 centimeters (cm)	= 1 meter	cm
1,000 millimeters (mm)	= 1 meter	**Smallest** mm
10 millimeters	= 1 centimeter	

To change a larger unit to a smaller unit, multiply.

▶ **EXAMPLE 1**

Change 1.2 kilometers to meters.

STEP 1 Choose the fact you need.   1 kilometer = 1,000 meters

STEP 2 Decide whether to   1.2 kilometers to ■ meters
multiply or divide.   larger to smaller: multiply

STEP 3 Multiply. $1.2 \times 1,000 = 1,200$

There are 1,200 meters in 1.2 kilometers.

To change a smaller unit to a larger unit, divide.

▶ **EXAMPLE 2**

Change 30 millimeters to centimeters.

STEP 1 Choose the fact you need.   10 millimeters = 1 centimeter

STEP 2 Decide whether to   30 millimeters to ■ centimeters
multiply or divide.   smaller to larger: divide

STEP 3 Divide. $30 \div 10 = 3$

There are 3 centimeters in 30 millimeters.

Practice

Common Error The decimal point is incorrectly placed in the answer. Review proper placement when multiplying or dividing by a power of 10.

Multiply to change each measurement.

1. 3 kilometers = ■ meters 3,000

2. 5 meters = ■ centimeters 500

3. 4 hectometers = ■ meters 400

4. 2 meters = ■ millimeters 2,000

5. 4 centimeters = ■ millimeters 40

6. 2.1 meters = ■ centimeters 210

Divide to change each measurement.

7. 50 centimeters = ■ meter .5

8. 3,400 meters = ■ kilometers 3.4

9. 6,000 millimeters = ■ meters 6

10. 10 centimeters = ■ meter .1

11. 1,700 meters = ■ kilometers 1.7

12. 5 millimeters = ■ centimeter .5

Everyday Problem Solving

Give the length of each item below in centimeters and meters.

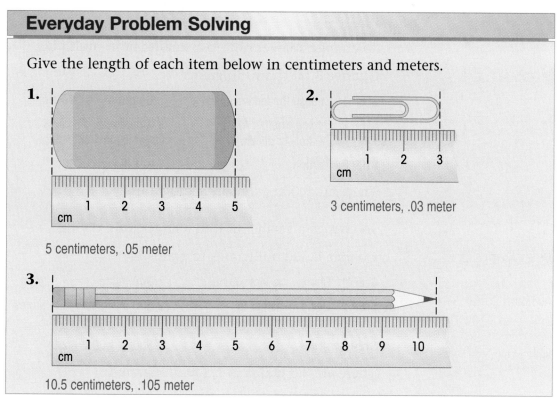

1.

5 centimeters, .05 meter

2.

3 centimeters, .03 meter

3.

10.5 centimeters, .105 meter

Extra Practice for this lesson is provided on page 446.

More Practice is provided in Exercise 138 of the *Workbook*.

15·3 ▶ Mass

The gram is used to measure mass. At the earth's surface, the mass and the weight of an object are considered to be the same.

Useful Facts	
1 kilogram (kg)	= 1,000 grams (g)
1 hectogram (hg)	= 100 grams
1 dekagram (dag)	= 10 grams
1 gram	= 1 gram
10 decigrams (dg)	= 1 gram
100 centigrams (cg)	= 1 gram
1,000 milligrams (mg)	= 1 gram
10 milligrams	= 1 centigram

Largest   kg
           hg
           dag
           g
           dg
           cg
Smallest   mg

To change a larger unit to a smaller unit, multiply.

▶ **EXAMPLE 1**

Change 3 kilograms to grams.

STEP 1	Choose the fact you need.	1 kilogram = 1,000 grams
STEP 2	Decide whether to multiply or divide.	3 kilograms to ▪ grams larger to smaller: multiply
STEP 3	Multiply.	3 × 1,000 = 3,000

There are 3,000 grams in 3 kilograms.

To change a smaller unit to a larger unit, divide.

▶ **EXAMPLE 2**

Change 2,500 milligrams to grams.

STEP 1	Choose the fact you need.	1,000 milligrams = 1 gram
STEP 2	Decide whether to multiply or divide.	2,500 milligrams to ▪ grams smaller to larger: divide
STEP 3	Divide.	2,500 ÷ 1,000 = 2.5

There are 2.5 grams in 2,500 milligrams.

Practice

Multiply to change each measurement.

1. 11 grams = ▦ milligrams 11,000

2. 4.9 kilograms = ▦ grams 4,900

3. 2.8 grams = ▦ centigrams 280

4. 3.8 grams = ▦ decigrams 38

5. .5 gram = ▦ milligrams 500

6. 2.3 kilograms = ▦ grams 2,300

Divide to change each measurement.

7. 900 milligrams = ▦ gram .9

8. 7,700 grams = ▦ kilograms 7.7

9. 400 centigrams = ▦ grams 4

10. 4,500 grams = ▦ kilograms 4.5

11. 50 grams = ▦ dekagrams 5

12. 200 grams = ▦ hectograms 2

Everyday Problem Solving

Use the nutrition fact label to answer the questions below. Grams are abbreviated as g, and milligrams are abbreviated as mg.

1. How many <u>milligrams</u> of total fat are in one serving of crackers? Multiply. 4,500 mg

2. How many <u>grams</u> of sodium are in one serving of crackers? Divide. .29 g

3. How many <u>milligrams</u> of protein are contained in one serving of crackers? 2,000 mg

4. Is there more sodium than protein in one serving of crackers? Explain your answer. No; 290 mg of sodium is less than 2,000 mg of protein.

Nutrition Facts	
1 Serving = 1 Cracker	
Total fat	4.5g
Sodium	290m
Total carbohydrates	21g
Protein	2g

Extra Practice for this lesson is provided on page 446.

15·4 Capacity (Liquid Measure)

Number Sense
Have students think of reference measures that are about 1 kiloliter (twice the capacity of a bathtub), 1 liter (a carton of milk), and 1 milliliter (a drop from an eyedropper).

The liter is used to measure liquid capacity. All other measures of liquid capacity are based on the liter.

Useful Facts		
1 kiloliter (kL)	= 1,000 liters (L)	**Largest** kL
1 hectoliter (hL)	= 100 liters	hL
1 dekaliter (daL)	= 10 liters	daL
1 liter	= 1 liter	L
10 deciliters (dL)	= 1 liter	dL
100 centiliters (cL)	= 1 liter	cL
1,000 milliliters (mL)	= 1 liter	**Smallest** mL
10 milliliters	= 1 centiliter	

To change a larger unit to a smaller unit, multiply.

► EXAMPLE 1

Change $1\frac{1}{2}$ kiloliters to liters.

STEP 1	Choose the fact you need.	1 kiloliter = 1,000 liters
STEP 2	Decide whether to multiply or divide.	$1\frac{1}{2}$ kiloliters to ▧ liters larger to smaller: multiply
STEP 3	Multiply.	$1\frac{1}{2} \times 1,000 = 1.5 \times 1,000 = 1,500$

There are 1,500 liters in $1\frac{1}{2}$ kiloliters.

To change a smaller unit to a larger unit, divide.

► EXAMPLE 2

Change 3,200 milliliters to liters.

STEP 1	Choose the fact you need.	1,000 milliliters = 1 liter
STEP 2	Decide whether to multiply or divide.	3,200 milliliters to ▧ liters smaller to larger: divide
STEP 3	Divide.	$3,200 \div 1,000 = 3.2$

Avoiding Errors
Point out the similarity in changing metric units. The prefixes remain the same; only the basic unit changes.

There are 3.2 liters in 3,200 milliliters.

Practice

Common Error Incorrect facts are chosen to change the measurements. Have students write the facts on index cards for easy reference.

Multiply to change each measurement.

1. 3 kiloliters = ■ liters 3,000

2. 3.4 liters = ■ milliliters 3,400

3. 4 liters = ■ milliliters 4,000

4. 55 liters = ■ milliliters 55,000

5. 6 liters = ■ milliliters 6,000

6. 4.7 liters = ■ dekaliters 47

Divide to change each measurement.

7. 60 deciliters = ■ liters 6

8. 9,300 liters = ■ kiloliters 9.3

9. 2,900 milliliters = ■ liters 2.9

10. 5,800 liters = ■ kiloliters 5.8

11. 800 liters = ■ hectoliters 8

12. 15,000 milliliters = ■ liters 15

Everyday Problem Solving

Beverage containers always show their capacity.

1. How many milliliters of juice are in the apple juice bottle? 1,890 milliliters

2. How many liters of cola are in the soda can? .34 liters

3. Is the amount of the sports drink greater than or less than a half liter? Explain.
less; 473 milliliters is .473 liter, which is less than .5 liter.

4. How many more milliliters of beverage are in the apple juice bottle than in the water bottle? 390 milliliters

340 milliliters   473 milliliters

1.5 liter   1.89 liter

Extra Practice for this lesson is provided on page 446.

More Practice is provided in Exercise 140 of the *Workbook*.

15·5 **Comparing Metric and Customary Measurements**

You can use either customary or metric units to describe the length, weight, or capacity of an item.

► **EXAMPLE**

Number Sense
Give students a sense of inch and centimeter lengths. Have them measure items around the classroom with both metric and customary rulers.

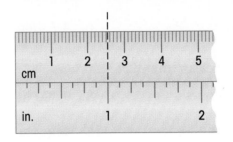

2.5 centimeters is about 1 inch.

1 liter is about 1 quart.

Avoiding Errors
Emphasize the difference between exact measurements and approximate measurements.

1.6 kilometers is about 1 mile.

28 grams is about 1 ounce.

Common Error An unrelated unit measurement is used for the equivalent expression. Have students determine whether the given quantity is a measure of weight, length, or capacity and then choose the conversion units accordingly.

Practice

Complete each sentence.

1. 5 centimeters is about 2 __?__.
  inches

2. 2 liters is about 2 __?__.
  quarts

3. 8 kilometers is about 5 __?__.
  miles

4. 56 grams is about 2 __?__.
  ounces

5. 10 centimeters is about 4 __?__.
  inches

6. 4 liters is about 4 __?__ or 1 __?__.
  quarts, gallon

7. 16 kilometers is about 10 __?__.
  miles

8. 14 grams is about $\frac{1}{2}$ __?__.
  ounce

USING YOUR CALCULATOR
Changing Measurements

You can use a calculator to change between metric and customary measurements.

Use the chart to the right to find the fact you need. Then, follow the instructions.

Change 14 inches to centimeters.

PRESS [1] [4] [×] [2] [.] [5] [4] [=] [____35.56]

There are 35.56 centimeters in 14 inches.

Change each measure. Use a calculator and a fact from the chart.

1. Change 4 feet to centimeters.
   121.92 centimeters

2. Change 22 pounds to kilograms.
   9.9792 kilograms

3. Change 26 pints to liters.
   12.3032 liters

4. Change 20 gallons to liters.
   75.7 liters

5. Change 12 inches to centimeters.
   30.48 centimeters

6. Change 17 yards to meters.
   15.5448 meters

7. Change 16 quarts to liters.
   15.1424 liters

8. Change 32 miles to kilometers.
   51.488 kilometers

inches x 2.54 → centimeters

feet x 30.48 → centimeters

yards x .9144 → meters

miles x 1.609 → kilometers

pints x .4732 → liters

quarts x .9464 → liters

gallons x 3.785 → liters

pounds x .4536 → kilograms

Calculator Tip

When you enter numbers to multiply, always check to be sure they are correct. Incorrect numbers will give you the wrong product!

Which is greater? Use a calculator and a fact from the chart.

9. 25 miles or 25 kilometers?
   25 miles

10. 6 yards or 6 meters?
    6 meters

11. 10 quarts or 10 liters?
    10 liters

12. 15 pounds or 15 kilograms?
    15 kilograms

More Practice is provided in Exercise 141 of the *Workbook*.

15·6 Problem Solving: Two-Part Problems

Some word problems are solved by working on one part at a time.

EXAMPLE

Number Sense
Have students read only the measurement units in the problem to emphasize the changes required.

Avoiding Errors
Be sure students complete each step before moving to the next step.

Marlene bought 2 kilograms of flour. She used 250 grams of flour on Saturday. On Sunday, she used 50 grams, and on Tuesday, she used 300 grams. How many kilograms of flour are left?

STEP 1 **READ   What do you need to find out?**
You need to find out how many kilograms of flour were left. But first, you need to find how much flour Marlene used.

STEP 2 **PLAN   What do you need to do?**
Add to find out how much flour Marlene used.
Subtract to find out how many grams were left.

STEP 3 **DO   Follow the plan.**

Add	Subtract
250 grams	Change 2 kilograms to 2,000 grams
50 grams	2,000 grams
+ 300 grams	− 600 grams
600 grams	1,400 grams or 1.4 kilograms

STEP 4 **CHECK   Does your answer make sense?**
Is your answer less than what Marlene started with? 1,400 grams is less than 2,000 grams. ✓

Marlene has 1.4 kilograms of flour left.

Problem Solving

READ the problem. Answer the questions under PLAN. DO the plan to solve the problem.

1. The vocational school is building a new 400-meter running track. The first day, 130 meters of track were laid. The second day, 110 meters were laid. On the third day, 90 meters of track were laid. How many meters of track are left to lay?   400 meters − 330 meters = 70 meters

   DO
   130 meters
   110 meters
   + 90 meters
   ──────────
   330 meters

   PLAN
   How many meters of track were laid in 3 days? 330 meters
   How many meters of track are left to lay? 70 meters

2. Marlene made 1 liter of lemonade for herself and her friends. She drank 200 milliliters. One friend drank 350 milliliters. Another friend drank 175 milliliters. How much lemonade is left?   1,000 milliliters − 725 milliliters = 275 milliliters

   DO
   1 liter = 1,000 milliliters
   200 milliliters
   350 milliliters
   + 175 milliliters
   ──────────────
   725 milliliters

   PLAN
   How many milliliters in 1 liter? 1,000 milliliters
   How many milliliters did the 3 friends drink altogether? 725 milliliters
   How many milliliters were left after they all drank their lemonade? 275 milliliters

Problem Solving Strategy

Sometimes, making a table can help you solve a problem.

Al's fruit drink has .5 liter of seltzer for every 2.5 liters of grape juice. How many liters of seltzer are needed to make 12 liters of fruit drink?

Copy the table. Fill in the blanks.

Seltzer	.5	?1	1.5	?2
Grape juice	2.5	5	7.5	?10
Fruit drink	3	?6	9	?12

gram
liter
meter
metric system
unit price

Vocabulary Review

Match a word from the list to its description.

1. A system of measurement based on the number 10. metric system

2. A basic unit of length. meter

3. The price of one unit of an item. unit price

4. A basic unit of mass. gram

5. A basic unit of liquid capacity. liter

6. **Writing** Make a sentence with each vocabulary word. Each sentence should give an example of something that is measured with the given unit.

Chapter Quiz

Identifying Prefixes

LESSON 15·1

Test Tip
The prefix tells how many of a unit. The suffix tells the type of unit.

Answer each question.

1. How many liters in a kiloliter? 1,000

2. How many grams in a dekagram? 10

3. How much of a meter is a millimeter? .001

4. How much of a liter is a centiliter? .01

5. How many meters in a kilometer? 1,000

Changing Metric Units

LESSONS 15·2 to 15·4

Test Tip
To change a larger unit to a smaller unit, multiply. The prefix tells how many of a unit. The suffix tells the type of unit.

Change each measurement.

6. 4 liters = ▪ milliliters 4,000

7. 45 meters = ▪ kilometer .045

8. 10 kilometers = ▪ meters 10,000

9. 7,600 milligrams = ▪ grams 7.6

10. 19.2 meters = ▪ centimeters 1,920

11. .008 kilogram = ▮ milligrams 8,000

12. 250 grams = ▮ kilogram .25

13. .012 kilometer = ▮ centimeters 1,200

14. 15,000 liters = ▮ kiloliters 15

15. 7,100 milliliters = ▮ liters 7.1

LESSON 15·5

Test Tip
2.5 centimeters → 1 inch
1 liter → 1 quart
1.6 kilometers → 1 mile
28 grams → 1 ounce

Comparing Metric and Customary Units
Complete each sentence.

16. 5 ounces is about __?__ grams. 140

17. 3 miles is about __?__ kilometers. 4.8

18. 8 inches is about __?__ centimeters. 20

19. 8 liters is about __?__ quarts. 8

LESSON 15·6

Test Tip
Solve by working on one part of the problem at a time.

Problem Solving
Solve.

20. Scott bought 2.5 kilograms of peanuts, pecans, and walnuts. There were 470 grams of peanuts and 780 grams of pecans. How many grams were walnuts? 1,250 grams

Group Activity See the *Teacher Planning Guide* for a Scoring Rubric for this activity.
With your group, make a Tourist's Guide on using the metric system while traveling. The guide should help travelers understand the different metric units they might see. Assume that they know nothing at all about the metric system. The guide should provide diagrams. It should be clearly written and easy to understand.

Many artists use geometry in their work. This sculpture is a solid shape called a cube. What flat shapes do you see?

336   Chapter 16 • Geometry

Caption Students may see a square, rectangle, circle, or oval. Some may notice that the circle is actually a cylinder.

Chapter 16 ▷ Geometry

ESL Note Geometry vocabulary is similar in many languages. Have students identify words in the list below that have the same roots as words in their native language.

Words to Know

angle	figure formed by two rays with the same endpoint
protractor	a tool used to measure angles
polygons	plane figures with three or more sides; examples are *triangles*, *quadrilaterals*, *pentagons*, *hexagons*, and *octagons*
perimeter	the distance around a figure
area	the amount of space inside a figure
parallelogram	a quadrilateral whose opposite sides are parallel; examples are *rectangles* and *squares*
circumference	the distance around a circle
radius	the distance from the center of a circle to its edge
space figure	a three-dimensional figure that has length, width, and height
volume	the amount of space inside a three-dimensional figure

Words to Know Have students come up with categories to place the words in, such as flat shapes, 3-D shapes, and measurements.

Box Project

Find a box of any size, and number its sides 1 to 6. Keep a record of the lengths of each side, the perimeter and area of each side, and the volume of your box.

Project This project can be done individually or in groups. The recorded measurements can be kept in a journal, and the boxes can be displayed.

Learning Objectives

- Recognize points and lines.
- Use a protractor and calculate angles in a triangle.
- Identify polygons.
- Find perimeter, circumference, area, and volume.
- Solve area word problems.
- Apply angle measurement to physical therapy.

More Practice is provided in Exercise 142 of the *Workbook*.

16·1 ▶ Points and Lines

The table below shows the basic figures in geometry.

Figure	Picture	Name
A **point** is a location in space.	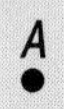 A •	point A
A **line** is made up of many points. It extends endlessly in both directions.	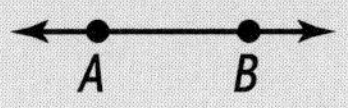 A B	line AB
A **line segment** is a part of a line. It has two endpoints.	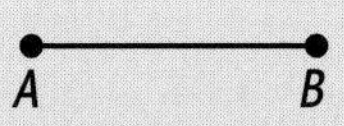 A B	line segment AB
A **ray** is part of a line. It has one endpoint. When you name a ray, name the endpoint first.	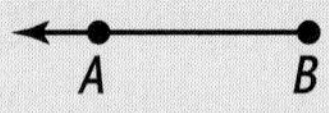 A B	ray BA

You can use the chart to identify the basic figures.

Name the figure on the right.

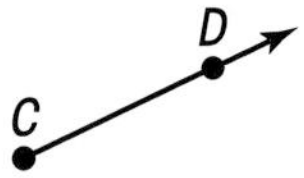

▶ **EXAMPLE**

STEP 1 Match the given figure to a figure in the chart above. → One endpoint ray –

STEP 2 Name the figure. → Ray CD

The figure is ray *CD*.

When you name a ray, you name the endpoint first.

Practice A

Common Error Lines and line segments are often confused. Point out that lines extend in both directions, as indicated by the arrows.

Name each figure. Write *point*, *line*, *line segment*, or *ray*.

1. ray *RS*

2. •A point *A*

3.  line *XY* or line *YX*

4. 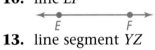 ray *SR*

5. ray *MN*

6. line *QR* or line *RQ*

7. •M point *M*

8. E F line segment *EF* or line segment *FE*

9. B C line segment *BC* or line segment *CB*

Practice B

Draw and label a picture for each name.

10. line *EF*
E F

11. ray *LM*
L M

12. point *X* •X

13. line segment *YZ*
Y Z

14. ray *YZ*
Y Z

15. ray *ZY*
Y Z

16. point *Q*
•Q

17. line *AB*
A B

18. line segment *GH*
G H

Everyday Problem Solving

Trace the drawing. Find points, lines, line segments, and rays.
Answers will vary. Check students' responses.

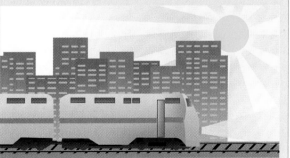

More Practice is provided in Exercise 143 of the *Workbook*.

16·2 Measuring Angles

Spatial Sense
Hold two rulers together to form various angles. Begin by showing the students a 90° angle. Then ask whether subsequent angles are greater than 90° or less than 90°.

An **angle** is formed by two rays with the same endpoint. The endpoint is called the vertex of the angle.

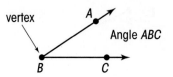

You measure the space between the two rays with a **protractor**. An angle is measured in degrees. The symbol for degrees is °.

▶ **EXAMPLE 1**

Measure angle *ABC*.

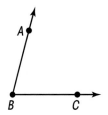

STEP 1   Place the center of the protractor's straight edge on the vertex. One ray must pass through 0° on the protractor.

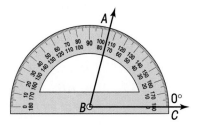

STEP 2   Read the number of degrees where the second ray crosses the protractor. Use the scale that reads 0° on the first ray.

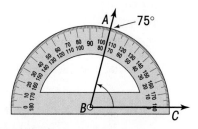

Angle *ABC* measures 75°.

Use the other scale on the protractor to measure angles that open to the left.

Measure angle *DEF*.

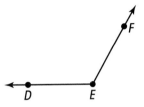

Avoiding Errors
Have students decide whether the angle is open on the right or open on the left before measuring. This will help them use the correct scale on the protractor.

STEP 1 Place the center of the protractor's straight edge on the vertex. One ray must pass through 0° on the protractor.

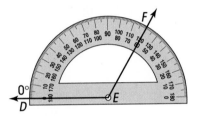

STEP 2 Read the number of degrees where the second ray crosses the protractor. Use the scale that reads 0° on the first ray.

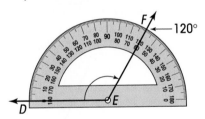

Angle *DEF* measures 120°.

Common Error If the angle is drawn smaller than the protractor, students often do not know how to position the protractor. Have students trace the angle onto their paper, and then extend the rays for an inch or two.

Practice

Use a protractor to measure each angle.

1. 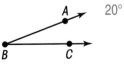 20°

2. 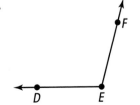 105°

3.  65°

More Practice is provided in Exercise 144 of the *Workbook*.

16·3 ▶ Drawing Angles

You can use a protractor to draw angles.

▶ **EXAMPLE**

Draw a 115° angle.

STEP 1 Draw a ray.

Spatial Sense
Draw several angles that are
less than 90° and several that
are greater than 90°.
Encourage students to
recognize the shapes of
these angles.

STEP 2 Place the protractor on the ray so that the center is over the endpoint and the ray goes through 0°.

Then find the number of degrees for the angle to be drawn. Use the scale that starts with 0° on your ray. Draw a point next to the number 115°.

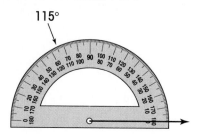

115°

STEP 3 Draw a ray from the endpoint of the first ray to the point marked for 115°.

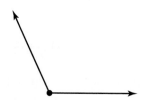

Practice

Common Error Students use the wrong scale. Have students begin at 0° and count to the number of degrees needed to form each angle.

Use a protractor to draw an angle with each measure. Check students' drawings.

1. 30°   **2.** 60°   **3.** 90°   **4.** 120°

5. 150°   **6.** 180°   **7.** 25°   **8.** 75°

ON-THE-JOB MATH
Physical Therapist

Stephanie is a physical therapist. She shows injured people how to improve the use of their joints and muscles.

This is a good job for Stephanie because she likes to help people and she knows how the body works.

Stephanie uses a tool that looks like a protractor to measure how far a person can bend his or her arm or leg. She takes a measurement before and after a person exercises to see how well they are doing.

The measurement on the right is 90°.

Write the degree measure for each measurement below.

1. shoulder 15°

2. knee 60°

3. entire leg 120°

Critical Thinking

Donna could only bend her wrist 40°. After she exercised, she could bend her wrist 110°, what is the percent increase in the movement of her wrist? 175%

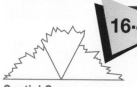

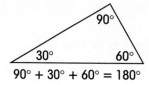

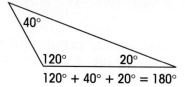

16·4 ► Angles in a Triangle

Spatial Sense
Cut several large triangles from construction paper. Show visually that if you tear off a triangle's three corners and place them with their vertices together, they form a straight line (180°).

A triangle is a plane figure with three sides.
The sum of the angles in a triangle is always 180°.

90° + 30° + 60° = 180°

120° + 40° + 20° = 180°

If you know the size of two angles, you can find the size of the third angle without measuring.

► **EXAMPLE**

Avoiding Errors
Be sure that students subtract the sum of the *two* given angles from 180°, not just *one* of the angles.

Find the measure of the third angle in triangle *ABC*.

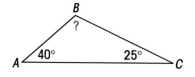

STEP 1	Find the sum of the known angles.	40° + 25° —— 65°
STEP 2	Subtract the sum from 180°.	180° − 65° —— 115°

The measure of the third angle is 115°.

Common Error The student makes an arithmetic error. Have the students check their answers by adding the three angles to be sure that the sum is 180°.

Find the measure of the third angle in each triangle.

1. 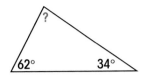 84°

2. 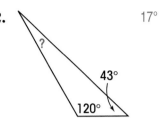 17°

3. 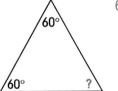 90°

4. 105°

5. 60°

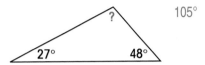

6. 132°

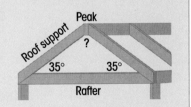

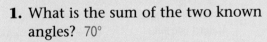

Everyday Problem Solving

Abdul is helping his father build a shed. He knows that the roof supports meet the rafters at an angle of 35°, as shown in the diagram.

1. What is the sum of the two known angles? 70°

2. What is the measure of the angle at the peak of the roof? 110°

3. Abdul built another shed. The angle at the peak of the roof is 90°. What is the measure of each angle at the bottom of the triangle, where the roof supports meet the rafters? 45°

More Practice is provided in Exercise 146 of the *Workbook*.

16-5 ▶ Polygons

Spatial Sense
Review the prefixes *tri-, quad-, penta-, hexa-,* and *octa-*.

Polygons are plane figures with three or more sides. Polygons are named by the number of sides they have.

▶ **EXAMPLE 1**

Count the number of sides. Name each polygon.

Avoiding Errors
Students can make a list of the names of all the figures. Have them draw a picture next to each word.

A triangle has three sides.

A quadrilateral has four sides.

A pentagon has five sides.

A hexagon has six sides.

An octagon has eight sides.

Triangles have special names. The names are based on their sides.

▶ **EXAMPLE 2**

Look at the sides. Then name each triangle.

5 in. 6 in.

3 in.
Scalene triangle
No sides are equal.

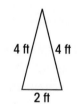

4 ft 4 ft

2 ft
Isosceles triangle
At least two sides are equal.

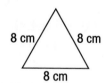

8 cm 8 cm

8 cm
Equilateral triangle
Three sides are equal.

Quadrilaterals also have special names.

EXAMPLE 3

Look at the sides and angles. Name the figure.

Avoiding Errors
Students can make a list of the names of all four-sided figures.

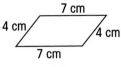

Parallelogram
A quadrilateral with the opposite sides parallel and equal in length.

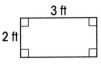

Rectangle
A parallelogram with all four angles equal to 90°.

Square
A rectangle with sides equal.

Practice A

Common Error The number of sides is miscounted. Have students mark the first side they count so they do not count it twice.

Name each polygon.

1.  pentagon

2. octagon

3. hexagon

Practice B

Name each triangle or quadrilateral.

4. 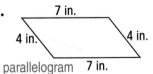 parallelogram

5. 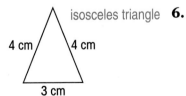 isosceles triangle

6. 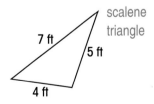 scalene triangle

7. 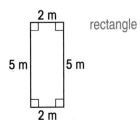 rectangle

8. 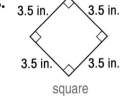 square

9. 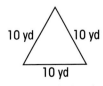 equilateral triangle

16·6 ▶ Perimeter

The **perimeter** is the total distance around a figure.

▶ **EXAMPLE 1**

Find the perimeter of this pentagon.

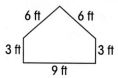

Spatial Sense
Ask students to imagine walking around a baseball diamond, starting and ending at home plate. The distance between any two bases is 90 ft. How far do you walk? This walk represents the perimeter of the baseball diamond.

STEP   Add the lengths of the sides.

$$
\begin{array}{r}
3 \text{ ft} \\
6 \text{ ft} \\
6 \text{ ft} \\
3 \text{ ft} \\
+\ 9 \text{ ft} \\
\hline
27 \text{ ft}
\end{array}
$$

The perimeter of the pentagon is 27 ft.

In an equilateral triangle, three sides are equal. You can find the perimeter if you know the length of one side.

▶ **EXAMPLE 2**

Find the perimeter of an equilateral triangle whose sides measure 5 inches.

Avoiding Errors
As a check, be sure that the number of measurements being added is the same as the number of sides.

STEP 1   Draw the triangle. Label every side. All of the sides of an equilateral triangle are equal.

5 in.   5 in.
5 in.

STEP 2   Add the lengths of the sides.

5 in. + 5 in. + 5 in. = 15 in.

The perimeter of the triangle is 15 inches.

In a rectangle, the opposite sides are equal. You can find the perimeter if you know the length and the width.

▶ **EXAMPLE 3**

Find the perimeter of a rectangle with width 6 feet and length 10 feet.

STEP 1 Draw the rectangle.
Label each side.

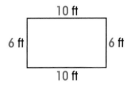

STEP 2 Add the lengths
of the sides.

6 ft + 10 ft + 6 ft + 10 ft = 32 ft

The perimeter of the rectangle is 32 feet.

Common Error Students add only the measurements noted on the figure. Have students draw the figure and write in a measurement for each side before adding.

Practice

Find the perimeter of each figure.

1.

8 cm   8 cm
9 cm
25 cm

2.
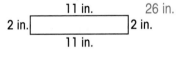
2 in.   11 in.   26 in.
2 in.
11 in.

3.
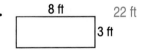
8 ft   22 ft
3 ft

4.
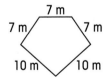
7 m
7 m   7 m
10 m   10 m
41 m

5.
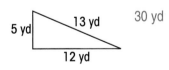
5 yd   13 yd   30 yd
12 yd

6.
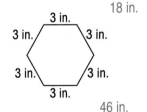
3 in.   18 in.
3 in.   3 in.
3 in.   3 in.
3 in.
46 in.

7.
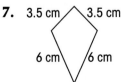
3.5 cm   3.5 cm   19 cm
6 cm   6 cm

8.
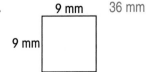
9 mm   36 mm
9 mm

9.
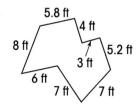
5.8 ft
4 ft
8 ft   5.2 ft
3 ft
6 ft
7 ft   7 ft

Extra Practice for this lesson
is provided on page 448.

More Practice is provided in Exercise 148 of the *Workbook*.

16·7 ▸ Area of Squares and Rectangles

The **area** of a figure is the amount of space inside the shape. Area is measured in square units.

To find the area of a square or rectangle, multiply the length times the width. You can write a formula to help you to remember what to do.

Area = length × width

▸ **EXAMPLE 1**

Find the area of this rectangle.

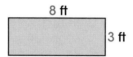

8 ft

3 ft

STEP 1	Write the formula. Substitute 8 ft for the length and 3 ft for the width.	Area = length x width Area = 8 ft × 3 ft
STEP 2	Multiply the length times the width.	Area = 24 sq ft

The area of the rectangle is 24 sq ft. You read 24 sq ft as 24 square feet.

▸ **EXAMPLE 2**

Find the area of this square.

4 in.

STEP 1	Write the formula. Substitute 4 in. for the length and 4 in. for the width.	Area = length × width Area = 4 in. × 4 in.
STEP 2	Multiply the length times the width.	Area = 16 sq in.

The area of the square is 16 sq in. You read 16 sq in. as 16 square inches.

Practice

Find the area of each figure.

1.

7 in.

3 in.

21 sq in.

2.

5.5 cm

3.5 cm

19.25 sq cm

3.

7 yd

49 sq yd

4.

13.8 ft

1 ft

13.8 sq ft

5.

8 in.

64 sq in.

6.

6.5 m

8.2 m

53.3 sq m

Everyday Problem Solving

Mr. Torres wants to plant a garden. A picture of the garden is shown below.

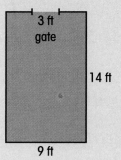

3 ft
gate

14 ft

9 ft

1. Mr. Torres needs to build a fence around the garden. How much fencing does he need? Do <u>not</u> include the gate. 43 ft

2. Fencing costs $8 a foot. The gate costs $35. How much will it cost to fence the garden? Include the cost of the gate. $379

3. What is the area of the garden? 126 sq ft

4. One-half of the garden will have corn. How much of the garden will have corn? Multiply the area by $\frac{1}{2}$. 63 sq ft

5. Three-eighths of the garden will have tomatoes. How much of the garden will have tomatoes? 47.25 sq ft

More Practice is provided in Exercise 149 of the *Workbook*.

16·8 ▶ Area of Parallelograms

Spatial Sense
Point out that the height
makes a 90° angle with
the base. For a rectangle
or a square, the height is
one of the sides.

To find the area of a **parallelogram**, multiply the base
times the height. The height of the parallelogram may
not be one of the sides.

$$\text{Area} = \text{base} \times \text{height}$$

▶ **EXAMPLE**

Find the area of this parallelogram.

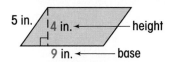

Avoiding Errors
Make sure that students are
aware that the height can be
drawn inside or outside a
parallelogram.

STEP 1	Write the formula. Substitute 9 in. for the base and 4 in. for the height.	Area = base × height Area = 9 in. × 4 in.
STEP 2	Multiply the length times the width.	Area = 36 sq in.

The area of the parallelogram is 36 square inches.

Common Error Students may use a side of the parallelogram as the
height. Discuss how you measure your height (standing straight up).
This is a way to identify the height of the parallelogram.

Practice

Find the area of each parallelogram.

1.
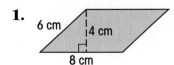
6 cm, 4 cm, 8 cm

32 sq cm

2.
5 ft, 4 ft, 7 ft

28 sq ft

3.
5 in., 4.2 in., 3.5 in.

14.7 sq in.

4.
9.2 m, 6 m, 9 m

54 sq m

5.
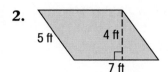
1 in., 2 in., 3.5 in.

3.5 sq in.

6.
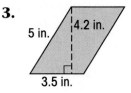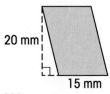
20 mm, 15 mm

300 sq mm

Extra Practice for this lesson
is provided on page 448.

USING YOUR CALCULATOR
Finding Perimeter and Area

You can use a calculator to find the perimeter and area of figures. Play this game with a classmate.

The Rules: Player 1 will use a calculator to find perimeter.

Player 2 will use a calculator to find area.

Find the perimeter and area of this rectangle.

Calculator Tip
Remember to key in the measure of all of the sides to find the perimeter.

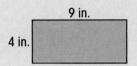

9 in.

4 in.

Player 1:   PRESS | 9 | + | 4 | + | 9 | + | 4 | = | 26.

Player 2:   PRESS | 9 | × | 4 | = | 36.

**Take turns being Player 1 and Player 2.
Find the perimeter and area.**

1.   6 in. P = 24 in.; A = 36 sq in.   **2.** P = 20 cm; A = 21 sq cm

3 cm

7 cm

3.   4 in.   3 in. P = 24 in.; A = 24 sq in.   **4.**   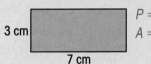 P = 35.4 ft; A = 65 sq ft

8 in.   5.2 ft

12.5 ft

5.   8.5 m   10 m P = 53.4 m; A = 141.95 sq m   **6.**   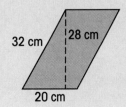 P = 104 cm; A = 560 sq cm

16.7 m   32 cm   28 cm

20 cm

More Practice is provided in Exercise 150 of the *Workbook*.

16-9 ▶ Area of Triangles

When you cut a parallelogram in half, you get two triangles. The area of a triangle is one-half the area of the parallelogram.

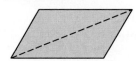

To find the area of a triangle, use this formula:

$$\text{Area} = \tfrac{1}{2} \times \text{base} \times \text{height}$$

▶ **EXAMPLE 1**

Find the area of this triangle.

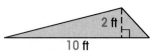

10 ft

STEP 1	Write the formula. Substitute 10 ft for the base and 2 ft for the height.	$\text{Area} = \tfrac{1}{2} \times \text{base} \times \text{height}$ $\text{Area} = \tfrac{1}{2} \times 10 \text{ ft} \times 2 \text{ ft}$
STEP 2	Multiply.	$\text{Area} = 10 \text{ sq ft}$

The area of the triangle is 10 square feet.

Sometimes, the height will be outside the triangle.

▶ **EXAMPLE 2**

Find the area of this triangle.

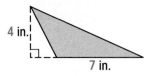

4 in.

7 in.

STEP 1	Write the formula. Substitute 7 in. for the base and 4 in. for the height.	$\text{Area} = \tfrac{1}{2} \times \text{base} \times \text{height}$ $\text{Area} = \tfrac{1}{2} \times 7 \text{ in.} \times 4 \text{ in.}$
STEP 2	Multiply.	$\text{Area} = 14 \text{ sq in.}$

The area of the triangle is 14 square inches.

Practice

Common Error Students use an incorrect side as the base. Show students that they should use the side to which the height is drawn. This is not always at the "bottom." The height always meets the base at a 90° angle.

Find the area of each triangle.

1.
15 cm
23 cm

172.5 sq cm

2.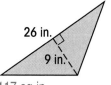
26 in.
9 in.

117 sq in.

3.
12 ft
14.4 ft

86.4 sq ft

4.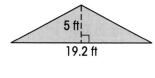
2 m
6.5 m

6.5 sq m

5.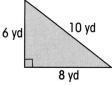
6 yd
10 yd
8 yd

24 sq yd

6.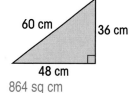
27 cm
9.5 cm

128.25 sq cm

7.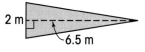
5 ft
19.2 ft

48 sq ft

8.
25 m
40 m

500 sq m

9.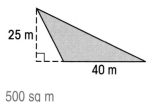
60 cm
36 cm
48 cm

864 sq cm

Everyday Problem Solving

Which takes more felt to make: the rectangular pennant or the triangular pennant?

1. What is the area of the rectangular pennant? 72 sq in.

2. What is the area of the triangular pennant? 76 sq in.

3. Which pennant takes more felt to make? How much more felt? triangular pennant; 4 sq in. more felt

4. CHALLENGE What would the height of the triangular pennant have to be for both pennants to have the same area? Keep the base of the triangle at 8 inches. 18 in.

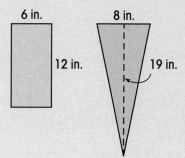
6 in.
12 in.
8 in.
19 in.

Extra Practice for this lesson is provided on page 448.

More Practice is provided in Exercise 151 of the *Workbook*.

16·10 ▶ Circumference of Circles

Spatial Sense
Show students a large can and ask them to guess how many times longer it is around the can than across the middle (diameter) of the can. Use string to measure. Try this several times with different-sized circular objects. (It is always about 3 times longer around than across.)

The **circumference** of a circle is the distance around the circle. To find circumference, you need to know the length of the diameter or **radius**. You also need to know pi.

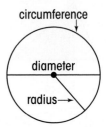

Pi is a special number you use with circles. The symbol for pi is π. The value of π is about 3.14 or $\frac{22}{7}$.

To find the circumference, use either formula below.

$$\text{Circumference} = \pi \times \text{diameter}$$
$$\text{or} \quad \text{Circumference} = \pi \times 2 \times \text{radius}$$

▶ **EXAMPLE 1**

The symbol $\approx$ means *about*.

Find the circumference of this circle.

STEP 1 Write the formula. Use 3.14 for π and substitute 6 in. for the diameter.
Circumference = $\pi \times$ diameter
Circumference $\approx 3.14 \times 6$ in.

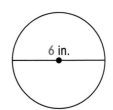

STEP 2 Multiply.
Circumference ≈ 18.84 in.

The circumference of the circle is about 18.84 inches.

▶ **EXAMPLE 2**

Find the circumference of this circle.

STEP 1 Write the formula. Use $\frac{22}{7}$ for π and substitute 7 ft for the radius.
Circumference = $\pi \times 2 \times$ radius
Circumference $\approx \frac{22}{7} \times 2 \times 7$ ft

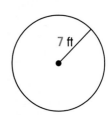

Avoiding Errors
Make sure that students understand the difference between radius and diameter, so that they choose the correct formula for the circumference.

STEP 2 Multiply.
Circumference ≈ 44 ft

The circumference is about 44 feet.

Practice A

Find the circumference of each circle. Use $\frac{22}{7}$ for π.

1.

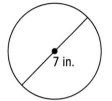

22 in.

7 in.

2.

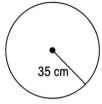

220 cm

35 cm

3.

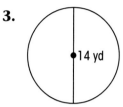

44 yd

14 yd

Practice B

Find the circumference of each circle. Use 3.14 for π.

4. radius = 4 in.
   25.12 in.

5. diameter = 9 yd
   28.26 yd

6. diameter = 7 m
   21.98 m

7. radius = 6.5 cm
   40.82 cm

8. radius = 10 ft
   62.8 ft

9. diameter = 3.75 in.
   11.775 in.

10. radius = 5.25 ft
   32.97 ft

11. diameter = 21 m
   65.94 m

12. radius = 9 mm
   56.52 mm

Everyday Problem Solving

The members of the Hornets Marching Band want to decorate their drums with a strip of green tape. The tape will wrap around a drum with no overlap.

1. One drum has a diameter of 18 inches. About how long will the tape be? The length of the tape is the circumference of the drum. about 56.52 in.

2. The diameter of a snare drum is 9 inches. Will you need half as much tape as in Question 1? Explain.
   Yes, the fact that the diameter is cut in half means that the circumference will be cut in half. You will need about 28.26 inches of tape.

Extra Practice for this lesson is provided on page 449.

More Practice is provided in Exercise 152 of the *Workbook*.

16·11 Area of Circles

Number Sense
Review squaring numbers.

To find the area of a circle, you need to square the radius. Remember that to square the radius, you multiply the radius by itself.

To find the area of a circle, use this formula:

$$\text{Area} = \pi \times (\text{radius})^2$$

▶ **EXAMPLE 1**

Find the area of this circle.

STEP 1 Write the formula. Use 3.14 for π and substitute 4 in. for the radius.
Area $= \pi \times (\text{radius})^2$
Area $\approx 3.14 \times 4$ in. $\times 4$ in.

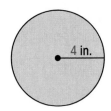

4 in.

STEP 2 Multiply.
Area ≈ 50.24 sq in.

The area of the circle is about 50.24 square inches.

You can find the area of a circle if you know the diameter. Just divide the diameter by 2 to get the radius. Then use the formula above.

▶ **EXAMPLE 2**

Find the area of this circle.

Avoiding Errors
Students need to divide the diameter by 2. The quotient is the radius, which is to be used in the formula.

STEP 1 Write the formula. Use 3.14 for π. Divide the diameter of 10 ft by 2. Use 5 ft for the radius.
Area $= \pi \times (\text{radius})^2$
Area $\approx 3.14 \times 5$ ft $\times 5$ ft

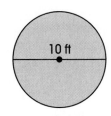

10 ft

STEP 2 Multiply.
Area ≈ 78.5 sq ft

The area of the circle is about 78.5 square feet.

Practice A

Common Error The diameter is used in place of radius in the formula. Have students begin <u>each</u> problem by noting "radius = ___" on their paper.

Find the area of each circle. Use 3.14 for π.

1.

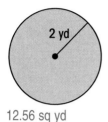

2 yd

12.56 sq yd

2.

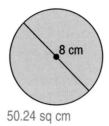

8 cm

50.24 sq cm

3.

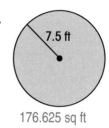

7.5 ft

176.625 sq ft

Practice B

Find the area of each circle. Use 3.14 for π. Round your answers to one decimal place.

4. radius = 7 ft
153.9 sq ft

5. diameter = 10 yd
78.5 sq yd

6. diameter = 6.5 in.
33.2 sq in.

7. radius = 9 cm
254.3 sq cm

8. radius = 7.2 m
162.8 sq m

9. diameter = 23 in.
415.3 sq in.

10. diameter = 8.5 mm
56.7 sq mm

11. radius = 6.25 ft
122.7 sq ft

12. diameter = 10.5 yd
86.5 sq yd

Everyday Problem Solving

Every winter, City Center Park has a circular skating rink with a flagpole at its exact center.

1. The distance from the flagpole to the edge of the rink is 50 feet. What is the radius of the rink? 50 ft

2. What is the area of the skating rink? 7,850 sq ft

3. The rink is surrounded by a wall. How long is this wall? Find the circumference of the circle. 314 ft

50 ft

Extra Practice for this lesson is provided on page 449.

More Practice is provided in Exercise 153 of the *Workbook*.

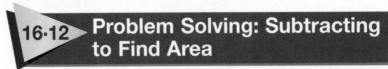

16·12 Problem Solving: Subtracting to Find Area

▶ **EXAMPLE**

Spatial Sense
Using square tiles, have students construct a rectangle measuring 4 units by 8 units and find its area. Then have them remove the "inside" tiles, leaving just the border. Ask: What is the area of this border? Discuss different ways to figure this out.

Avoiding Errors
Be sure that students draw and label a diagram for each problem so they can see what is being done.

Some word problems can be solved by breaking them down into smaller problems.

Mary bought a frame for an 8 in. × 10 in. picture. If the outside of the frame is 9 in. × 11 in., what is the area of the frame?

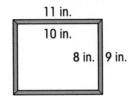

11 in.

10 in.

8 in. 9 in.

STEP 1 READ What do you need to find out?
You need to find the area of the frame.

STEP 2 PLAN What do you need to do?
What is the area of the large rectangle?
Multiply to find out.
What is the area of the small rectangle?
Multiply to find out.
What is the area of the frame?
Subtract to find out.

STEP 3 DO Follow the plan.

Multiply

Area = length × width
Area = 9 × 11
Area = 99 sq in.

Multiply

Area = length × width
Area = 8 × 10
Area = 80 sq in.

Subtract
99 sq in. − 80 sq in. = 19 sq in.

STEP 4 CHECK Does your answer make sense?
Does 19 sq in. + 80 sq in. = 99 sq in.?
                99 sq in. = 99 sq in. ✓

The area of the frame is 19 square inches.

Problem Solving

Draw a diagram. Then answer the questions under PLAN to solve each problem.

1. Brenda has a square picture frame with a square picture in it. The picture measures 4 inches on each side, and the outer edge of the frame is 7 inches on each side. What is the area of the frame?

   PLAN

   What is the area of the large rectangle? 49 sq in.
   What is the area of the small rectangle? 16 sq in.
   What is the area of the frame? 33 sq in.

   DO

   $7 \times 7 = 49$
   $4 \times 4 = 16$
   $49 - 16 = 33$

2. A fenced-in yard is 35 ft × 70 ft. A rectangular pool measures 25 ft × 60 ft. What is the area between the fence and the pool?

   PLAN

   What is the area of the large rectangle? 2,450 sq ft
   What is the area of the small rectangle? 1,500 sq ft
   What is the area of the walkway? 950 sq ft

   DO

   $35 \times 70 = 2,450$
   $25 \times 60 = 1,500$
   $2,450 - 1,500 = 950$

3. Amina put a blue border around the edge of a quilt. The quilt is 100 in. × 60 in. With the border it is 120 in × 80 in. What is the area of the blue border?

   PLAN

   What is the area of the large rectangle? 9,600 sq in.
   What is the area of the small rectangle? 6,000 sq in.
   What is the area of the border? 3,600 sq in.

   DO

   $120 \times 80 = 9,600$
   $100 \times 60 = 6,000$
   $9,600 - 6,000 = 3,600$

Problem Solving Strategy

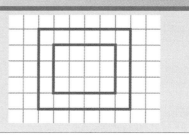

Sometimes, you can draw the diagram on graph paper and count the square units.

What is the area of the frame in square units? 18 square units

More Practice is provided in Exercise 154 of the *Workbook*.

16-13 Volume of Prisms

Spatial Sense
Show the students a box. Have them identify the length, width, and height of the box.

A **space figure** is a three-dimensional figure that has length, width, and height. A rectangular prism and a cube are space figures.

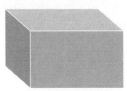

Rectangular Prism   Cube

Volume is the amount of space inside a space figure. Volume is measured in cubic units. To find the volume of a rectangular prism, use this formula:

Volume = length × width × height

▶ **EXAMPLE 1**

Avoiding Errors
Be sure that students use cubic units. Since they multiply by the three dimensions, the units must be cubed.

Find the volume of this prism.

STEP 1   Write the formula.
Place the values you know into the formula.
Volume = length × width × height
Volume = 10 in. × 6 in. × 7 in.

STEP 2   Multiply.
Volume = 420 cu in.

The volume of the prism is 420 cubic inches.

▶ **EXAMPLE 2**

Find the volume of this cube.

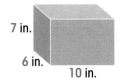

STEP 1   Write the formula.
Place the values you know in the formula.
Volume = length × width × height
Volume = 4 cm × 4 cm × 4 cm

STEP 2   Multiply.
Volume = 64 cu cm

The volume of the cube is 64 cubic centimeters.

Practice

Common Error Students calculate the area of the base instead of volume. Remind students that to find volume, they must multiply all three dimensions.

Find the volume of each prism.

1. 2 in. 12 in. 15 in.

360 cu in.

2. 7 cm 3 cm 3 cm

63 cu cm

3. 8 ft 13 ft 9 ft

936 cu ft

4. 11 m 17 m 9 m

1,683 cu m

5. 8 mm 8 mm 8 mm

512 cu mm

6. 3 in. 11 in. 8.5 in.

280.5 cu in.

Everyday Problem Solving

Allen has a fish tank that is 24 inches long, 14 inches wide, and 18 inches tall.

1. What is the capacity (volume) of the fish tank? 6,048 cu in.

2. Allen fills the tank with water. He leaves 1 inch of space between the waterline and the top of the tank. What is the capacity of the water?
5,712 cu in.

3. A gallon is 231 cubic inches of water. How many gallons of water are needed to fill this tank? Divide the answer you found to question 2 by 231. Round your answer to the nearest whole number. 25 gal

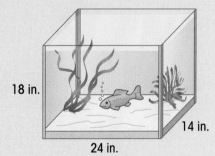

18 in.

24 in.

14 in.

16·14 ▶ Volume of Cylinders

A cylinder is a space figure that has circles for the bases. These two circles are the same size. To find the volume of a cylinder, use this formula:

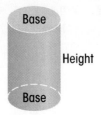

$$\text{Volume} = \pi \times (\text{radius})^2 \times \text{height}$$

Spatial Sense
Point out that in the formula for the volume of a cylinder, the expression $\pi \times (\text{radius})^2$ is the area of the circular base.

▶ **EXAMPLE 1**

Find the volume of this cylinder.

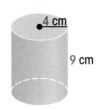

STEP 1 Write the formula. Place the values you know into the formula. Use 3.14 for π.
Volume $= \pi \times (\text{radius})^2 \times \text{height}$
Volume $\approx 3.14 \times (4 \text{ cm})^2 \times 9 \text{ cm}$
Volume $\approx 3.14 \times 4 \text{ cm} \times 4 \text{ cm} \times 9 \text{ cm}$

Avoiding Errors
It is easy to omit one of the factors. Be sure that students multiply four numbers to find volume: π, the radius, the radius again, and the height.

STEP 2 Multiply.
Volume ≈ 452.16 cu cm

The volume is 452.16 cubic centimeters.

▶ **EXAMPLE 2**

Find the volume of this cylinder.

STEP 1 Find the radius.
Divide the diameter by 2.
radius $= 12$ in. $\div 2$
radius $= 6$ in.

STEP 2 Use the formula. Use 3.14 for π.
Volume $= \pi \times (\text{radius})^2 \times \text{height}$
Volume $\approx 3.14 \times (6 \text{ in.})^2 \times 15$ in.

STEP 3 Multiply.
Volume $\approx 1,695.6$ cu in.

The volume of this cylinder is 1,695.6 cubic inches.

Practice

Find the volume of each cylinder. Use 3.14 for π.

1.

1 in.

2.5 in.

7.85 cu in.

2.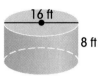

16 ft

8 ft

1,607.68 cu ft

3.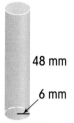

48 mm

6 mm

5,425.92 cu mm

4.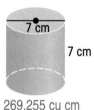

7 cm

7 cm

269.255 cu cm

5.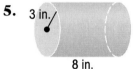

3 in.

8 in.

226.08 cu in.

6.

8.6 cm

2 cm

116.1172 cu cm

Everyday Problem Solving

A water tank is shaped like a cylinder. The diameter of the tank is 12 feet. The tank is 20 feet high.

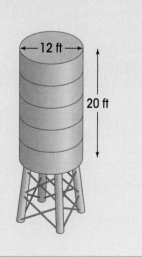

12 ft

20 ft

1. What is the radius of the base of the tank? 6 ft

2. What is the area of the base of the tank? 113.04 sq ft

3. What is the volume of the tank? 2,260.8 cu ft

4. The tank is $\frac{2}{3}$ full. What is $\frac{2}{3}$ of the volume? 1,507.2 cu ft

Chapter

16 Review

LESSONS 16·1 to 16·4

Test Tip
Be sure to use the correct scale on the protractor.

Possible Answer for Vocabulary Review
6. Prisms and cylinders are both space figures. To find the volume of each one, you multiply the area of its base times its height. Prisms have rectangular sides, and their bases are polygons. In contrast, cylinders have circular bases.

Vocabulary Review

Answer *true* or *false* for statements 1–5. If the statement is false, rewrite it so that it becomes true.

1. A *protractor* is used to measure *angles*. true

2. The *circumference* is $\pi \times 2 \times$ radius. true

3. The *area* of a figure measures the distance around the outside of the figure. false; perimeter

4. A *parallelogram* is a three-dimensional figure. false; space figure

5. The *volume* of a prism is length $\times$ width $\times$ height. true

6. **Writing** Compare *prisms* and *cylinders*. How are they alike? How are they different?

Chapter Quiz

Points, Lines, and Angles
Name each figure.

1. • *B*   point *B*

2. •*L*   ray *LM*
    •*M*

3. ←•——•→   line *WX* or line *XW*
       W   *X*

Draw an angle with each measure. check students' drawings

4. 12°   5. 145°   6. 80°

Find the measure of the third angle in the triangle.

7.   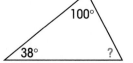   42°

Perimeter and Area of Polygons

Name each figure. Then find its perimeter.

8.

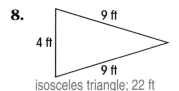

isosceles triangle; 22 ft

9.

hexagon; 22 mm

Find the area of each figure.

10. parallelogram with base = 11 in. and height = 3 in.   33 sq in.

11. triangle with base = 7 yd and height = 6 yd   21 sq yd

Circles

Find the circumference and area of each circle.

12. radius = 3 in.
$C = 18.84$ in. $A = 28.26$ sq in.

13. diameter = 8 cm
$C = 25.12$ cm $A = 50.24$ sq cm

Problem Solving

14. A window measures 30 inches by 60 inches.
There is a wood frame around the window that is
6 inches wide. What is the area of the wood frame?
1,224 sq in.

Prisms and Cylinders

Find the volume of each space figure.

15. prism with length = 9 m, width = 7 m, and
height = 6 m   378 cu m

16. cylinder with diameter = 10 m and height = 3 m
235.5 cu m

Group Activity   See the *Teacher Planning Guide* for a Scoring Rubric for this activity.

Each member of the group should bring in three different-sized cans or boxes
from food products. Have them guess the volume of the containers. Then
measure and calculate the actual volumes. Were your predictions accurate?
Did any of the results surprise you? Write a summary of your results.

Unit 4 **Review**

Choose the letter for the correct answer.

Use the graph to answer Questions 1 and 2.

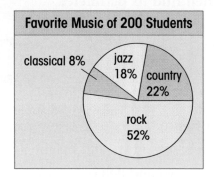

Favorite Music of 200 Students

classical 8%
jazz 18%
country 22%
rock 52%

1. Which statement is true?

Incorrect. **A.** More students like jazz than country music.

Incorrect. **B.** More students like classical than country music.

Correct. **C.** Most students like rock music.

Incorrect. **D.** Fewer students like country than classical music.

A, B, and D reversed word order

2. How many students like jazz music?

Incorrect. **A.** 182   200 − 18

Incorrect. **B.** 44   found number for country

Correct. **C.** 36

Incorrect. **D.** 3,600   no decimal point

3. Gen went to work at 7:55 A.M. He left work at 4:45 P.M. Find the elapsed time.

Incorrect. **A.** 3 hours 10 minutes   7:55 − 4:45

Correct. **B.** 8 hours 50 minutes

Incorrect. **C.** 12 hours   7:55 + 4:45

Incorrect. **D.** None of the above

B. Incorrect; 5L = 500cL then subtracted

4. Suki made 5 liters of punch. She used 1,200 milliliters of ginger ale. Then she added fruit juice. How many milliliters of juice did she add to the punch?

A. 1,700 ml   Incorrect; 5L = 500cL then added

B. 700 ml   See above

C. 6,000 ml   Incorrect; 5L × 1,200 mL

D. None of the above   Correct; 5000mL − 1,200mL = 3,800mL

5. Find the area of the parallelogram below.

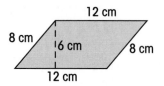

12 cm
8 cm
6 cm
8 cm
12 cm

A. 36 sq cm   Incorrect; found area of triangle

B. 40 sq cm   Incorrect; found perimeter

C. 96 sq cm   Incorrect; used side, not height

D. 72 sq cm   Correct.

Critical Thinking

The area of a rectangle is 36 sq cm. What are some of the possible widths and lengths of this rectangle?

CHALLENGE The area of the rectangle is 36 sq cm. What is the largest possible perimeter of this rectangle?

Critical Thinking: 1 by 36, 2 by 18, 3 by 12, 4 by 9, and 6 by 6
Challenge: 1 × 36 cm.

Chapter 17 **Integers**

Chapter 18 **Algebra**

Opening the Unit Have students record Fahrenheit temperatures from newspapers or television. Tell students that to snow, the temperature has to be at or below the freezing temperature of 32°F. Ask students if the temperatures they have are colder or warmer than 32°F.

New York City, 1995	
Month	**Snowfall in Inches**
January	7.5
February	8.6
March	5.0
April	.9
May	0
June	0
July	0
August	0
September	0
October	0
November	.9
December	5.4

The total snowfall in New York City for 1995 was only 28.3 inches. In January 1996, a blizzard dropped about 20 inches of snow on the city.

The graph and table give information on the snowfall in New York City in 1995.

1. Using the line graph, which month in 1995 had the most snowfall? How do you know?

2. Which 6 months have zero inches of snowfall? Why was there no snowfall during these months?

3. How much more snow fell in March than in April. 4.1 inches

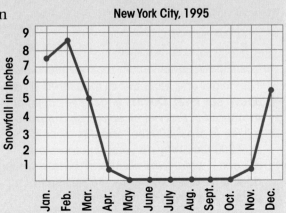

New York City, 1995

1. February; the point on the graph for that month was the highest point
2. May through October; during these months, it is too warm to snow.

Photo Discuss different heights and depths around the world. For example, the tallest mountain is Mt. Everest in Nepal/Tibet, which is +29,028 ft, and the lowest point on Earth is the Marianas Trench in the Pacific Ocean, which is −38,635 ft. New Orleans is a city that is below sea level.

The height of a mountain is measured in feet above sea level. Depths under the ocean are measured in feet below sea level. Suppose a hiker is at +8,500 feet and this diver is at − 200 feet. Why do you think there are a + and − before the numbers? What number do you think would signify the position of a person in a kayak on the ocean?

Caption The + signifies "above sea level" and the − signifies "below sea level." A kayaker is at sea level, so her position would be 0.

Chapter 17 ▷ Integers

ESL Note Discuss the word *opposite.* Have students name words that are opposites, and then tie this discussion into the numerical meaning of opposites.

Words to Know

integers	numbers in the set {..., $^-3$, $^-2$, $^-1$, 0, $^+1$, $^+2$, $^+3$, ...}
positive integers	integers to the right of zero on the number line
negative integers	integers to the left of zero on the number line
opposites	two numbers that are the same distance from zero on the number line but are on opposite sides of zero

Words to Know The words *positive, negative,* and *opposite* have many different meanings. Have students think of several meanings for these terms, and then discuss the mathematical definitions.

Integer Search Project

Search for five different integers. Find one example of each topic listed below.

- Temperature
- Stock market
- Money
- Height/depth
- Sports

Be sure to copy each topic. Look in magazines, newspapers, and an atlas. Next to the topic, write the example you found. Then, write what the example is about.

| Temperature | $^+32$ | degrees |
| Stock | $^-1$ | stock points |

Learning Objectives

- Identify and write integers.
- Add integers with like signs.
- Add integers with unlike signs.
- Subtract integers.
- Multiply integers.
- Divide integers.
- Solve problems using integers.
- Apply integers to wind chill temperatures.

Project Answers will vary. More examples are: +1,000 feet, magazines; or −40 dollars, magazines/newspapers

More Practice is provided in Exercise 156 of the *Workbook.*

17·1 ▶ What Is an Integer?

Integers are numbers that describe direction and quantity. **Positive integers** are greater than zero. **Negative integers** are less than zero. Zero is neither positive nor negative.

Decimals and fractions are **not** integers. For example, 3.5 and ⁻3.5 are not integers.

The integer ⁺4 is read: positive four or four. The integer ⁻4 is read: negative four.

You can write a positive integer without the positive sign. The integers ⁺4 and 4 are the same number.

The numbers ⁺4 and ⁻4 are called **opposites.** Opposites are the same distance from zero on the number line but are on opposite sides of zero.

▶ **EXAMPLE 1**

Number Sense
Draw a large number line the length of the board, with numbers about 2 feet apart. Have students represent different integers by having them stand in front of the line. Ask who is positive, who is negative, which two are the same distance from zero, etc.

What integer describes point *A*? Write its opposite.

STEP 1   Find point *A* on the number line.

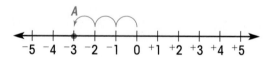

Point *A* is 3 units to the left of 0. Point *A* is at ⁻3.

STEP 2   Find the opposite of ⁻3.

Count 3 units to the right of 0. The opposite of ⁻3 is ⁺3.

STEP 3   Write the integers that describe these points. ⁻3 and ⁺3

⁻3 describes point *A*. The opposite of ⁻3 is ⁺3.

Integers often describe real-life situations.

▶ **EXAMPLE 2**

Use an integer to describe 10 degrees below 0.

STEP 1 Should the integer be positive or negative? Use a **negative** integer to describe **below** zero.   −

Avoiding Errors
Make sure the students say "positive seven" and "negative seven," not "plus seven" and "minus seven." This will help them avoid confusion later in the chapter.

STEP 2 Write the integer.   ⁻10

The integer ⁻10 describes 10 degrees below 0.

Practice A

Common Error Units on a number line may not be drawn uniformly. Have the students use graph paper or a ruler.

Copy the number line. Then, on the line, mark a point for each integer below.

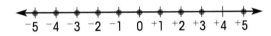

1. ⁺2   **2.** ⁻5   **3.** ⁺3   **4.** ⁺1   **5.** ⁻2

6. ⁻1   **7.** 0   **8.** ⁺5   **9.** ⁻4   **10.** ⁻3

Practice B

Write the integer that describes each point. Then write its opposite.

11. point A ⁻2; ⁺2   **12.** point B ⁺3; ⁻3   **13.** point C ⁺4; ⁻4

14. point D ⁺1; ⁻1   **15.** point E ⁻4; ⁺4   **16.** point F ⁻5; ⁺5

Practice C

Write an integer to describe each situation.

17. a $5 profit ⁺5   **18.** a $7 loss ⁻7   **19.** 12° above zero ⁺12

20. 9 ft below sea level ⁻9   **21.** a 6-point gain ⁺6   **22.** a 5-point loss ⁻5

More Practice is provided in Exercise 157 of the *Workbook*.

17·2 ▶ Adding Integers with Like Signs

You can use a number line to add integers. Start at 0. Move to the right to add a positive integer. Move to the left to add a negative integer. You can make the number line any size you need.

▶ **EXAMPLE 1**

Number Sense
Have students explain in their own words what addition means. Ask them for real-life examples of addition, and ask for guesses as to how you might add integers.

Add. $^+3 + {}^+6$

STEP 1   Start at 0. Move right 3 spaces to $^+3$.

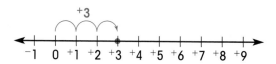

STEP 2   Then, to add $^+6$, move to the right 6 spaces.

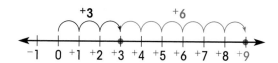

STEP 3   The number you end at is the sum. Write the sum.

$$^+3 + {}^+6 = {}^+9$$

The sum of $^+3$ and $^+6$ is $^+9$.

▶ **EXAMPLE 2**

Avoiding Errors
Emphasize that the sum of two negative integers is (also) a negative integer.

Add. $^-4 + {}^-2$

STEP 1   Start at 0. Move left 4 spaces to $^-4$.

STEP 2   Then, to add $^-2$, move to the left 2 spaces.

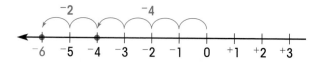

STEP 3   The number you end at is the sum. Write the sum.

$$^-4 + {}^-2 = {}^-6$$

The sum of $^-4$ and $^-2$ is $^-6$.

Practice

Common Error Negative integers are subtracted. Have students circle numbers on a number line.

Add.

1. $^+2 + {}^+8$ $^+10$

2. $^-5 + {}^-3$ $^-8$

3. $^+9 + {}^+7$ $^+16$

4. $^-10 + {}^-11$ $^-21$

5. $^-5 + {}^-8$ $^-13$

6. $^+6 + {}^+8$ $^+14$

7. $^-3 + {}^-9$ $^-12$

8. $^+5 + {}^+14$ $^+19$

9. $^-3 + {}^-16$ $^-19$

10. $^+4 + {}^+6$ $^+10$

11. $^-5 + {}^-5$ $^-10$

12. $^-6 + {}^-2$ $^-8$

13. $^-7 + {}^-8$ $^-15$

14. $^+8 + {}^+4$ $^+12$

15. $^-9 + {}^-5$ $^-14$

16. $^-9 + {}^-9$ $^-18$

17. $^+7 + {}^+6$ $^+13$

18. $^-8 + {}^-3$ $^-11$

Everyday Problem Solving

Dana hiked down a mountain from the peak. She went down 500 feet, and then she rested. Then she went down 400 feet more to her camp site.

1. What are the two integers described in this problem? $^-500$ and $^-400$

2. How far did Dana hike from the peak to the camp site? Use an integer to describe the distance and direction. $^-900$; 900 for distance, negative sign for downward

3. Dana's car is parked 600 feet below the camp site. How far did Dana hike from the peak to the car? 1,500 feet

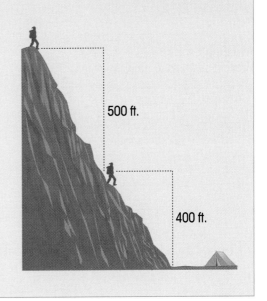

500 ft.

400 ft.

Extra Practice for this lesson is provided on page 450.

More Practice is provided in Exercise 158 of the *Workbook*.

17·3 ▸ Adding Integers with Unlike Signs

You can use a number line to add integers with unlike signs. Start at 0. Move to the right to add a positive integer. Move to the left to add a negative integer.

▸ **EXAMPLE 1**

Number Sense
Draw a big number line the length of the board with numbers spaced about 2 feet apart. Have students "act out" addition problems.

Add. $^-2 + {}^+5$

STEP 1   Start at 0. Move left 2 spaces to $^-2$.

STEP 2   Then, to add 5, move to the right 5 spaces.

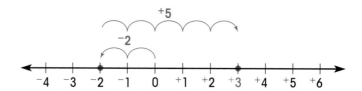

STEP 3   The number you end at is the sum. Write the sum.

$$^-2 + {}^+5 = {}^+3$$

The sum of $^-2$ and $^+5$ is $^+3$.

▸ **EXAMPLE 2**

Avoiding Errors
Remind students to move to the left on the number line to add a negative integer.

Add. $^+6 + {}^-8$

STEP 1   Start at 0. Move right 6 spaces to $^+6$.

STEP 2   Then, to add $^-8$, move to the left 8 spaces.

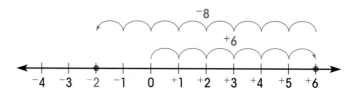

STEP 3   The number you end at is the sum. Write the sum.

$$^+6 + {}^-8 = {}^-2$$

The sum of $^+6$ and $^-8$ is $^-2$.

Practice

Common Error Students may be unsure as to which number to mark on the number line. Since we read a number sentence from left to right, the first number in the sentence is the one marked.

Add.

1. $^-2 + {}^+7$ $^+5$

2. $^+9 + {}^-6$ $^+3$

3. $^-8 + {}^+6$ $^-2$

4. $^-7 + {}^+1$ $^-6$

5. $^-4 + {}^+8$ $^+4$

6. $^+3 + {}^-3$ 0

7. $^+9 + {}^-10$ $^-1$

8. $^-1 + {}^+6$ $^+5$

9. $^+8 + {}^-6$ $^+2$

10. $^-11 + {}^+8$ $^-3$

11. $^+10 + {}^-4$ $^+6$

12. $^-6 + {}^+4$ $^-2$

13. $^+5 + {}^-11$ $^-6$

14. $^+5 + {}^-9$ $^-4$

15. $^-12 + {}^+2$ $^-10$

16. $^-2 + {}^+12$ $^+10$

17. $^+9 + {}^-12$ $^-3$

18. $^-8 + {}^+17$ $^+9$

19. $^-15 + {}^+1$ $^-14$

20. $^+1 + {}^-9$ $^-8$

21. $^+13 + {}^-4$ $^+9$

22. $^-8 + {}^+8$ 0

23. $^+100 + {}^-100$ 0

24. $^-15 + {}^+9$ $^-6$

25. $^+7 + {}^-5$ $^+2$

26. $^-7 + {}^+5$ $^-2$

27. $^-8 + {}^+9$ $^+1$

28. $^-9 + {}^+6$ $^-3$

29. $^+10 + {}^-2$ $^+8$

30. $^-12 + {}^+8$ $^-4$

Everyday Problem Solving

In a football game, Jeff started on the 40 yard line. He lost 4 yards on one play. Then he gained 7 yards on the next play.

1. Use an integer to describe a 4-yard loss. $^-4$

2. Use an integer to describe a 7-yard gain. $^+7$

3. In all, how many yards did Jeff gain or lose on the two plays? $^-4 + {}^+7 = {}^+3$; Jeff gained 3 yards on the two plays.

Extra Practice for this lesson is provided on page 450.

More Practice is provided in Exercise 159 of the *Workbook*.

17·4 ▶ Subtracting Integers

Number Sense
Put this problem on the board:

$$5 + {}^-2 = 3$$

Then ask students if they can think of another way of getting an answer of 3 by using 5 and 2. Write:
$5 - 2 = 3$. Have students try other numbers.

You can use a number line to see how subtracting integers is like adding the opposite integers.

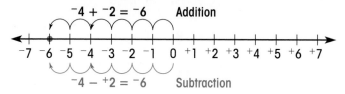

This shows the addition: $\qquad {}^-4 + {}^-2 = {}^-6$
This shows the subtraction: $\qquad {}^-4 - {}^+2 = {}^-6$
Notice that **subtracting** ${}^+2$ is just like **adding** ${}^-2$.

To subtract an integer, add its opposite.

▶ **EXAMPLE 1**

Subtract. $\quad {}^-4 - {}^-3$

STEP 1 Write the problem as given. $\qquad\qquad {}^-4 - {}^-3$

Avoiding Errors
Remind students that they must change the sign of the second number when they rewrite the subtraction as an addition.

STEP 2 ${}^+3$ is the opposite of ${}^-3$. $\qquad\qquad {}^-4 + {}^+3$
Change the problem to adding ${}^+3$.

STEP 3 Use the number line to add.
$${}^-4 + {}^+3 = {}^-1$$

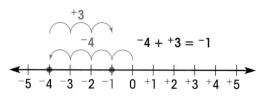

STEP 4 The number you end at is the answer to the problem as given. Write the answer.
$${}^-4 - {}^-3 = {}^-1$$

The difference between ${}^-4$ and ${}^-3$ is ${}^-1$.

► **EXAMPLE 2**   Subtract. $^-2 - {}^+7$

STEP 1 Write the problem as given. $^-2 - {}^+7$

STEP 2 $^-7$ is the opposite of $^+7$. $^-2 + {}^-7$
Change the problem to adding $^-7$.

STEP 3 Use the number line to add. $^-2 + {}^-7 = {}^-9$

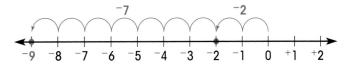

STEP 4 The number you end at is the $^-2 - {}^+7 = {}^-9$
answer to the problem as given.
Write the answer.

The difference between $^-2$ and $^+7$ is $^-9$.

Common Error Students may change the signs of both numbers.
Explain that the first number stays the same. Students should
remember the rule: "Add the opposite of the second number."

Practice A

Rewrite each subtraction as an addition.

1. $^-2 - {}^-1$ $^-2 + {}^+1$

2. $^-5 - {}^+2$ $^-5 + {}^-2$

3. $^+4 - {}^-3$ $4 + {}^+3$

4. $^+6 - {}^-2$ $6 + {}^+2$

5. $^+6 - {}^+2$ $6 + {}^-2$

6. $^+1 - {}^-4$ $1 + {}^+4$

7. $^-10 - {}^-1$ $^-10 + {}^+1$

8. $^-8 - {}^+7$ $^-8 + {}^-7$

9. $^-5 - {}^-5$ $^-5 + {}^+5$

10. $^-12 - {}^-12$ $^-12 + {}^+12$

Lesson continues on next page.

Practice B

Subtract. Remember to rewrite each subtraction as an addition first.

11. $^-2 - {}^-4$ $^+2$

12. $^+4 - {}^+2$ $^+2$

13. $^+3 - {}^+8$ $^-5$

14. $^-8 - {}^-4$ $^-4$

15. $^-2 - {}^+4$ $^-6$

16. $^+5 - {}^-11$ $^+16$

17. $^+6 - {}^-3$ $^+9$

18. $^-3 - {}^+2$ $^-5$

19. $^+10 - {}^-7$ $^+17$

20. $^-5 - {}^-1$ $^-4$

21. $^-1 - {}^-9$ $^+8$

22. $^+9 - {}^+5$ $^+4$

23. $^-5 - {}^+6$ $^-11$

24. $^-7 - {}^+2$ $^-9$

25. $^+4 - {}^-9$ $^+13$

26. $^+2 - {}^-7$ $^-9$

27. $^-12 - {}^-10$ $^-2$

28. $^+3 - {}^-4$ $^+7$

29. $^+7 - {}^+5$ $^+2$

30. $^+8 - {}^-7$ $^+15$

31. $^-9 - {}^-6$ $^-3$

Everyday Problem Solving

Sam went scuba diving. He dove 12 feet below the surface of the water. Sam went down another 5 feet.

1. Write a subtraction problem to describe the situation. $^-12 - {}^+5$

2. Write an addition problem to describe the situation. $^-12 + {}^-5$

3. In all, how far below the surface of the water did Sam dive? $^-17$ feet

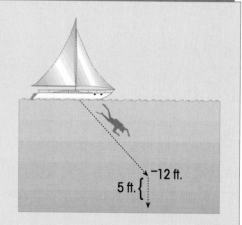

Then, Sam rose 9 feet toward the surface of the water.

4. How far below the surface of the water is he now? $^-8$ feet

Extra Practice for this lesson is provided on page 450.

You can use your calculator to add and subtract integers. Most calculators have a button that looks like this: [+/-]

This button will change the sign of the number shown on the calculator. For example, if you press [3] [+/-], the result will be ⁻3. Practice entering negative integers in your calculator. Be sure you press the [+/-] button <u>after</u> entering the number, not before. For a positive number, just enter the number itself.

Now you are ready to learn how to add and subtract integers on your calculator. Here are some examples.

To add ⁻3 + 5:

PRESS [3] [+/-] [+] [5] [=] [2.]

To subtract ⁻6 − ⁻4:

PRESS [6] [+/-] [−] [4] [+/-] [=] [⁻2.]

Use a calculator to add or subtract.

1. ⁻2 + ⁺7   5
2. ⁺5 + ⁻8   ⁻3
3. ⁻3 − ⁺2   ⁻5

4. ⁺4 + ⁻3   1
5. ⁻8 − ⁻2   ⁻6
6. ⁻6 + ⁻8   ⁻14

7. ⁻5 + ⁻7   ⁻12
8. ⁺6 − ⁺10   ⁻4
9. ⁺12 − ⁻3   15

10. ⁺9 + ⁻10   ⁻1
11. ⁻1 − ⁻5   4
12. ⁺8 − ⁺12   ⁻4

Calculator Tip

To make a number negative, be sure you do not use the [−] button by mistake. It will just subtract the next integer you enter.

More Practice is provided in Exercise 160 of the *Workbook*.

17·5 ▶ Multiplying Integers

Number Sense
Review the basic multiplication facts.

When you multiply integers, you need to decide if the product is positive or negative.

Multiplication is the process of adding the same number one or more times. Adding $^-2 + {^-2} + {^-2}$ is the same as multiplying $3 \times {^-2}$. You can use the number line to find the product.

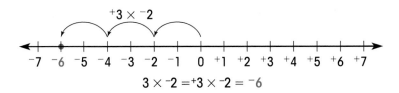

$$3 \times {^-2} = {^+3} \times {^-2} = {^-6}$$

Remember:
A positive number can be written without the + sign.

Notice that a positive integer times a negative integer is a negative integer.

Remember this rule:
  If the signs are **different**, the product is **negative**.

▶ **EXAMPLE 1**

Multiply. $^-7 \times {^+8}$

STEP 1 Look at the signs. Are the signs the same or different?

$^-7 \times {^+8}$
The signs are different.

STEP 2 Multiply the numbers without the signs.

$7 \times 8 = 56$

STEP 3 Decide on the sign of the product. The signs are different. The product is negative.

$^-7 \times {^+8} = {^-56}$

The product of $^-7$ and $^+8$ is $^-56$.

The product of two positive integers is positive.

$$^+2 \times {}^+3 = {}^+6$$

Is the product of two negative integers positive? To find out, look at the pattern below. Begin with what you know: $^+3 \times {}^-2 = {}^-6$.

$^+3 \times {}^-2 = {}^-6$	Each product is 2 more.
$^+2 \times {}^-2 = {}^-4$	
$^+1 \times {}^-2 = {}^-2$	
$0 \times {}^-2 = 0$	
$^-1 \times {}^-2 = {}^+2$	
$^-2 \times {}^-2 = {}^+4$	
$^-3 \times {}^-2 = {}^+6$	

Notice that $^-3 \times {}^-2 = {}^+6$. A negative integer times a negative integer is a positive integer.

Remember this rule:
> If the signs are the **same**, the product is **positive**.

▶ **EXAMPLE 2**

Multiply. $^-7 \times {}^-8$

STEP 1 Look at the signs. Are the signs the same or different?

$^-7 \times {}^-8$
The signs are the **same**.

STEP 2 Multiply the numbers without the signs.

$7 \times 8 = 56$

STEP 3 Decide on the sign of the product. The signs are the same. The product is **positive**.

$^-7 \times {}^-8 = {}^+56$

The product of $^-7$ and $^-8$ is $^+56$.

Practice A

Common Error Students may confuse multiplication with addition. Have students compare and contrast the rules for + and × before beginning these exercises.

Multiply. If the signs are different, the product is negative.

1. $^-4 \times {}^+3$ $^-12$

2. $^-5 \times {}^+8$ $^-40$

3. $^+7 \times {}^-9$ $^-63$

4. $^+6 \times {}^-5$ $^-30$

5. $^-1 \times {}^+9$ $^-9$

6. $^+8 \times {}^-3$ $^-24$

7. $^+2 \times {}^-2$ $^-4$

8. $^-6 \times {}^+3$ $^-18$

9. $^-5 \times {}^+7$ $^-35$

10. $^-100 \times {}^+1$ $^-100$

11. $^+100 \times {}^-1$ $^-100$

12. $^+1 \times {}^-1$ $^-1$

Practice B

Multiply. If the signs are the same, the product is positive.

13. $^-5 \times {}^-4$ $^+20$

14. $^+6 \times {}^+9$ $^+54$

15. $^-8 \times {}^-7$ $^+56$

16. $^+8 \times {}^+2$ $^+16$

17. $^+6 \times {}^+7$ $^+42$

18. $^-3 \times {}^-9$ $^+27$

19. $^-7 \times {}^-4$ $^+28$

20. $^+8 \times {}^+8$ $^+64$

21. $^-8 \times {}^-6$ $^+48$

22. $^+9 \times {}^+6$ $^+54$

23. $^-9 \times {}^-6$ $^+54$

24. $^-50 \times {}^-2$ $^+100$

Practice C

Multiply. Decide if the product is positive or negative.

25. $^-7 \times {}^-3$ $^+21$

26. $^-8 \times {}^+9$ $^-72$

27. $^+4 \times {}^+6$ $^+24$

28. $^-8 \times {}^+4$ $^-32$

29. $^+5 \times {}^-5$ $^-25$

30. $^-9 \times {}^-4$ $^+36$

31. $^+5 \times {}^+9$ $^+45$

32. $^+9 \times {}^-9$ $^-81$

33. $^-7 \times {}^+7$ $^-49$

34. $^-6 \times {}^+9$ $^-54$

35. $^-8 \times {}^-5$ $^+40$

36. $^+9 \times {}^+7$ $^+63$

Extra Practice for this lesson is provided on page 451.

MATH IN YOUR LIFE
Wind Chill Temperature

The wind can make you feel colder than the temperature that is on a thermometer. Suppose the thermometer reads 10°F. A wind blowing at 10 mph makes the air feel as if it were ⁻9°F. This is called the *wind chill temperature*.

Louise heard on the five day weather report that the temperatures and wind speeds would vary.

Wind Chill					
Wind Speed	Temperature				
0 mph	0°F	10°F	20°F	30°F	40°F
5 mph	⁻5	6	16	27	37
10 mph	⁻22	⁻9	3	16	28
15 mph	⁻31	⁻18	⁻5	9	23
20 mph	⁻39	⁻24	⁻10	4	19
25 mph	⁻44	⁻29	⁻15	1	16

Use the table to answer the questions.

1. On Monday, the temperature was 10°F. The wind speed was 15 mph. What was the wind chill temperature? ⁻18°F

2. On Tuesday, the temperature was 20°F. The wind blew at 25 mph. What was the wind chill temperature? ⁻15°F

3. On Wednesday, the temperature was 30°F. The wind speed was 5 mph. What was the wind chill temperature? ⁺27°F

4. On Thursday, the temperature was 0°F. The wind blew at 20 mph. What was the wind chill temperature? ⁻39°F

5. On Friday, the temperature was still 0°F. But wind speed was only 5 mph. What was the wind chill temperature? ⁻5°F

6. What was the difference in wind chill temperatures between Thursday and Friday? ⁻39 − ⁻5 = ⁻34. The wind chill temperature became 5 degrees warmer.

Critical Thinking
Why is wind chill important to consider?

Wind chill may be dangerous to people who are unprepared for its effect.

More Practice is provided in Exercise 161 of the *Workbook*.

17·6 ▶ Dividing Integers

Number Sense
Discuss the connection
between multiplication and
division. If $^-2 \times {}^+4 = {}^-8$,
then $^-8 \div {}^+4 = {}^-2$
and $^-8 \div {}^-2 = {}^+4$.

When you divide integers, you need to decide if the
quotient is positive or negative. The rules for dividing
integers are the same as the rules for multiplying
integers.

Follow these rules:
> If the signs are **different**, the quotient is **negative**.
> If the signs are the **same**, the quotient is **positive**.

▶ **EXAMPLE 1**

Divide. $^-32 \div {}^+4$

STEP 1	Look at the signs. Are the signs the same or different?	$^-32 \div {}^+4$ The signs are different.
STEP 2	Divide the numbers without the signs.	$32 \div 4 = 8$
STEP 3	Decide on the sign of the quotient. The signs are different. The quotient is negative.	$^-32 \div {}^+4 = {}^-8$

The quotient of $^-32$ and $^+4$ is $^-8$.

▶ **EXAMPLE 2**

Divide. $^-10 \div {}^-2$

Avoiding Errors
Show students how they can
check their answers,
including the signs, by using
multiplication:

$12 \div {}^-4 = {}^-3$

$^-4 \times {}^-3 = 12$

STEP 1	Look at the signs. Are the signs the same or different?	$^-10 \div {}^-2$ The signs are the same.
STEP 2	Divide the numbers without the signs.	$10 \div 2 = 5$
STEP 3	Decide on the sign of the quotient. The signs are the same. The quotient is positive.	$^-10 \div {}^-2 = {}^+5$

The quotient of $^-10$ and $^-2$ is $^+5$.

Practice A

Divide. If the signs are different, the quotient is negative.

1. $^-4 \div {}^+2$ $^-2$

2. $^+21 \div {}^-3$ $^-7$

3. $^-32 \div {}^+8$ $^-4$

4. $^-45 \div {}^+9$ $^-5$

5. $^+42 \div {}^-7$ $^-6$

6. $^+81 \div {}^-9$ $^-9$

7. $^+54 \div {}^-9$ $^-6$

8. $^-40 \div {}^+5$ $^-8$

9. $^-9 \div {}^+9$ $^-1$

10. $^-15 \div {}^+5$ $^-3$

11. $^-81 \div {}^+9$ $^-9$

12. $^+24 \div {}^-3$ $^-8$

Practice B

Divide. If the signs are the same, the quotient is positive.

13. $^+16 \div {}^+2$ $^+8$

14. $^-35 \div {}^-5$ $^+7$

15. $^+24 \div {}^+8$ $^+3$

16 $^-49 \div {}^-7$ $^+7$

17. $^+20 \div {}^+5$ $^+4$

18. $^-72 \div {}^-9$ $^+8$

19. $^-28 \div {}^-4$ $^+7$

20. $^+12 \div {}^+4$ $^+3$

21. $^-30 \div {}^-6$ $^+5$

22. $^+16 \div {}^+4$ $^+4$

23. $^-40 \div {}^-5$ $^+8$

24. $^-2 \div {}^-2$ $^+1$

Practice C

Divide. Decide if the sign of the quotient is positive or negative.

25. $^-18 \div {}^+3$ $^-6$

26. $^-56 \div {}^-7$ $^+8$

27. $^-64 \div {}^-8$ $^+8$

28. $^+36 \div {}^-6$ $^-6$

29. $^+27 \div {}^-3$ $^-9$

30. $^+48 \div {}^+6$ $^+8$

31. $^+63 \div {}^+7$ $^+9$

32. $^-24 \div {}^+6$ $^-4$

33. $^+36 \div {}^-9$ $^-4$

34. $^-20 \div {}^-4$ $^+5$

35. $^+49 \div {}^-7$ $^-7$

36. $^+72 \div {}^-8$ $^-9$

Extra Practice for this lesson is provided on page 451.

More Practice is provided in Exercise 162 of the *Workbook*.

17·7 Problem Solving: Using Integers

Sometimes you can use integers to solve word problems.

Number Sense
Ask students to relate positive and negative integers to real-life gains and losses.

Avoiding Errors
Have students use a number line to compute with integers.

The Evergreen football team lost 5 yards on its first play and gained 12 yards on the second play. What was the team's total gain?

STEP 1 **READ** **What do you need to find out?**
You need to find the total gain in yards.

STEP 2 **PLAN** **What do you need to do?**
Add the yards lost (a negative integer) and the yards gained (a positive integer).

STEP 3 **DO** **Follow the plan.**
Add. $^-5 + {}^+12$

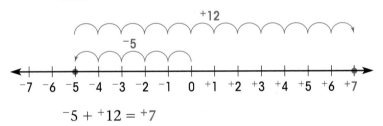

$$^-5 + {}^+12 = {}^+7$$

STEP 4 **CHECK** **Does your answer make sense?**
Yes. Look at the numbers.

The yards gained are greater than the yards lost. The total should be positive.
The sum is $^+7$.

One number is positive. The other number is negative. The total should be less than the yards gained.
7 is less than 12. ✓

The Evergreen team gained 7 yards for the two plays.

Practice

READ the problem. Answer the questions under PLAN.
DO the plan to solve the problem.

1. The Clarksville Hornets football team lost 5 yards on its first play, and it lost 6 yards on the second play. What was the team's total for the two plays? 11-yard loss

PLAN
What operation will you use? addition
What integers will you use? ⁻5 and ⁻6

DO
⁻5 + ⁻6 = ⁻11

2. The Hawks football team gained 7 yards on its first play and lost 9 yards on the second play. What was the team's total for the two plays? 2-yard loss

PLAN
What operation will you use? addition
What integers will you use? ⁺7 and ⁻9

DO
⁺7 + ⁻9 = ⁻2

3. The Eagles football team lost 2 yards on each of 3 plays. What was the team's total loss for the 3 plays? 6-yard loss

PLAN
What operation will you use? addition or multiplication
What integers will you use? ⁻2 and ⁺3 for multiplication
⁻2 for addition

DO
⁻2 × ⁺3 = ⁻6

Problem-Solving Strategy

Often, problems can be solved by drawing a diagram.

Rick lost 4 yards on each of the last two plays.
Draw a diagram to find the total number of yards he gained or lost.

Draw a number line. Use a negative integer to describe yards lost.

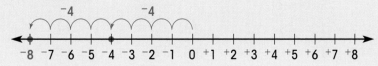

Chapter

integers
negative integers
opposites
positive integers

5. Possible answers include situations involving temperature, altitude, money, and football.

Vocabulary Review
Fill in each blank with a word from the list.

1. The integers to the left of zero on the number line are called __?__. negative integers

2. The numbers $^+6$ and $^-6$ are called __?__ because they are the same distance from zero but on different sides of zero. opposites

3. __?__ are any numbers in the set $\{...,^-3,\ ^-2,\ ^-1,\ 0,\ ^+1,\ ^+2,\ ^+3,...\}$. integers

4. The integers to the right of zero on the number line are called __?__. positive integers

5. **Writing** Explain two situations where negative numbers are used in "real life."

Chapter Quiz

LESSON 17·1

Writing Integers
Write an integer to describe each situation.

1. a $3 loss $^-3$

2. a 9 point gain $^+9$

LESSONS 17·2 and 17·3

Test Tip
The sum of positive integers is positive. The sum of negative integers is negative. If the signs are different, use the number line.

Adding Integers
Add.

3. $^-5 + ^-3$ $^-8$ 4. $^+4 + ^+6$ $^+10$ 5. $^+7 + ^-3$ $^+4$

6. $^-8 + ^-2$ $^-10$ 7. $^+6 + ^+6$ $^+12$ 8. $^-9 + ^+7$ $^-2$

9. $^-3 + ^-3$ $^-6$ 10. $^+12 + ^-13$ $^-1$ 11. $^+4 + ^-4$ 0

LESSON 17·4

Test Tip
To subtract, add the opposite of the second integer.

Subtracting Integers
Subtract.

12. $^+8 - ^+7$ $^+1$ 13. $^+7 - ^+9$ $^-2$ 14. $^-3 - ^+2$ $^-5$

15. $^-10 - ^-4$ $^-6$ 16. $^+6 - ^-8$ $^+14$ 17. $^-4 - ^-5$ $^+1$

18. $^+9 - ^+15$ $^-6$ 19. $^-3 - ^-6$ $^+3$ 20. $^+4 - ^-4$ $^+8$

Multiplying and Dividing Integers

Multiply.

21. $^-2 \times ^-8$ $^+16$ **22.** $^+9 \times ^-6$ $^-54$ **23.** $^-8 \times ^+3$ $^-24$

24. $^+7 \times ^+7$ $^+49$ **25.** $^-8 \times ^-9$ $^+72$ **26.** $^+4 \times ^-7$ $^-28$

27. $^+3 \times ^+11$ $^+33$ **28.** $^-5 \times ^-2$ $^+10$ **29.** $^-1 \times ^+15$ $^-15$

Divide.

30. $^+24 \div ^+3$ $^+8$ **31.** $^+18 \div ^-3$ $^-6$ **32.** $^-5)\overline{^-25}$ $^+5$

33. $^-80 \div ^+10$ $^-8$ **34.** $^-32 \div ^-8$ $^+4$ **35.** $^-7)\overline{^+21}$ $^-3$

36. $^-24 \div ^-4$ $^+6$ **37.** $^+54 \div ^-6$ $^-9$ **38.** $^-81 \div ^+9$ $^-9$

Solving Problems Using Integers

Solve.

39. A stock in the stock market was worth 1 point when it first came on the market. It then rose 4 points, dropped 3 points, and then dropped 2 more points by the end of the day. Where did the stock end? 0 points

40. This morning, the temperature was $^-4°$. By noon, the temperature had risen by $^+21°$. What was the temperature at noon? $^+17°$

Group Activity   See the *Teacher Planning Guide* for a Scoring Rubric for this activity.
Make sure that each member on the team has an atlas. Each student should look through the atlas and try to find the highest place above sea level and the lowest place below sea level. Compare these places and choose the highest and lowest from the group. Next, draw a picture of the places and label their heights or depths. Then find the difference between the two.

This acrobat is balancing himself on the tightrope. He does this by using his arms. He likes to keep an equal number of circles on each arm. This is much like an algebra equation. The two sides need to balance, or be the same. If he puts six rings on his right arm, how many will he want to put on his left arm?

Caption He will need six rings. Note that the photo shows three rings on each arm. Some students may think to add three to each side. Tell students that the rings in his mouth and on his leg do not count.

Chapter 18 ▷ Algebra

ESL Note Tell students that the rules for doing algebra, such as the order of operations, are the same everywhere in the world. Students solving an equation here and in Egypt, for example, will arrive at the same solution.

Words to Know

equation	a mathematical sentence stating that two quantities are equal
variable	a letter that stands for a number
number expression	a number or numbers together with operation symbols
solution	the value of a variable that makes an equation true
simplify	to write a shorter or easier form of an expression; or to find its value
parentheses ( )	marks around an operation that should be done first
order of operations	the specific order to do the four basic operations when more than one operation is in an equation

Words to Know Discuss students' previous understanding of these terms and ask them for examples.

Equation Project

In this chapter, you will learn about the equation $d = r \times t$. In the equation, d stands for distance, r stands for rate, and t stands for time. Research to find five more equations with letters. Look in your math book, your science book, or a reference book. Write each equation. Describe what each letter represents. Then explain one important use of the equation.

Project Students may work alone or in pairs. Have them share their equations and create a class list. Explain that banks use the equation $I = prt$ to calculate simple interest.

Learning Objectives

- Identify solutions to equations.
- Simplify expressions with parentheses and using the order of operations.
- Solve equations with one operation.
- Solve equations with more than one operation.
- Solve problems using one-step equations and two-step equations.
- Apply algebra to computer programming.

More Practice is provided in Exercise 163 of the *Workbook*.

18·1 ▶ What Is an Equation?

Look at the scale below. This scale is balanced when *x* is 5.

Number Sense
Draw balanced scales on the board. Have students find numbers that will balance each scale.

■ + 20 = 25 [5]
7 + ■ = 5 + 5 [3]
12 − ■ = 4 + 3 [5]

$x = 5$ ← equation

An **equation** is like a balanced scale. An equation states that two quantities are equal. The equation above contains the **variable** *x*. A variable is a letter that stands for a number.

An equation may contain one or more operations.

$$y + 8 = 10 \qquad 3m = 6 \qquad 2x + 1 = 7$$

To solve an equation, you find the value of the variable that makes the equation true. This value is called the **solution.**

▶ **EXAMPLE 1**

Is $y = 2$ the solution to the equation $y + 8 = 10$?

STEP 1 Replace *y* with 2 in the equation. Is this a true statement?

$y + 8 = 10$
Does $2 + 8$ equal 10?

STEP 2 Do the calculation. If the new statement is true, you have found the solution to the given equation.

$2 + 8 ? 10$
$10 = 10$ ✓

Yes, $y = 2$ is the solution to the equation $y + 8 = 10$.

A number next to a variable means multiply. For example, the expression $3m$ means 3 times m.

> **EXAMPLE 2**

Avoiding Errors
If a variable has a coefficient, be sure that students understand that they have to multiply the coefficient by the value of the variable.

Is $m = 7$ the solution to the equation $3m = 24$?

STEP 1 Replace m with 7 in the equation. Is this a true statement?

$3m = 24$
Does 3×7 equal 24?

STEP 2 Do the calculation. If the new statement is false, you have not found the solution to the given equation.

$3 \times 7 ? 24$
$21 \neq 24$

No, $m = 7$ is <u>not</u> a solution to the equation $3m = 24$.

Common Error Student does not know how to interpret the results once a number replaces the variable. Remind students to think of a balance scale. If the scale is balanced, then the number they substituted for the variable is a solution to the equation.

Practice

Tell whether the number is a solution to the equation. Write *Yes* or *No*.

1. $x + 2 = 5$; $x = 3$ yes

2. $m - 5 = 4$; $m = 9$ yes

3. $f - 7 = 1$; $f = 5$ no

4. $a + 4 = 9$; $a = 4$ no

5. $p + 1 = 10$; $p = 11$ no

6. $m - 6 = 3$; $m = 9$ yes

7. $h - 11 = 0$; $h = 12$ no

8. $k \div 3 = 8$; $k = 24$ yes

9. $g - 4 = 5$; $g = 9$ yes

10. $y + 3 = 32$; $y = 20$ no

11. $4c = 25$; $c = 3$ no

12. $17 - v = 9$; $v = 8$ yes

13. $5e = 20$; $e = 4$ yes

14. $10 - x = 5$; $x = 6$ no

15. $2w = 12$; $w = 6$ yes

16. $15 \div n = 10$; $n = 3$ no

17. $a \div 3 = 6$; $a = 9$ no

18. $8q = 45$; $q = 5$ no

More Practice is provided in Exercise 164 of the *Workbook*.

18·2 ▶ Using Parentheses

Number Sense
Provide a quick review of
basic facts for all operations.

A **number expression** is a number or numbers
together with operation symbols. When you find the
value of an expression, you **simplify** the expression.
Some expressions contain **parentheses**. Parentheses
around an operation tell you to do this operation first.

▶ **EXAMPLE 1**

The four operations are:
addition, subtraction,
multiplication, and division.

Simplify. $(7 + 4) - 6$

STEP 1 Do the addition inside the
parentheses first.

STEP 2 Then subtract.

$$(7 + 4) - 6$$
$$11 - 6$$
$$5$$

The value of $(7 + 4) - 6$ is 5.

Parentheses can also mean to multiply.

▶ **EXAMPLE 2**

Avoiding Errors
Be sure that students
write down each step
systematically. It is easy to
make errors when all of the
math is done mentally.

Simplify. $3(7 - 3)$

STEP 1 Do the subtraction inside the
parentheses first.

STEP 2 Then multiply.

$$3(7 - 3)$$
$$3(4)$$
$$12$$

The value of $3(7 - 3)$ is 12.

Common Error Students multiply the number beside the parentheses
by only one of the numbers inside the parentheses. Remind students to
always do what is inside the parentheses first.

Practice

Simplify each expression.

1. $(3 + 9) - 7$ 5

2. $38 - (9 \times 2)$ 20

3. $(3 \times 8) + 1$ 25

4. $(7 \times 8) - 26$ 30

5. $2(8 + 1)$ 18

6. $27 + (5 \times 12)$ 87

7. $4(15 - 8)$ 28

8. $(5 + 7) - (6 + 3)$ 3

9. $(24 + 8) \times 9$ 288

10. $93 - (63 - 9)$ 39

11. $(12 \times 8) - (4 \times 7)$ 68

12. $5(6 + 9) + (2 \times 8)$ 91

Extra Practice for this lesson
is provided on page 452.

ON-THE-JOB MATH
Computer Programmer

Andrea is a computer programmer. She writes programs in special languages for computers. Other people use these programs to make their jobs easier.

Andrea uses algebra in almost every program she writes. One computer language that Andrea uses is called Basic. Here is an example of a Basic program.

```
10 PRINT:"Type a number from 1 to 10" for x
20 LET   y=2*x
30 LET   z=5+y
40 LET   a=-z
50 PRINT:"We changed your number to:"
60 PRINT a
```

Line 10 identifies your number as x. Suppose you choose 3 for x.

Line 20 multiplies 3 by 2 and calls the answer y. Now $y = 6$.

Line 30 adds 5 to 6 and calls the answer z. Now $z = 11$.

Line 40 takes the opposite of this number and calls the answer a. Now $a = {}^-11$.

The computer then prints: "We changed your number to: ${}^-11$."

Work with a partner. Use the number given for x. Find the number the computer will print.

1. 1 ${}^-7$ **2.** 6 ${}^-17$ **3.** 5 ${}^-15$ **4.** 10 ${}^-25$ **5.** 7 ${}^-19$

Critical Thinking
Andrea has a printout of her friend's results. Her friend entered a number into the program. How can Andrea find out what number her friend entered?

Critical Thinking
Andrea can work backward from her friend's result. She can take the opposite of the number, then subtract 5, and then divide by 2. The result will be the number her friend entered.

More Practice is provided in Exercise 165 of the *Workbook*.

18-3 ▶ Order of Operations

Number Sense
Ask students to find:
$12 - 2 \times 3$
Incorrectly subtract first:
$12 - 2 \times 3$ is 10×3, or 30.
Correctly multiply first:
$12 - 2 \times 3$ is $12 - 6$, or 6.
Point out the need for rules.

Some expressions do not contain parentheses that tell you what to do first. Then you need to follow the **order of operations**. This means that you do the operations in this order:

1. Multiply and divide from left to right.
2. Add and subtract from left to right.

▶ **EXAMPLE 1**

Simplify. $8 - 2 \times 3$

STEP 1   Do all multiplication and division first. $8 - 2 \times 3$

Avoiding Errors
Students will be tempted to do the operations from left to right. Remind them that all multiplication and division must be done first.

STEP 2   Then do all addition and subtraction. $8 - 6$

2

The value of $8 - 2 \times 3$ is 2.

Sometimes a problem contains just multiplication and division or just addition and subtraction. Do the operations in order from left to right.

▶ **EXAMPLE 2**

Simplify. $22 \div 2 \times 3$

STEP   Do all multiplication and division in order from left to right. $22 \div 2 \times 3$

11×3

33

The value of $22 \div 2 \times 3$ is 33.

Common Error Students do the multiplication before the division. Tell them that multiplication and division are grouped together. They do any multiplication and division in the order given, from left to right.

Practice A

Simplify each expression. Remember to multiply or divide first.

1. $7 + 6 \div 2$ 10

2. $33 - 3 \times 4$ 21

3. $6 + 6 \times 15$ 96

4. $9 - 2 \times 3$ 3

5. $19 - 1 \times 8$ 11

6. $64 - 8 \div 8$ 63

7. $40 + 6 \times 8$ 88

8. $18 - 4 \times 4$ 2

9. $37 - 7 \times 3$ 16

Practice B

Simplify each expression. Remember to follow the order of operations.

10. $10 + 7 \times 6$ 52

11. $52 \div 2 \times 2$ 52

12. $14 - 2 \times 6$ 2

13. $99 + 11 - 8$ 102

14. $56 \div 7 + 3$ 11

15. $25 - 2 \times 7$ 11

16. $24 + 4 \times 9$ 60

17. $8 \times 5 - 6$ 34

18. $6 \div 6 \times 13$ 13

19. $32 - 8 \times 3$ 8

20. $70 + 25 \div 5$ 75

21. $49 - 7 + 1$ 43

22. $45 - 12 \div 4$ 42

23. $18 + 2 \times 9$ 36

24. $3 \times 8 \div 6$ 4

Everyday Problem Solving

Jackson is shopping for clothes for a new job. The store is having a sale.

1. If Jackson buys 3 T-shirts, how much does each T-shirt cost? Use the expression $36 \div 3$ to find the cost of one T-shirt. $12

STORE WIDE SALE

T-Shirt Sale   3 for $36

Tie Sale   3 for $45

Dress Shirt Sale   4 for $76

2. How much would only 2 T-shirts cost? The expression 12×2 tells you what to do. $24

3. If he buys 4 dress shirts, how much does each one cost? Write an expression that tells you what to do. $19; $76 \div 4$

4. How much would 5 ties cost altogether? Write an expression that tells you what to do. $75; $45 \div 3 \times 5$

5. Is the expression $45 \div 3 \times 5$ the same as $45 \div (3 \times 5)$? why or why not?   No; $45 \div 3 \times 5 = 15 \times 5 = 75$; $45 \div (3 \times 5) = 45 \div 15 = 3$

More Practice is provided in Exercise 166 of the *Workbook*.

18·4 ▶ Solving Equations with Addition and Subtraction

Number Sense
Review fact families to show that addition and subtraction are related.

$8 + 6 = 14$ $14 - 6 = 8$
$6 + 8 = 14$ $14 - 8 = 6$

To solve equations, you will need to *undo* operations. Look at the examples below.

$5 - 2 + 2$ $5 + 2 - 2$

$3 + 2$ $7 - 2$

5 5

To solve an equation that has addition, undo the addition with subtraction.

▶ **EXAMPLE 1**

Solve. $x + 8 = 15$

Remember:
Whatever you do to one side of an equation, you must do to the other side to keep the equation balanced.

STEP 1 Undo addition with subtraction. Subtract 8 from both sides of the equation.

$x + 8 = 15$
$x + 8 - 8 = 15 - 8$

STEP 2 Simplify each side.

$x + 0 = 7$
$x = 7$

STEP 3 Check your work. Replace the variable in the equation with your solution.

$x + 8 = 15$
$7 + 8 ? 15$
$15 = 15$ ✓

The solution to the equation $x + 8 = 15$ is $x = 7$.

To solve an equation that has subtraction, undo the subtraction with addition.

▶ **EXAMPLE 2**

Solve. $y - 3 = 10$

Avoiding Errors
Be sure students notice when the variable appears on the right. You might have them rewrite the equation so that the variable is on the left.
$2 = h - 8$
$h - 8 = 2$

STEP 1 Undo subtraction with addition. Add 3 to both sides of the equation.

$y - 3 = 10$
$y - 3 + 3 = 10 + 3$

STEP 2 Simplify each side.

$y + 0 = 13$
$y = 13$

STEP 3 Check your work. Replace the variable in the equation with your solution.

$y - 3 = 10$
$13 - 3 ? 10$
$10 = 10$ ✓

The solution to the equation $y - 3 = 10$ is $y = 13$.

Practice

Common Error Students use the same operation as in the equation to solve it. Remind students that they must undo the appropriate operation.

Solve each equation.

1. $x + 6 = 13$ $x = 7$

2. $y + 5 = 14$ $y = 9$

3. $p - 7 = 8$ $p = 15$

4. $2 = h - 8$ $h = 10$

5. $c + 3 = 9$ $c = 6$

6. $f - 2 = 4$ $f = 6$

7. $m - 4 = 10$ $m = 14$

8. $15 = r - 7$ $r = 22$

9. $9 = w + 2$ $w = 7$

10. $12 = k - 7$ $k = 19$

11. $n - 11 = 3$ $n = 14$

12. $x - 8 = 5$ $x = 13$

13. $20 = j - 9$ $j = 29$

14. $m + 15 = 23$ $m = 8$

15. $e - 13 = 19$ $e = 32$

16. $50 + k = 75$ $k = 25$

17. $h + 8 = 26$ $h = 18$

18. $30 = x - 45$ $x = 75$

19. $27 = r - 8$ $r = 35$

20. $s + 7 = 22$ $s = 15$

21. $g - 19 = 40$ $g = 59$

Everyday Problem Solving

Algebra can be used to represent everyday situations.

1. Mary is 8 years older than Tom. Tom is t years old. Which expression shows how old Mary is? **a.** $t + 8$

 (a) $t + 8$ (b) $t - 8$ (c) $8t$ (d) $t \div 8$

2. Mary is 8 years older than Tom. Tom is t years old. Mary is 12 years old. Which equation shows this relationship? **a.** $t + 8 = 12$

 (a) $t + 8 = 12$ (b) $t - 8 = 12$ (c) $8t = 12$ (d) $t \div 8 = 12$

3. How old is Tom? To find out, solve the equation $t + 8 = 12$. 4 years old

4. Eileen is 5 years younger than Peter. She is 23 years old. How old is Peter? Write an equation and solve. 28 years old; $p - 5 = 23$ or $p = 23 + 5$

5. Nora is 15 years old. She is 6 years older than her brother Abel. How old is Abel? Write an equation and solve. 9 years old; $a + 6 = 15$ or $a = 15 - 6$

More Practice is provided in Exercise 167 of the *Workbook*.

18·5 ▸ Solving Equations with Multiplication and Division

Number Sense
Review fact families to show that multiplication and division are related.

$3 \times 4 = 12$ $12 \div 4 = 3$
$4 \times 3 = 12$ $12 \div 3 = 4$

To solve equations with multiplication or division, you will need to *undo* each operation. Look at the examples below.

$$6 \times 3 \div 3 \qquad\qquad 6 \div 3 \times 3$$
$$18 \div 3 \qquad\qquad 2 \times 3$$
$$6 \qquad\qquad\qquad 6$$

To solve an equation that has multiplication, divide.

▶ **EXAMPLE 1**

Remember:
$2m$ means $2 \times m$.

Solve. $2m = 10$

STEP 1	Undo multiplication with division. Divide both sides of the equation by 2.	$2m = 10$ $2m \div 2 = 10 \div 2$
STEP 2	Simplify each side.	$m = 5$
STEP 3	Check your work. Replace the variable in the equation with your solution.	$2m = 10$ $2 \times 5 ? 10$ $10 = 10 ✓$

The solution to the equation $2m = 10$ is $m = 5$.

To solve an equation that has division, multiply.

▶ **EXAMPLE 2**

Remember:
$\frac{y}{3}$ means $y \div 3$

Solve. $\frac{y}{3} = 7$

STEP 1	Undo division with multiplication. Multiply each side of the equation by 3.	$y \div 3 = 7$ $y \div 3 \times 3 = 7 \times 3$
STEP 2	Simplify each side.	$y = 21$
STEP 3	Check your work. Replace the variable in the equation with your solution.	$\frac{y}{3} = 7$ $\frac{21}{3} ? 7$ $7 = 7 ✓$

Avoiding Errors
Be sure students understand that division can be written as a fraction: t divided by 6 can be written as $\frac{t}{6}$ or $t \div 6$.

The solution to the equation $\frac{y}{3} = 7$ is $y = 21$.

Common Error Students divide the numbers in a division equation instead of multiplying. Remind students that to solve an equation, they must undo the operation.

Solve each equation.

1. $24 = 4c$ $c = 6$

2. $\dfrac{m}{5} = 4$ $m = 20$

3. $4n = 20$ $n = 5$

4. $\dfrac{k}{8} = 18$ $k = 144$

5. $36 = 9f$ $f = 4$

6. $9s = 144$ $s = 16$

7. $9 = \dfrac{x}{5}$ $x = 45$

8. $24 = 3m$ $m = 8$

9. $\dfrac{s}{17} = 2$ $s = 34$

10. $16v = 80$ $v = 5$

11. $\dfrac{g}{12} = 9$ $g = 108$

12. $52 = 13k$ $k = 4$

13. $7 = \dfrac{y}{8}$ $y = 56$

14. $12x = 72$ $x = 6$

15. $4 = \dfrac{w}{12}$ $w = 48$

16. $8a = 808$ $a = 101$

17. $\dfrac{c}{3} = 70$ $c = 210$

18. $75 = 25x$ $x = 3$

Everyday Problem Solving

Algebra can be used to represent everyday situations.

1. Tasha is twice as old as Barbara. Barbara is b years old. Which expression shows how old Tasha is? **c.** $2b$

    (a) $b + 2$ **(b)** $b - 2$ **(c)** $2b$ **(d)** $b \div 2$

2. Tasha is twice as old as Barbara. Barbara is b years old. Tasha is 20 years old. Which equation shows this relationship? **c.** $2b = 20$

    (a) $b + 2 = 20$ **(b)** $b - 2 = 20$ **(c)** $2b = 20$ **(d)** $b \div 2 = 20$

3. How old is Barbara? To find out, solve the equation $2b = 20$. 10 years old

4. Sam is three times as old as Carol. He is 48. How old is Carol? Write an equation and solve. 16 years old; $3c = 48$

5. Vince is half as old as Gail. Vince is 14 years old. How old is Gail? Write an equation and solve. 28 years old; $\dfrac{g}{2} = 14$

Extra Practice for this lesson is provided on page 452.

More Practice is provided in Exercise 168 of the *Workbook*.

18-6 ▶ Problem Solving: Using a One-Step Equation

Number Sense
Have students study the relationship among distance, rate, and time. Lead them to realize that multiplication is needed to find the distance. To find the time or the rate, division is needed.

Suppose that a car travels 55 miles per hour for 3 hours. How far does the car travel? You can solve an equation to find out.

$$\text{Distance} = \text{rate} \times \text{time}$$
$$d \quad = \quad r \times t$$
$$d = 55 \times 3 = 165 \text{ miles}$$

If you know two of the three values in the equation, you can find the third value.

Michael drove 78 miles in 2 hours. At what rate (in miles per hour) did he drive?

▶ **EXAMPLE**

Avoiding Errors
Discuss the meaning of the word *replace*. Remind students that one player can replace another during a basketball game. In the same way, a variable can be replaced with a number in an equation.

STEP 1   READ   What do you need to find out?
You need to find how fast Michael drove.

STEP 2   PLAN   What do you need to do?
Write the equation.
Replace d with 78 miles.
Replace t with 2 hours.
Solve for r.

STEP 3   DO   Follow the plan.
Write the equation. Replace.

$$d = r \times t \qquad\qquad 78 = r \times 2$$
$$78 \div 2 = r \times 2 \div 2$$
$$39 = r$$

STEP 4   CHECK   Does your answer make sense?
Replace the variable with the solution.

$$r \times t = d$$
$$39 \times 2 = 78 \text{ miles } \checkmark$$

Michael drove at a rate of 39 miles per hour.

Common Error Students put the numbers in the wrong places in the formula. Students should write the formula each time and carefully put in the given information, paying close attention to the units. (Rate is miles per hour, time is hours, and distance is miles.)

READ the problem. Follow the instructions under PLAN.
DO the plan to solve the problem.

1. Lucia drove for 6 hours at an average speed of 47 mph. How far did she travel? 282 miles

PLAN
What is the equation? $d = r \times t$
What given values can be replaced in the equation? rate and time
Substitute given values in the equation and solve.

DO
$d = 47 \times 6$
$d = 282$

2. A plane went 945 miles in 3 hours. What was the plane's average rate, in miles per hour? 315 mph

PLAN
What is the equation? $d = r \times t$
What given values can be replaced in the equation? distance and time
Substitute given values in the equation and solve.

DO
$945 = r \times 3$
$315 = r$

3. A train went 375 miles at 75 mph. How long did the trip take? 5 hours

PLAN
What is the equation? $d = r \times t$
What given values can be replaced in the equation? distance and rate
Substitute given values in the equation and solve.

DO
$375 = 75 \times t$
$5 = t$

Problem Solving Strategy

Sometimes, distance problems can be solved by making a table.

A train went 248 miles at 62 mph.
How long did the trip take? 4 hours

Complete the table to find the time.

Time	62 mph × t	Distance
1	62 × 1	62
2	62 × 2	? 124
? 3	?62 × 3	? 186
? 4	?62 × 4	? 248

Extra Practice for this lesson is provided on page 453.

More Practice is provided in Exercise 169 of the *Workbook*.

18·7 Solving Equations with More Than One Operation

Number Sense
Mention that since you undo operations to solve for *x*, you need to reverse the order of operations.

To solve equations involving more than one operation, do the following steps:

1. First undo any addition and subtraction.
2. Then undo any multiplication or division.

▶ **EXAMPLE 1**

Solve for *x*. $2x + 5 = 15$

Avoiding Errors
Be sure that students perform the necessary operations on <u>both sides</u> of the equation.

STEP 1	First undo the addition with subtraction. Subtract 5 from both sides.	$2x + 5 - 5 = 15 - 5$ $2x = 10$
STEP 2	Then undo the multiplication with division. Divide both sides by 2.	$2x \div 2 = 10 \div 2$ $x = 5$
STEP 3	To check, replace the variable in the equation with your answer.	$2x + 5 = 15$ $2 \times 5 + 5 \,?\, 15$ $10 + 5 \,?\, 15$ $15 = 15 \checkmark$

The solution to the equation $2x + 5 = 15$ is $x = 5$.

▶ **EXAMPLE 2**

Solve for *y*. $\frac{y}{3} - 7 = 5$

Remember:
$\frac{y}{3} = y \div 3$

STEP 1	First undo the subtraction with addition. Add 7 to both sides.	$\frac{y}{3} - 7 + 7 = 5 + 7$ $\frac{y}{3} = 12$
STEP 2	Then undo the division with multiplication. Multiply both sides by 3.	$y \div 3 \times 3 = 12 \times 3$ $y = 36$
STEP 3	To check, replace the variable in the equation with your answer.	$\frac{y}{3} - 7 = 5$ $\frac{36}{3} - 7 \,?\, 5$ $12 - 7 \,?\, 5$ $5 = 5 \checkmark$

The solution to the equation $\frac{y}{3} - 7 = 5$ is $y = 36$.

Practice A

Solve each equation. First undo the addition or the subtraction. Then undo the multiplication.

1. $2a + 8 = 28$ $a = 10$
2. $3w - 5 = 16$ $w = 7$

3. $3x + 2 = 8$ $x = 2$
4. $4m - 6 = 10$ $m = 4$

5. $11v + 8 = 19$ $v = 1$
6. $4a + 7 = 19$ $a = 3$

7. $4n - 1 = 11$ $n = 3$
8. $9f + 5 = 32$ $f = 3$

9. $5k + 8 = 28$ $k = 4$
10. $2r + 6 = 10$ $r = 2$

11. $7y + 13 = 48$ $y = 5$
12. $8c - 30 = 2$ $c = 4$

13. $6x - 15 = 15$ $x = 5$
14. $12n + 10 = 58$ $n = 4$

Practice B

Solve each equation. First undo the addition or the subtraction. Then undo the division.

15. $\frac{z}{7} - 1 = 3$ $z = 28$
16. $\frac{u}{3} + 9 = 18$ $u = 27$

17. $\frac{e}{4} + 14 = 16$ $e = 8$
18. $\frac{y}{5} - 3 = 2$ $y = 25$

19. $\frac{n}{9} - 6 = 0$ $n = 54$
20. $\frac{s}{3} - 5 = 3$ $s = 24$

21. $\frac{w}{8} + 4 = 8$ $w = 32$
22. $\frac{a}{9} + 7 = 16$ $a = 81$

23. $\frac{f}{5} - 7 = 2$ $f = 45$
24. $\frac{h}{6} + 8 = 11$ $h = 18$

25. $\frac{m}{6} + 13 = 19$ $m = 36$
26. $\frac{r}{7} - 5 = 1$ $r = 42$

27. $\frac{x}{2} - 6 = 9$ $x = 30$
28. $\frac{x}{12} + 6 = 10$ $x = 48$

Lesson continues on the next page.

Practice C

Solve each equation

29. $\frac{x}{8} - 1 = 7$ $x = 64$

30. $4u + 9 = 37$ $u = 7$

31. $\frac{t}{2} - 14 = 36$ $t = 100$

32. $9y - 30 = 150$ $y = 20$

33. $\frac{p}{7} - 3 = 4$ $p = 49$

34. $3s - 15 = 75$ $s = 30$

35. $6w + 4 = 46$ $w = 7$

36. $\frac{n}{5} + 7 = 18$ $n = 55$

37. $8f - 7 = 65$ $f = 9$

38. $\frac{y}{6} + 9 = 17$ $y = 48$

Everyday Problem Solving

A Portland taxi had this sign about its fares.

1. How much will it cost to ride 1 mile?
$3; Add $1.75 and $1.25

2. How much will it cost to ride 2 miles?
What did you do to find out? $4.25;
multiply $1.25 by 2 and add $1.75.

3. How much will it cost to ride *m* miles?
Choose an equation. Let *c* represent the cost.
(a) $c = \$1.25m$ (b) $c = \$1.25m + \$1.75$
b. $c = \$1.25m + \$1.75$

4. How much will it cost to ride 5 miles?
Use the equation $c = \$1.25m + \$1.75$.
Replace *m* with 5 in the equation and
calculate the cost. $8

5. How many miles can you travel for $20.50?
Replace *c* in your equation with $20.50 and
solve the equation for *m*. 15 miles

TAXI FARES
$1.75 Initial Charge
$1.25 per mile or
part of a mile

Extra Practice for this lesson
is provided on page 453.

You can use your calculator to check the solution to an equation.

John solved the equation $3x + 5 = 20$. He found that the solution was $x = 5$. He now needs to check his answer.

John can check his answer on paper.

$$3x + 5 = 20$$
$$3 \times 5 + 5 \ ? \ 20$$
$$15 + 5 \ ? \ 20$$
$$20 = 20 \ \checkmark$$

Calculator Tip

On some calculators, the first product may be displayed before the final answer.

Or, John can use a calculator.

PRESS [3] [×] [5] [+] [5] [=] [20.] ✓

John's solution of $x = 5$ is correct.

Use your calculator to check each solution.

1. $2x + 7 = 19$; $x = 6$ yes

2. $3y - 13 = 5$; $y = 10$ no

3. $5n + 6 = 20$; $n = 3$ no

4. $27 = 5m + 7$; $m = 4$ yes

5. $19 = 4w - 9$; $w = 7$ yes

6. $14x = 98$; $x = 7$ yes

7. $f + 25 = 8$; $f = 17$ no

8. $26 = 8y - 6$; $y = 4$ yes

9. $5t - 4 = 49$; $t = 9$ no

10. $29 = 7v + 8$; $v = 3$ yes

11. $15 = 3r + 3$; $r = 6$ no

12. $26 = 7s - 2$; $s = 4$ yes

More Practice is provided in Exercise 170 of the *Workbook*.

18·8 Problem Solving: Using a Two-Step Equation

Number Sense
Discuss why the total cost of renting an item increases when the number of days increases or when the rate per day increases.

▶ **EXAMPLE**

Remember:
In a two-step equation, first undo addition or subtraction, then undo multiplication or division.

Avoiding Errors
Be sure that students know what information is given and what they need to solve for.

The equation below shows how to find the cost of renting an item by the day.

Cost = rate per day × number of days + renter's fee

$$c = r \times d + f$$

The cost to rent a tent is $4 per day plus a renter's fee of $10. Shawn paid $22 to rent a tent. For how many days will he rent the tent?

STEP 1   **READ   What do you need to find out?**
You need to find the number of days that Shawn will rent the tent.

STEP 2   **PLAN   What do you need to do?**
Write the equation.
Replace r with $4.
Replace f with $10.
Replace c with $22.
Solve for d.

STEP 3   **DO   Follow the plan.**

Write the equation.   Replace and solve.
$$c = r \times d + f$$
$$22 = 4 \times d + 10$$
$$22 - 10 = 4 \times d + 10 - 10$$
$$12 = 4 \times d$$
$$12 \div 4 = 4 \times d \div 4$$
$$3 = d$$

STEP 4   **CHECK   Does your answer make sense?**
Work backward. If Shawn rents the tent for 3 days, how much will it cost?

$$3 \times 4 + 10 \,?\, 22$$
$$12 + 10 \,?\, 22$$
$$22 = 22 \checkmark$$

Shawn will rent the tent for 3 days.

Common Error Students confuse the two dollar amounts given in the problem. Reinforce that the *rate per day* is multiplied by the number of days. The *fee* is added to this product.

READ the problem. Follow the instructions under PLAN. DO the plan to solve the problem.

1. The cost to rent a car is $35 per day plus a fee of $20. Mr. Hillwig rented a car for $195. For how many days did he rent the car? 5 days

PLAN
Write the equation. $c = r \times d + f$
Substitute the given values in the equation and solve.

DO
$195 = 35 \times d + 20$
$175 = 35 \times d$
$5 = d$

2. The cost to rent a table is $5 per day plus a fee of $20. The drama club paid a total of $30 to rent a table. For how many days did they rent the table? 2 days

PLAN
Write the equation. $c = r \times d + f$
Substitute the given values in the equation and solve.

DO
$30 = 5 \times d + 20$
$10 = 5 \times d$
$2 = d$

3. The cost to rent a lawn tent is $16 per day plus a fee of $41. Ms. Fare rented a lawn tent for $89. For how many days did she rent the tent? 3 days

PLAN
Write the equation. $c = r \times d + f$
Substitute given values in the equation and solve.

DO
$89 = 16 \times d + 41$
$48 = 16 \times d$
$3 = d$

Problem Solving Strategy

Rental problems sometimes can be solved by making a table.

The cost to rent a tent is $15 per day plus a fee of $38. Al paid $113 to rent a tent. How many days did he rent it? 5 days

Copy and complete the table to find the number of days.

Number of Days	$15 × d + $38	Total Cost
1	$15 × 1 + $38	$53
2	$15 × 2 + $38	? $68
3	? a.	? $83
? 4	? b.	? $98
? 5	? c.	? $113

a. $15 × 3 + $38
b. $15 × 4 + $38
c. $15 × 5 + $38

Extra Practice for this lesson is provided on page 453.

Vocabulary Review

| equation |
| order of operations |
| parentheses |
| simplify |
| solution |
| variable |

Choose a word from the list to complete each sentence.

1. $6x + 1 = 13$ is an example of a(n) __?__. equation

2. The __?__ of $3y = 24$ is $y = 8$. solution

3. Following the __?__ means to do all multiplication and division before addition and subtraction. order of operations

4. The __?__ in $5y + 7 = 12$ is y. variable

5. You can __?__ to find the value of an expression. simplify

6. You can write __?__ around an expression to show that it should be done first. parentheses

7. **Writing** Explain in words how to find the solution to $4r + 12 = 24$. Subtract 12 from both sides, then divide both sides by 4. The solution is $r = 3$.

Chapter Quiz

LESSON 18·1

Test Tip
The solution to an equation makes the equation true.

Identifying Solutions
Is the number a solution? Write *Yes* or *No*.

1. $x + 5 = 9$; $x = 10$ no

2. $3y = 15$; $y = 5$ yes

3. $a \div 6 = 3$; $a = 18$ yes

LESSONS 18·2 and 18·3

Test Tip
Remember to do what is in the parentheses first. Then, follow the order of operations.

Simplifying Expressions
Solve.

4. $3(10 - 4)$ 18

5. $9 - 2 + 4$ 11

6. $24 - 16 \div 8$ 22

7. $5 + 5 \times 2$ 15

8. $(8 + 3) - (6 + 1)$ 4

9. $(18 - 6) \div 2$ 6

Solving Equations with One Operation

Solve.

10. $9 + c = 29$ $c = 20$

11. $4m = 16$ $m = 4$

12. $n - 5 = 34$ $n = 39$

13. $\frac{y}{5} = 9$ $y = 45$

Problem Solving: Using a One-Step Equation

Solve. Use the formula $d = r \times t$.

14. Jenny drove for 5 hours at 55 mph. How far did she drive?   275 miles

15. When Lee went on vacation, he flew 1,140 miles in 4 hours. What was the plane's average rate of speed?   285 mph

Solving Equations with More Than One Operation

Solve.

16. $4a - 7 = 17$ $a = 6$

17. $5n + 23 = 33$ $n = 2$

18. $\frac{c}{3} - 6 = 3$ $c = 27$

19. $\frac{x}{6} + 2 = 4$ $x = 12$

Problem Solving: Using a Two-Step Equation

Solve each problem. Use $c = r \times d + f$.

20. Van rented a pair of skates for $19.The rental cost $5 plus a daily rate of $2. For how many days did he rent the skates?   7 days

Group Activity See the *Teacher Planning Guide* for a Scoring Rubric for this activity.
With your group, decide on an item to rent. Some examples might be a car, a television set, tools, or sports equipment. Contact local businesses to ask about rental fees. Record the fees. Then calculate the total cost of renting the item for 1 week, 12 days, and 1 month. Is it less expensive to rent on a daily, weekly, or monthly basis? Write a paragraph about your findings.

Unit 5 **Review**

Choose the letter for the correct answer.

Use the graph to answer Questions 1 and 2.

Day	°F
Monday	−4
Tuesday	3
Wednesday	18
Thursday	−7

1. How much warmer was Tuesday than Monday?

   A. $^+7°$ Correct
   B. $^-7°$ Incorrect; included negative sign
   C. $^+1°$ Incorrect; $^+4\ ^-3$
   D. $^+3°$ Incorrect; chose a temperature

2. Find the coldest and warmest temperatures in the table. What is the difference between these temperatures?
   A. $^+11°$ Incorrect; added temperatures
   B. $^+15°$ Incorrect; used 3° as coldest temp.
   C. $^+25°$ Correct
   D. None of the above. Incorrect

3. Which expression simplifies to 4?

   A. $(12 - 4) \div 2$ Correct
   B. $2 + 10 \div 3$ Incorrect; added first
   C. $4 \div 2 - 2$ Incorrect; added
   D. $(4 + 8) \div 2$ Incorrect

4. Which equation has a solution of $x = -4$?

   A. $2x = 2$ Incorrect; multiplied by 2
   B. $4x - 6 = ^+22$ Incorrect; subtracted 6
   C. $4x - 5 = ^+11$ Correct
   D. $x - 4 = 8$ Incorrect; subtracted 4

5. Adam drove 165 miles at 55 mph. How long did it take?

   A. 220 minutes Incorrect; added
   B. 110 hours Incorrect; subtracted
   C. 3 minutes Incorrect; incorrect unit
   D. 3 hours Correct

6. Which is not true?

   A. $^-4 \times ^-5 = ^+20$ Incorrect; neg. product
   B. $^-4 + ^-5 = ^+9$ Correct
   C. $^-20 \div ^-4 = ^+5$ Incorrect; neg. quotient
   D. $^+5 - ^-4 = ^+9$ Incorrect; changed subtraction to addition

---

Critical Thinking

Look at the table above. It was colder on Friday than it was on Thursday. What could have been Friday's temperature? Explain.

CHALLENGE What was the average temperature for the four days. (Add the temperatures. Then divide by 4.)

Critical Thinking Answers will vary.
Challenge Possible Answer: any 3 temperatures with a sum equal to $^-45°F$.

Extra Practice Chapter 1

5. 3 hundred thousands + 4 thousands + 7 hundreds

▶ Lessons 1·3 and 1·4 *Pages 6–11*

Rename each number to show the place value of each digit.

1. 403
4 hundreds + 3 ones

2. 2,067
2 thousands + 6 tens + 7 ones

3. 6,050
6 thousands + 5 tens

4. 12,090
4. 1 ten thousand + 2 thousands + 9 tens

5. 304,700
5. See above.

6. 70,007
6. 7 ten thousands + 7 ones

Write each number using digits and in words.

7. 5 thousands + 7 tens 5,070; five thousand, seventy

8. 7 ten thousands + 2 hundreds + 4 ones 70,204; seventy thousand, two hundred, four

9. 8 millions + 3 thousands + 9 hundreds 8,003,900; eight million, three thousand, nine hundred

▶ Lesson 1·6 *Pages 12–13*

Compare each pair of numbers from left to right.
Use the symbol >, <, or =.

1. 345 < 354

2. 2,760 > 990

3. 45,302 = 45,302

4. 72,909 < 72,911

5. 3,749 > 3,689

6. 1,000,843 > 1,000,782

▶ Lesson 1·8 *Pages 16–18*

Round each number to the nearest hundred.

1. 567 600

2. 34,181 34,200

3. 70,338 70,300

4. 1,850 1,900

5. 56,987 57,000

6. 219,843 219,800

Round each number to the nearest ten thousand.

7. 34,931 30,000

8. 193,722 190,000

9. 49,604 50,000

10. 1,208,306 1,210,000

11. 371,672 370,000

12. 389,682 390,000

Extra Practice Chapter 2

▶ **Lessons 2·1 and 2·2**   *Pages 26–27*

Add. Use the basic addition facts.

1. 4
 + 8
 12

2. 8
 + 1
 9

3. 9
 + 7
 16

4. 5
 + 5
 10

5. 6
 + 2
 8

6. 3
 + 7
 10

7. 0
 + 4
 4

8. 7
 + 5
 12

9. 4 + 6 10

10. 5 + 7 12

11. 6 + 5 11

12. 8 + 9 17

13. 3 + 6 9

14. 8 + 7 15

▶ **Lessons 2·3 and 2·4**   *Pages 29–31*

Add. Remember to line up the digits by place value.

1. 3 + 8 + 6 17

2. 7 + 7 + 5 19

3. 3 + 8 + 4 + 6 21

4. 4 + 5 + 1 + 9 19

5. 9 + 3 + 1 + 4 17

6. 3 + 8 + 2 13

7. 34 + 11 45

8. 67 + 10 77

9. 23 + 44 67

10. 231 + 600 831

11. 171 + 515 686

12. 249 + 440 689

▶ **Lessons 2·6 and 2·7**   *Pages 34–37*

Add. Regroup if needed.

1.   56
 + 15
 71

2. 345
 + 444
 789

3. 1,284
 + 1,417
 2,701

4. 623
 + 455
 1,078

5. 6,084
 + 1,659
 7,743

6. 591
 + 2,777
 3,368

7. 2,385
 + 9,368
 11,753

8. 2,655
 + 8,329
 10,984

Extra Practice Chapter 3

▶**Lessons 3·1 and 3·2** *Pages 44–45*

Subtract. Use the basic subtraction facts.

1. 9 − 3 6	**2.** 18 − 9 9	**3.** 17 − 8 9	**4.** 15 − 7 8
5. 16 − 9 7	**6.** 13 − 7 6	**7.** 11 − 7 4	**8.** 13 − 5 8

▶**Lesson 3·3** *Page 47*

Subtract. Remember to line up the digits by place value.

1. 45 − 22 23

2. 284 − 251 33

3. 598 − 316 282

4. 656 − 431 225

5. 7,415 − 305 7,110

6. 5,493 − 1,272 4,221

▶**Lessons 3·5 and 3·6** *Pages 50–55*

Subtract. Regroup if needed.

1. 314 − 75 239

2. 3,456 − 83 3,373

3. 6,493 − 675 5,818

4. 938 − 93 845

5. 8,763 − 988 7,775

6. 7,573 − 5,832 1,741

▶**Lesson 3·7** *Pages 56–57*

Subtract. Regroup if needed.

1. 3,000 − 2,675 325	**2.** 5,005 − 2,184 2,821	**3.** 7,000 − 371 6,629	**4.** 10,000 − 371 9,629
5. 80,090 − 5,500 74,590	**6.** 35,000 − 23,485 11,515	**7.** 79,000 − 39,722 39,278	**8.** 70,070 − 53,091 16,979

Extra Practice Chapter 4

Lessons 4·1 and 4·2 *Pages 64–65*

Multiply. Use the basic multiplication facts.

1. 4×6 24

2. 3×5 15

3. 8×7 56

4. 9×8 72

5. 7×6 42

6. 4×8 32

7. 3×8 24

8. 5×8 40

9. 9×7 63

10. 6×6 36

11. 3×7 21

12. 8×6 48

13.
$$\begin{array}{r} 7 \\ \times\ 4 \\ \hline 28 \end{array}$$

14.
$$\begin{array}{r} 4 \\ \times\ 9 \\ \hline 36 \end{array}$$

15.
$$\begin{array}{r} 7 \\ \times\ 5 \\ \hline 35 \end{array}$$

16.
$$\begin{array}{r} 5 \\ \times\ 6 \\ \hline 30 \end{array}$$

17.
$$\begin{array}{r} 9 \\ \times\ 9 \\ \hline 81 \end{array}$$

18.
$$\begin{array}{r} 3 \\ \times\ 9 \\ \hline 27 \end{array}$$

Lesson 4·3 *Pages 66–68*

Multiply. Add partial products, if needed.

1.
$$\begin{array}{r} 23 \\ \times\ 3 \\ \hline 69 \end{array}$$

2.
$$\begin{array}{r} 11 \\ \times\ 8 \\ \hline 88 \end{array}$$

3.
$$\begin{array}{r} 343 \\ \times\ 2 \\ \hline 686 \end{array}$$

4.
$$\begin{array}{r} 73 \\ \times\ 21 \\ \hline 1,533 \end{array}$$

5.
$$\begin{array}{r} 54 \\ \times\ 12 \\ \hline 648 \end{array}$$

6.
$$\begin{array}{r} 23 \\ \times\ 33 \\ \hline 759 \end{array}$$

7.
$$\begin{array}{r} 32 \\ \times\ 13 \\ \hline 416 \end{array}$$

8.
$$\begin{array}{r} 84 \\ \times\ 21 \\ \hline 1,764 \end{array}$$

Lesson 4·4 and 4·5 *Pages 70–73*

Multiply. Regroup if needed.

1.
$$\begin{array}{r} 47 \\ \times\ 34 \\ \hline 1,598 \end{array}$$

2.
$$\begin{array}{r} 86 \\ \times\ 42 \\ \hline 3,612 \end{array}$$

3.
$$\begin{array}{r} 192 \\ \times\ 75 \\ \hline 14,400 \end{array}$$

4.
$$\begin{array}{r} 864 \\ \times\ 56 \\ \hline 48,384 \end{array}$$

5.
$$\begin{array}{r} 712 \\ \times\ 87 \\ \hline 61,944 \end{array}$$

6.
$$\begin{array}{r} 1,345 \\ \times\ 732 \\ \hline 984,540 \end{array}$$

7.
$$\begin{array}{r} 40 \\ \times\ 67 \\ \hline 2,680 \end{array}$$

8.
$$\begin{array}{r} 105 \\ \times\ 93 \\ \hline 9,765 \end{array}$$

Extra Practice Chapter 5

► Lessons 5·1 and 5·2   *Pages 86–87*

Divide. Use the basic division facts.

1. 45 ÷ 9 5   **2.** 32 ÷ 8 4   **3.** 16 ÷ 4 4   **4.** 20 ÷ 5 4

5. 36 ÷ 4 9   **6.** 18 ÷ 2 9   **7.** 56 ÷ 8 7   **8.** 12 ÷ 3 4

9. 5)$\overline{15}$ 3   **10.** 8)$\overline{48}$ 6   **11.** 3)$\overline{24}$ 8   **12.** 7)$\overline{35}$ 5

13. Forty-five divided by nine 5   **14.** Forty-two divided by seven 6

15. Forty divided by five 8   **16.** Eighty-one divided by nine 9

► Lesson 5·3   *Pages 88–89*

Divide. If the reminder is 0, do not write it.

1. 25 ÷ 6 4 R1   **2.** 60 ÷ 7 8 R4   **3.** 33 ÷ 4 8 R1   **4.** 78 ÷ 8 9 R6

5. 11 ÷ 3 3 R2   **6.** 35 ÷ 5 7   **7.** 45 ÷ 7 6 R3   **8.** 89 ÷ 9 9 R8

9. 6)$\overline{56}$ 9 R2   **10.** 4)$\overline{90}$ 22 R2   **11.** 8)$\overline{90}$ 11 R2   **12.** 5)$\overline{67}$ 13 R2

► Lesson 5·4   *Pages 90–91*

1. 3)$\overline{696}$ 232   **2.** 5)$\overline{340}$ 68   **3.** 2)$\overline{678}$ 339   **4.** 4)$\overline{548}$ 137

5. 9)$\overline{558}$ 62   **6.** 6)$\overline{870}$ 145   **7.** 8)$\overline{295}$ 36 R7   **8.** 2)$\overline{976}$ 488

9. 410 ÷ 7 58 R4   **10.** 492 ÷ 4 123   **11.** 397 ÷ 3 132 R1 **12.** 709 ÷ 6 118 R1

13. 357 ÷ 8 44 R5 **14.** 381 ÷ 5 76 R1 **15.** 333 ÷ 9 37   **16.** 537 ÷ 7 76 R5

Extra Practice Chapter 5

▶ **Lessons 5·1 to 5·8** *Pages 86–99*

Find each quotient.

1. 25)‾325‾ 13   2. 32)‾897‾ 28 R1   3. 7)‾1,473‾ 210 R 3   4. 16)‾1,127‾ 70 R7

5. 11)‾957‾ 87   6. 27)‾2,270‾ 84 R2   7. 18)‾414‾ 23   8. 8)‾777‾ 97 R1

9. 9)‾972‾ 108   10. 6)‾4,845‾ 807 R3   11. 43)‾2,455‾ 57 R 4   12. 12)‾1,089‾ 90 R9

13. 869 ÷ 20 43 R9   14. 732 ÷ 38 19 R10   15. 2,421 ÷ 3 807   16. 502 ÷ 29 17 R9

17. 2,632 ÷ 56 47   18. 1,795 ÷ 5 359   19. 1,165 ÷ 36 32 R13   20. 7,932 ÷ 13 610 R2

▶ **Lessons 5·6 and 5·9** *Pages 94–95* and *100–101*

Solve each problem. Look for clue words whenever possible.

1. Exactly 210 students signed up for soccer. Each team has 14 players. How many teams can be formed? 15 teams

2. The soccer coach ordered 4 pairs of socks, 2 jerseys, 1 sweatshirt, and 3 pairs of shorts for each team member. If each team has 14 players, how many pairs of socks are ordered for each team? 56 pairs of socks

3. Last season, each soccer team practiced a total of 180 hours. If practice was held 2 hours each day, how many days did the team practice? 90 days

4. Each soccer team played 3 games in September, 6 games in October, and 5 games in November. Each game lasted 2 hours. How many total hours of game time did each team have? 28 hours

Extra Practice Chapter 6

▶Lessons 6·1 to 6·3   *Pages 106–112*

Use a divisibility test to answer each question.

   1. Is 5,632,380 divisible by 10? yes   **2.** Is 5,943 divisible by 6? no

   3. Is 7,236 divisible by 4? yes   **4.** Is 6,109 divisible by 9? no

▶Lesson 6·4   *Pages 114–115*

Find the greatest common factor of each pair of numbers.

   1. 8   28 4   **2.** 10   15 5   **3.** 18   24 6   **4.** 12   15 3

   5. 18   45 9   **6.** 12   20 4   **7.** 21   28 7   **8.** 18   30 6

▶Lesson 6·5   *Pages 116–117*

Find the least common multiple of each pair of numbers.

   1. 6   12 12   **2.** 3   4 12   **3.** 6   8 24   **4.** 25   50 50

   5. 9   15 45   **6.** 8   12 24   **7.** 5   6 30   **8.** 15   20 60

▶Lesson 6·6   *Page 118*

Write the prime factorization of each number.

   1. 12 $2 \times 2 \times 3$ **2.** 8 $2 \times 2 \times 2$ **3.** 10 2×5 **4.** 15 3×5 **5.** 20 $2 \times 2 \times 5$

▶Lessons 6·7 and 6·8   *Pages 119–120*

Find the value of each expression.

   1. 6^2 36   **2.** 2^3 8   **3.** 1^9 1   **4.** $\sqrt{36}$ 6   **5.** $\sqrt{25}$ 5 **6.** $\sqrt{49}$ 7

Extra Practice Chapter 7

▶ **Lesson 7·3**   *Pages 132–133*

Write each fraction in lowest terms.

1. $\dfrac{16}{40}$ $\dfrac{2}{5}$ 2. $\dfrac{44}{88}$ $\dfrac{1}{2}$ 3. $\dfrac{45}{81}$ $\dfrac{5}{9}$ 4. $\dfrac{15}{20}$ $\dfrac{3}{4}$ 5. $\dfrac{8}{100}$ $\dfrac{2}{25}$

6. $\dfrac{75}{100}$ $\dfrac{3}{4}$ 7. $\dfrac{70}{90}$ $\dfrac{7}{9}$ 8. $\dfrac{24}{32}$ $\dfrac{3}{4}$ 9. $\dfrac{49}{70}$ $\dfrac{7}{10}$ 10. $\dfrac{27}{36}$ $\dfrac{3}{4}$

11. $\dfrac{9}{99}$ $\dfrac{1}{11}$ 12. $\dfrac{30}{35}$ $\dfrac{6}{7}$ 13. $\dfrac{28}{56}$ $\dfrac{1}{2}$ 14. $\dfrac{16}{40}$ $\dfrac{2}{5}$ 15. $\dfrac{35}{100}$ $\dfrac{7}{20}$

▶ **Lesson 7·4**   *Pages 134–135*

Write each fraction in higher terms. Use the denominator shown.

1. $\dfrac{2}{3} = \dfrac{?}{6}$ 4   2. $\dfrac{13}{14} = \dfrac{?}{28}$ 26   3. $\dfrac{11}{20} = \dfrac{?}{40}$ 22   4. $\dfrac{1}{4} = \dfrac{?}{28}$ 7

5. $\dfrac{4}{10} = \dfrac{?}{50}$ 20   6. $\dfrac{3}{5} = \dfrac{?}{20}$ 12   7. $\dfrac{7}{15} = \dfrac{?}{45}$ 21   8. $\dfrac{5}{6} = \dfrac{?}{18}$ 15

▶ **Lesson 7·5**   *Pages 136–137*

Change each pair of fractions to like fractions.

1. $\dfrac{3}{4}$ $\dfrac{2}{3}$ $\dfrac{9}{12}, \dfrac{8}{12}$ 2. $\dfrac{2}{3}$ $\dfrac{5}{12}$ $\dfrac{8}{12}, \dfrac{5}{12}$ 3. $\dfrac{1}{2}$ $\dfrac{3}{8}$ $\dfrac{4}{8}, \dfrac{3}{8}$ 4. $\dfrac{1}{3}$ $\dfrac{1}{6}$ $\dfrac{2}{6}, \dfrac{1}{6}$

5. $\dfrac{1}{2}$ $\dfrac{2}{5}$ $\dfrac{5}{10}, \dfrac{4}{10}$ 6. $\dfrac{3}{4}$ $\dfrac{1}{8}$ $\dfrac{6}{8}, \dfrac{1}{8}$ 7. $\dfrac{5}{6}$ $\dfrac{7}{12}$ $\dfrac{10}{12}, \dfrac{7}{12}$ 8. $\dfrac{1}{2}$ $\dfrac{2}{3}$ $\dfrac{3}{6}, \dfrac{4}{6}$

▶ **Lesson 7·9**   *Page 144*

Change each mixed number to an improper fraction.

1. $3\dfrac{2}{3}$ $\dfrac{11}{3}$ 2. $2\dfrac{5}{6}$ $\dfrac{17}{6}$ 3. $5\dfrac{1}{2}$ $\dfrac{11}{2}$ 4. $8\dfrac{3}{4}$ $\dfrac{35}{4}$

Extra Practice Chapter 8

Lesson 8·1   *Pages 154–155*

Multiply.

1. $\frac{1}{3} \times \frac{1}{4}$ $\frac{1}{12}$

2. $\frac{1}{2} \times \frac{1}{9}$ $\frac{1}{18}$

3. $\frac{2}{5} \times \frac{3}{7}$ $\frac{6}{35}$

4. $\frac{1}{6} \times \frac{7}{9}$ $\frac{7}{54}$

5. $\frac{4}{5} \times \frac{1}{5}$ $\frac{4}{25}$

6. $\frac{1}{8} \times \frac{5}{6}$ $\frac{5}{48}$

Lesson 8·2   *Pages 156–157*

Multiply. Cancel, if possible.

1. $\frac{3}{8} \times \frac{8}{9}$ $\frac{1}{3}$

2. $\frac{4}{9} \times \frac{9}{16}$ $\frac{1}{4}$

3. $\frac{3}{5} \times \frac{10}{13}$ $\frac{6}{13}$

4. $\frac{11}{12} \times \frac{2}{3}$ $\frac{11}{18}$

5. $\frac{3}{4} \times \frac{8}{9}$ $\frac{2}{3}$

6. $\frac{5}{9} \times \frac{3}{10}$ $\frac{1}{6}$

Lessons 8·3 and 8·4   *Pages 158 and 160–161*

Multiply. Remember to change whole and mixed numbers to improper fractions.

1. $\frac{3}{4} \times 16$ 12

2. $20 \times \frac{4}{5}$ 16

3. $\frac{5}{9} \times 27$ 15

4. $9 \times 2\frac{2}{3}$ 24

5. $1\frac{3}{7} \times 7$ 10

6. $8 \times 3\frac{5}{8}$ 29

7. $\frac{5}{6} \times 1\frac{1}{2}$ $1\frac{1}{4}$

8. $2\frac{4}{9} \times 18$ 44

9. $2\frac{2}{3} \times \frac{9}{10}$ $2\frac{2}{5}$

10. $21 \times 2\frac{3}{7}$ 51

11. $\frac{5}{6} \times 2\frac{3}{10}$ $1\frac{11}{12}$

12. $15 \times 4\frac{2}{3}$ 70

13. $4\frac{5}{6} \times 1\frac{1}{2}$ $7\frac{1}{4}$

14. $2\frac{3}{8} \times 1\frac{2}{19}$ $2\frac{5}{8}$

15. $3\frac{3}{4} \times 2\frac{4}{5}$ $10\frac{1}{2}$

Extra Practice Chapter 8

Lesson 8·5 *Pages 162–163*

Divide. Remember to invert the second fraction and then multiply.

1. $\dfrac{1}{2} \div \dfrac{2}{3}$ $\dfrac{3}{4}$

2. $\dfrac{3}{4} \div \dfrac{1}{5}$ $3\dfrac{3}{4}$

3. $\dfrac{2}{3} \div \dfrac{1}{4}$ $2\dfrac{2}{3}$

4. $\dfrac{8}{9} \div \dfrac{1}{4}$ $3\dfrac{5}{9}$

5. $\dfrac{3}{7} \div \dfrac{1}{4}$ $1\dfrac{5}{7}$

6. $\dfrac{2}{5} \div \dfrac{3}{7}$ $\dfrac{14}{15}$

7. $\dfrac{2}{9} \div \dfrac{3}{4}$ $\dfrac{8}{27}$

8. $\dfrac{3}{8} \div \dfrac{1}{9}$ $3\dfrac{3}{8}$

9. $\dfrac{1}{6} \div \dfrac{1}{5}$ $\dfrac{5}{6}$

10. $\dfrac{4}{5} \div \dfrac{1}{5}$ 4

11. $\dfrac{2}{3} \div \dfrac{1}{6}$ 4

12. $\dfrac{5}{9} \div \dfrac{2}{3}$ $\dfrac{5}{6}$

13. $\dfrac{3}{4} \div \dfrac{3}{8}$ 2

14. $\dfrac{11}{12} \div \dfrac{1}{6}$ $5\dfrac{1}{2}$

15. $\dfrac{3}{14} \div \dfrac{2}{7}$ $\dfrac{3}{4}$

Lessons 8·6, 8·8, and 8·9 *Pages 164 and 168–171*

Divide. Remember to cancel, if possible.

1. $\dfrac{3}{5} \div 5$ $\dfrac{3}{25}$

2. $\dfrac{4}{9} \div 8$ $\dfrac{1}{18}$

3. $\dfrac{2}{3} \div 4$ $\dfrac{1}{6}$

4. $27 \div \dfrac{3}{4}$ 36

5. $36 \div \dfrac{4}{9}$ 81

6. $42 \div \dfrac{6}{7}$ 49

7. $\dfrac{1}{2} \div 2\dfrac{1}{2}$ $\dfrac{1}{5}$

8. $\dfrac{5}{6} \div 1\dfrac{1}{2}$ $\dfrac{5}{9}$

9. $\dfrac{9}{10} \div 2\dfrac{1}{4}$ $\dfrac{2}{5}$

10. $4\dfrac{3}{4} \div \dfrac{3}{8}$ $12\dfrac{2}{3}$

11. $3\dfrac{6}{7} \div \dfrac{3}{5}$ $6\dfrac{3}{7}$

12. $5\dfrac{1}{3} \div \dfrac{3}{4}$ $7\dfrac{1}{9}$

13. $5\dfrac{1}{2} \div 1\dfrac{2}{3}$ $3\dfrac{3}{10}$

14. $7\dfrac{1}{4} \div 2\dfrac{3}{4}$ $2\dfrac{7}{11}$

15. $6\dfrac{3}{5} \div \dfrac{3}{10}$ 22

16. $2\dfrac{5}{6} \div 1\dfrac{1}{2}$ $1\dfrac{8}{9}$

17. $3\dfrac{1}{8} \div 1\dfrac{1}{4}$ $2\dfrac{1}{2}$

18. $4\dfrac{3}{5} \div 1\dfrac{1}{10}$ $4\dfrac{2}{11}$

Extra Practice Chapter 9

Add or subtract. Remember to write each answer in lowest terms.

1. $\begin{array}{r} \frac{1}{9} \\ +\frac{7}{9} \\ \hline \frac{8}{9} \end{array}$

2. $\begin{array}{r} \frac{5}{6} \\ +\frac{5}{6} \\ \hline 1\frac{2}{3} \end{array}$

3. $\begin{array}{r} \frac{9}{10} \\ +\frac{7}{10} \\ \hline 1\frac{3}{5} \end{array}$

4. $\begin{array}{r} \frac{7}{8} \\ -\frac{3}{8} \\ \hline \frac{1}{2} \end{array}$

5. $\begin{array}{r} \frac{4}{5} \\ +\frac{3}{5} \\ \hline 1\frac{2}{5} \end{array}$

6. $\frac{9}{14} - \frac{3}{14}$ $\frac{3}{7}$

7. $\frac{7}{12} - \frac{5}{12}$ $\frac{1}{6}$

8. $\frac{8}{9} - \frac{5}{9}$ $\frac{1}{3}$

Add. Remember to write each answer in lowest terms.

1. $\begin{array}{r} 2\frac{1}{5} \\ +\ 1\frac{2}{5} \\ \hline 3\frac{3}{5} \end{array}$

2. $\begin{array}{r} 3\frac{3}{4} \\ +\ 4\frac{1}{4} \\ \hline 8 \end{array}$

3. $\begin{array}{r} 5\frac{3}{7} \\ +\ 2\frac{1}{7} \\ \hline 7\frac{4}{7} \end{array}$

4. $\begin{array}{r} 4\frac{5}{6} \\ +\ 2\frac{3}{6} \\ \hline 7\frac{1}{3} \end{array}$

5. $\begin{array}{r} 8\frac{5}{8} \\ +\ 1\frac{1}{8} \\ \hline 9\frac{3}{4} \end{array}$

6. $3\frac{2}{3} + 2\frac{2}{3}$ $6\frac{1}{3}$

7. $7\frac{5}{7} + 3\frac{2}{7}$ 11

8. $6\frac{1}{9} + 4\frac{5}{9}$ $10\frac{2}{3}$

Subtract. Remember to regroup, if needed.

1. $\begin{array}{r} 4\frac{4}{5} \\ -\ 3\frac{1}{5} \\ \hline 1\frac{3}{5} \end{array}$

2. $\begin{array}{r} 7\frac{5}{8} \\ -\ 3\frac{1}{8} \\ \hline 4\frac{1}{2} \end{array}$

3. $\begin{array}{r} 7\frac{8}{9} \\ -\ 4\frac{5}{9} \\ \hline 3\frac{1}{3} \end{array}$

4. $\begin{array}{r} 11\frac{1}{3} \\ -\ 5\frac{2}{3} \\ \hline 5\frac{2}{3} \end{array}$

5. $\begin{array}{r} 10\frac{2}{5} \\ -\ 6\frac{4}{5} \\ \hline 3\frac{3}{5} \end{array}$

6. $5\frac{5}{6} - 1\frac{2}{6}$ $4\frac{1}{2}$

7. $7\frac{3}{10} - 2\frac{7}{10}$ $4\frac{3}{5}$

8. $3\frac{3}{8} - 2\frac{7}{8}$ $\frac{1}{2}$

Extra Practice Chapter 9

▶Lesson 9·4 *Pages 184–185*

Subtract. Remember to regroup the whole number.

1. $\begin{array}{r} 5 \\ -\ \frac{3}{4} \\ \hline 4\frac{1}{4} \end{array}$
2. $\begin{array}{r} 7 \\ -\ 3\frac{1}{4} \\ \hline 3\frac{3}{4} \end{array}$
3. $\begin{array}{r} 8 \\ -\ 2\frac{4}{6} \\ \hline 5\frac{1}{3} \end{array}$
4. $\begin{array}{r} 9 \\ -\ 3\frac{2}{3} \\ \hline 5\frac{1}{3} \end{array}$
5. $\begin{array}{r} 8 \\ -\ 3\frac{3}{10} \\ \hline 4\frac{7}{10} \end{array}$

6. $6 - 2\frac{1}{7}$ $3\frac{6}{7}$
7. $11 - 5\frac{4}{9}$ $5\frac{5}{9}$
8. $12 - 10\frac{5}{7}$ $1\frac{2}{7}$

▶Lesson 9·5 *Page 186*

Add. Remember to rename as like fractions.

1. $\begin{array}{r} \frac{3}{14} \\ +\ \frac{1}{2} \\ \hline \frac{5}{7} \end{array}$
2. $\begin{array}{r} \frac{5}{8} \\ +\ \frac{3}{4} \\ \hline 1\frac{3}{8} \end{array}$
3. $\begin{array}{r} \frac{2}{3} \\ +\ \frac{8}{9} \\ \hline 1\frac{5}{9} \end{array}$
4. $\begin{array}{r} \frac{7}{10} \\ +\ \frac{1}{5} \\ \hline \frac{9}{10} \end{array}$
5. $\begin{array}{r} \frac{1}{2} \\ +\ \frac{2}{3} \\ \hline 1\frac{1}{6} \end{array}$

6. $\frac{1}{3} + \frac{5}{12}$ $\frac{3}{4}$
7. $\frac{3}{4} + \frac{2}{3}$ $1\frac{5}{12}$
8. $\frac{5}{6} + \frac{5}{12}$ $1\frac{1}{4}$

▶Lesson 9·6 *Page 188*

Subtract. Remember to rename as like fractions.

1. $\begin{array}{r} \frac{7}{8} \\ -\ \frac{1}{4} \\ \hline \frac{5}{8} \end{array}$
2. $\begin{array}{r} \frac{5}{6} \\ -\ \frac{2}{3} \\ \hline \frac{1}{6} \end{array}$
3. $\begin{array}{r} \frac{3}{4} \\ -\ \frac{5}{12} \\ \hline \frac{1}{3} \end{array}$
4. $\begin{array}{r} \frac{9}{14} \\ -\ \frac{1}{2} \\ \hline \frac{1}{7} \end{array}$
5. $\begin{array}{r} \frac{2}{3} \\ -\ \frac{2}{9} \\ \hline \frac{4}{9} \end{array}$

6. $\frac{11}{12} - \frac{1}{4}$ $\frac{2}{3}$
7. $\frac{3}{5} - \frac{1}{10}$ $\frac{1}{2}$
8. $\frac{5}{8} - \frac{1}{3}$ $\frac{7}{24}$

Extra Practice Chapter 9

Lesson 9·7 *Pages 190–191*

Add. Remember to rename as like mixed numbers.

1. $3\frac{1}{2}$
$+\ 9\frac{2}{3}$
$13\frac{1}{6}$

2. $7\frac{1}{3}$
$+\ 9\frac{2}{5}$
$16\frac{11}{15}$

3. $6\frac{2}{5}$
$+\ 1\frac{3}{10}$
$7\frac{7}{10}$

4. $5\frac{3}{4}$
$+\ 3\frac{5}{8}$
$9\frac{3}{8}$

5. $6\frac{1}{6}$
$+\ 6\frac{3}{5}$
$12\frac{23}{30}$

6. $8\frac{5}{6}$
$+\ 3\frac{2}{9}$
$12\frac{1}{18}$

7. $8\frac{1}{10}$
$+\ \ 5\frac{2}{5}$
$13\frac{1}{2}$

8. $2\frac{3}{8}$
$+\ 1\frac{1}{4}$
$3\frac{5}{8}$

9. $2\frac{3}{7}+3\frac{1}{3}$ $5\frac{16}{21}$

10. $7\frac{3}{11}+2\frac{1}{2}$ $9\frac{17}{22}$

11. $1\frac{1}{4}+8\frac{1}{3}$ $9\frac{7}{12}$

12. $9\frac{2}{5}+5\frac{3}{4}$ $15\frac{3}{20}$

Lesson 9·8 *Pages 192–193*

Subtract. Remember to rename as like mixed numbers. Regroup if needed.

1. $5\frac{3}{4}$
$-\ 1\frac{1}{8}$
$4\frac{5}{8}$

2. $7\frac{1}{2}$
$-\ 4\frac{2}{5}$
$3\frac{1}{10}$

3. $3\frac{4}{5}$
$-\ 1\frac{3}{10}$
$2\frac{1}{2}$

4. $6\frac{2}{3}$
$-\ 2\frac{7}{8}$
$3\frac{19}{24}$

5. $3\frac{8}{9}$
$-\ 1\frac{2}{3}$
$2\frac{2}{9}$

6. $\frac{19}{10}$
$-\ \ \frac{2}{5}$
$1\frac{1}{2}$

7. $6\frac{1}{3}$
$-\ 2\frac{1}{10}$
$4\frac{7}{30}$

8. $5\frac{7}{8}$
$-\ 2\frac{1}{6}$
$3\frac{17}{24}$

9. $3\frac{1}{7}-1\frac{1}{4}$ $1\frac{25}{28}$

10. $5\frac{3}{5}-5\frac{1}{3}$ $\frac{4}{15}$

Extra Practice Chapter 9

▶ **Lessons 9-1 to 9-8**   *Pages 178–193*

Add or subtract.

1. $\begin{array}{r} \frac{4}{5} \\ + 3\frac{1}{5} \\ \hline 4 \end{array}$

2. $\begin{array}{r} 6\frac{3}{5} \\ - 1\frac{3}{20} \\ \hline 5\frac{9}{20} \end{array}$

3. $\begin{array}{r} 8\frac{3}{4} \\ - 2\frac{2}{3} \\ \hline 6\frac{1}{12} \end{array}$

4. $\begin{array}{r} 8 \\ + 5\frac{6}{7} \\ \hline 13\frac{6}{7} \end{array}$

5. $9 - 5\frac{5}{9}$ $3\frac{4}{9}$

6. $12\frac{2}{3} + 6\frac{5}{6}$ $19\frac{1}{2}$

7. $5\frac{3}{8} - 1\frac{2}{3}$ $3\frac{17}{24}$

8. $7\frac{4}{9} + 3\frac{5}{9}$ 11

9. $\frac{3}{10} + \frac{6}{7}$ $1\frac{11}{70}$

10. $5\frac{2}{3} - 2\frac{4}{6}$ 3

▶ **Lesson 9-9**   *Pages 194–195*

Solve. Work on one part at a time.

1. Jamie practiced piano for $3\frac{1}{2}$ hours on Monday and $2\frac{3}{4}$ hours on Tuesday. On Wednesday, she practiced the drums for 5 hours. How much longer did she practice piano than drums? $1\frac{1}{4}$ hours

2. Reid decided to run 26 miles over three days. He ran $9\frac{7}{8}$ miles on Monday and $8\frac{1}{2}$ miles on Tuesday. How many miles should he run on Wednesday to complete the 26 miles? $7\frac{5}{8}$ miles

3. Stock for a carpet company closed at \$35 per share. The next day, it rose \$$1\frac{1}{2}$. The day after that, it dropped \$$2\frac{1}{4}$. What is the new closing price? \$$34\frac{1}{4}$

4. Marna, Sam, and Julie are weight training. Marna lost $5\frac{1}{2}$ pounds. Sam lost double Marna's amount. Julie lost $1\frac{3}{4}$ pounds more than Sam. How many pounds did Julie lose? $12\frac{3}{4}$ pounds

5. Mrs. Henderson had 12 pounds of peanuts. She divided them into three equal bags. Then she gave away two bags. From the bag that was left, she ate $\frac{1}{2}$ pound of peanuts. How many pounds of peanuts does she have left? $3\frac{1}{2}$ pounds

Extra Practice Chapter 10

▶**Lesson 10·2** *Pages 203–204*

Write each decimal in words.

1. 39.7

2. .046

3. 5.14

4. .799 seven hundred ninety-nine thousandths

thirty-nine and seven tenths   forty-six thousandths   five and fourteen hundredths

5. 160.52

6. 800

7. .008

8. 4.9

one hundred sixty and fifty-two hundredths   eight hundred   eight thousandths   four and nine tenths

Write each number as a decimal.

9. thirty-five thousandths .035

10. two hundred and seven tenths 200.7

11. eight and five hundredths 8.05

12. sixty-eight and seventeen thousandths 68.017

▶**Lesson 10·3** *Pages 205–206*

Compare each pair of numbers. Use <, >, or =.

1. 4.2 > 4.02

2. 5.1 < 5.11

3. 2.35 < 2.36

4. 6.899 < 6.9

5. 136.8 > 13.68

6. .027 < .127

7. .99 < 1

8. 1.1 > 1.059

9. 9.041 < 10.014

▶**Lesson 10·4** *Page 207*

Write the decimals in order from largest to smallest.

1. 4.063   4.31   4.03
    4.31   4.063   4.03

2. .148   .014   .483
    .483   .148   .014

3. .8   .081   .81
    .81   .8   .081

4. 3.144   3.15   3.158
    3.158   3.15   3.144

5. 7.81   7.18   7.03
    7.81   7.18   7.03

6. 41.28   41.6   40.31
    41.6   41.28   40.31

Extra Practice Chapter 10

Lesson 10·5 *Pages 208–209*

Add.

1.   1.3
     + 4.5
     —————
      5.8

2.   5.7
     + 3.8
     —————
      9.5

3. $12.45
     +   8.29
     —————————
      $20.74

4.   2.067
     + .200
     —————————
      2.267

5. 34.9 + 2.8 37.7

6. 8 + .6 8.6

7. $23.08 + $3.90 $26.98

8. 15.762 + 8.04 23.802

9. $24.99 + $18.49 $43.48

10. 10.4 + .08 + 1.349 11.829

Lesson 10·6 *Pages 210–211*

Subtract.

1.   4.8
     − 1.5
     —————
      3.3

2.   14.1
     − 5.7
     ——————
       8.4

3. $10.00
     −   4.99
     —————————
       5.01

4.   80.60
     − 6.03
     —————————
      74.57

5. 13.78 − 10.45 3.33

6. 15 − 3.22 11.78

7. $23.75 − $23.58 $.17

8. 4.088 − .726 3.362

9. 2.9 − 1.045 1.855

10. .5 − .025 .475

Lesson 10·7 *Pages 212–213*

Multiply.

1.   .4
     × .7
     ————
     .28

2.   .2
     × .3
     ————
     .06

3.   4.5
     × 1.5
     —————
     6.75

4.   13.25
     × .04
     —————
      .53

5. 3.5 × .8 2.8

6. $23.00 × 1.05 $24.15

7. 23.05 × 2.9 66.845

8. 34.89 × .1 3.489

9. 3.024 × 28 84.672

10. .005 × 12.8 .064

Extra Practice Chapter 10

▶**Lesson 10·9**   *Pages 216–217*

Divide.

1. $2\overline{).24}$ .12   **2.** $6\overline{).54}$ .09   **3.** $9\overline{).027}$ .003   **4.** $15\overline{)30.45}$ 2.03

5. .81 ÷ 6 .135   **6.** .75 ÷ 15 .05   **7.** 12.96 ÷ 40 .324

8. 4.3 ÷ 8 .5375   **9.** .008 ÷ 25 .00032   **10.** 18.32 ÷ 50 .3664

▶**Lesson 10·10**   *Pages 218–219*

Divide.

1. $.06\overline{).48}$ 8   **2.** $3.8\overline{)2.128}$ .56   **3.** $.05\overline{)21}$ 420   **4.** $.3\overline{)91.44}$ 304.8

5. 28.45 ÷ .15 $189.\overline{6}$ **6.** 12.09 ÷ .06 201.5   **7.** 4.8 ÷ .16 30

8. 6.75 ÷ .3 22.5   **9.** 15 ÷ .02 750   **10.** 34.3 ÷ 1.225 28

▶**Lesson 10·12**   *Pages 222–223*

Use the chart to solve each problem.

1. Find the price of each item with tax.
$1.36; $1.04; $14.70

2. What is the price with tax of
15 mechanical pencils? $15.60

3. A math club has 20 members. They need
10 rulers, 20 pencils, and 5 calculators.
The club will split the total cost equally
among themselves. How much will each
member pay, including tax? $5.40

School Supplies		
Item	Price	Tax
ruler	$ 1.29	$.07
mechanical pencil	.99	.05
calculator	14.00	.70

Extra Practice Chapter 10

▶ Mixed Practice

Calculate.

1. $\begin{array}{r} 5.27 \\ + 1.19 \\ \hline 6.46 \end{array}$

2. $\begin{array}{r} 4.96 \\ - 4.87 \\ \hline .09 \end{array}$

3. $\begin{array}{r} 35.8 \\ \times .5 \\ \hline 17.9 \end{array}$

4. $4.8\overline{)96}$ $\overset{20}{}$

5. $\begin{array}{r} 7.92 \\ \times 1.06 \\ \hline 8.3952 \end{array}$

6. $\begin{array}{r} 32.97 \\ - .055 \\ \hline 32.915 \end{array}$

7. $1.9\overline{)15.58}$ $\overset{8.2}{}$

8. $\begin{array}{r} 7.904 \\ + 3.176 \\ \hline 11.080 \end{array}$

9. $21 - .409$ 20.591

10. $.16 - .07$ .09

11. $1.007 + .08 + 7$ 8.087

12. $825 \div .25$ 3,300

13. 8.63×4.9 42.287

14. $1.4 \div 6$ .2$\overline{3}$

15. $\$39.58 + \$11.79$ $51.37

16. $\$155.40 \div 12$ $12.95

17. $\$18.98 \times 100$ $1,898

▶ Lesson 10·13 *Page 224*

Rename each decimal as a fraction. Reduce if possible.

1. .25 $\frac{25}{100} = \frac{1}{4}$

2. .04 $\frac{4}{100} = \frac{1}{25}$

3. .8 $\frac{8}{10} = \frac{4}{5}$

4. .125 $\frac{125}{1000} = \frac{1}{8}$

5. .4 $\frac{4}{10} = \frac{2}{5}$

6. .5 $\frac{5}{10} = \frac{1}{2}$

7. .75 $\frac{75}{100} = \frac{3}{4}$

8. .6 $\frac{6}{10} = \frac{3}{5}$

9. .625 $\frac{625}{1000} = \frac{5}{8}$

10. .05 $\frac{5}{100} = \frac{1}{20}$

▶ Lesson 10·14 *Page 225*

Rename each fraction as a decimal.

1. $\frac{3}{4}$ .75

2. $\frac{1}{2}$ .5

3. $\frac{3}{10}$ .3

4. $\frac{1}{8}$ .125

5. $\frac{2}{3}$.$\overline{6}$

6. $\frac{7}{8}$ .875

7. $\frac{3}{5}$ .6

8. $\frac{1}{4}$ .25

9. $\frac{2}{5}$ .4

10. $\frac{7}{10}$ .7

Extra Practice Chapter 11

▶ **Lesson 11·1** *Page 232*

Write the percent for each description.

1. 12 parts out of 100 are shaded. What percent is shaded? 12%

2. If 3 parts out of 100 are red, what percent is red? 3%

3. Each whole has 100 equal parts. 140 parts are shaded. What percent is shaded? 140%

4. What percent is shaded if 35 out of 100 parts are shaded? 35%

▶ **Lesson 11·2** *Page 233*

Change each percent to a decimal.

1. 43% .43   2. 28% .28   3. 2% .02   4. $2\frac{1}{2}$% .025

5. $8\frac{1}{2}$% .085   6. 8.5% .085   7. $14\frac{1}{2}$% .145   8. 2.5% .025

9. 118% 1.18   10. 255% 2.55   11. 6% .06   12. 145% 1.45

▶ **Lesson 11·3** *Pages 234–235*

Find the part in each problem.

1. 50% of 66 is ▩ 33   2. 25% of 36 is ▩ 9   3. 10% of 70 is ▩ 7

4. 19% of 100 is ▩ 19   5. 20% of 450 is ▩ 90   6. 125% of 32 is ▩ 40

7. What is 16% of 30? 4.8   8. What is 30% of 88? 26.4

9. What is 150% of 40? 60   10. What is 200% of 85? 170

Extra Practice Chapter 11

▶ Lesson 11·4   *Pages 236–237*

Solve each problem about sales tax.

1. The sales tax in New Jersey is 6%. Your purchases total $17.50. What is the amount of tax? $1.05

2. The sales tax in the city is 11%. Your purchase is $58. What is the amount of sales tax? $6.38

3. An ice cream cone costs $1.60. If the sales tax is 5%, what is the total cost of the ice cream cone? $1.68

4. The sales tax on home furnishings is 7%. How much tax will be paid on a purchase of $880? $61.60

5. A new kitchen table costs $148. The sales tax is 5%. What is the total cost of the table? $155.40

▶ Lesson 11·5   *Pages 238–239*

Solve each problem about discounts.

1. The television costs $450. It is on sale at 30% off. What is the discount? $135

2. A new washing machine, originally $360, is on sale at 25% off. What is the discount? $90

3. All tools are on sale at 10% off. At the original prices, your tool purchase totals $48. What is your sale price? $43.20

4. The radio is on sale at 25% off. The original price was $20. What is the sale price? $15

5. The original cost of a cassette player is $235. The salesperson offers you a 15% discount. How much will you save? $35.25

Extra Practice Chapter 11

▶**Lesson 11·6**   *Pages 240–241*

Solve each problem about commissions.

1. A new car costs $20,000. If the salesperson's commission is 3%, what is the amount of the commission? $600

2. Sally receives 7% commission on greeting card sales. If she sells $5,600 worth of cards, what is the amount of her commission? $392

3. At your new job, the base salary is $200 per week. In addition, the commission on sales is 4%. If you sell $4,000 in sales for the week, what is your gross salary? $360

4. The real estate commission on the property is 5%. If the property sells for $110,000, what is the amount of the commission? $5,500

▶**Lesson 11·7**   *Page 243*

Change each decimal to a percent.

1. .23 23%

2. .08 8%

3. .17 17%

4. .6 60%

5. 1.12 112%

6. 2.53 253%

7. .234 23.4%

8. 2.7 270%

▶**Lesson 11·8**   *Page 244*

Change each fraction to a percent.

1. $\frac{11}{100}$ 11%

2. $\frac{2}{5}$ 40%

3. $\frac{3}{20}$ 15%

4. $\frac{4}{25}$ 16%

5. $\frac{7}{10}$ 70%

6. $\frac{1}{8}$ 12.5%

7. $\frac{3}{50}$ 6%

8. $\frac{2}{5}$ 40%

Extra Practice Chapter 11

▶Lesson 11·9 *Pages 247–248*

Find the percent to solve each problem.

1. What percent of 60 is 30? 50%

2. What percent of 104 is 26? 25%

3. What percent of 100 is 450? 450%

4. What percent of 560 is 280? 50%

5. 16 is what percent of 80? 20%

6. 196 is what percent of 560? 35%

7. 200 is what percent of 50? 400%

8. 90 is what percent of 30? 300%

▶Lesson 11·10 *Pages 248–249*

Find the percent increase or decrease to solve each problem.

1. David's autographed baseball is worth $100 now. Last year, it was worth $80. What is the percent increase? $25%

2. Jan's stocks are worth $2,160 now. Last month, they were worth $2,400. What is the percent decrease? 10%

3. A car worth $10,000 last year is now worth $7,000. What is the percent decrease? 30%

4. Your $2,000 art collection is now worth $5,000. What is the percent increase? 150%

▶Lesson 11·11 *Pages 250–251*

Find the whole to solve each problem.

1. 20 is 10% of what number? 200

2. 23 is 50% of what number? 46

3. 11 is 25% of what number? 44

4. 60 is 75% of what number? 80

5. 80% of what number is 100? 125

6. 45% of what number is 90? 200

Extra Practice Chapter 11

► **Lesson 11·12** *Pages 252–253*

Find the original price to solve each problem.

1. Leo's book costs $20. All books are on sale at 20% off. What was the original price of the book? $25

2. A media rack is on sale for $19. This is 50% off the original price. What was the original price? $38

3. An art collection has increased in value by 10%. It is now worth $2,200. What was its original value? $2,000

4. Dues this year are $30. This is a 25% increase from last year. What were last year's dues? $24

► **Lesson 11·13** *Pages 254–255*

Solve each problem. Be careful: all three types of percent problems are used.

1. Nancy's workout is 90 minutes long. She spends 30% of her time swimming. How many minutes does she spend swimming? 27 minutes

2. Clark spends 25% of his workout time on the exercise bike. If he spends 30 minutes on the bike, how long is his workout? 120 minutes

3. Marianne spends 15 minutes of her 75-minute workout doing step aerobics. What percent of her workout is spent doing step aerobics? 20%

4. Thomas plays tennis 3 hours every week. This is 50% of his weekly exercise. How long is his weekly exercise? 6 hours

5. Caitlin jogs 25 miles each month. She jogs with a partner for 10 of those miles. What percent of her jogging is with a partner? 40%

Extra Practice Chapter 12

▶ **Lesson 12·1**   *Pages 260–261*

Write a ratio for each problem using fractions or ratio signs.

1. blue squares to all squares ☐ ☐ ☐ ☐ ☐ ☐ ☐ ☐ $\frac{7}{8}$, 7:8

2. In a class of 29 students, 13 students are male. What is the ratio of all students to male students? 29:13

3. Of the 32 total movies in John's collection, 13 are cartoons, 5 are action, and 14 are comedies. What is the ratio of action movies to the total number of movies? $\frac{5}{32}$, 5:32

▶ **Lesson 12·3**   *Page 264*

Find the missing number in each proportion.

1. $\frac{2}{?} = \frac{8}{12}$ 3

2. $\frac{3}{7} = \frac{?}{28}$ 12

3. $\frac{4}{?} = \frac{1}{4}$ 16

4. $\frac{?}{10} = \frac{2}{5}$ 4

5. $\frac{8}{56} = \frac{1}{?}$ 7

6. $\frac{3}{?} = \frac{18}{24}$ 4

7. $\frac{8}{?} = \frac{24}{36}$ 12

8. $\frac{5}{7} = \frac{15}{?}$ 21

▶ **Lesson 12·4 to 12·6**   *Pages 266–268 and 270–271*

Use a proportion to solve each problem.

1. Charlotte bought 3 pizzas for $12. How many pizzas can she buy for $36? 9 pizzas

2. Suppose that 2 buses can carry 44 people. How many buses are needed if there are 132 people? 6 buses

3. The scale on a map is 1 inch = 10 miles. The distance on the map is 5 inches. How many miles does this represent? 50 miles

4. Zachary can buy 7 plates for $14. How much will he pay for 21 plates? $42

Extra Practice Chapter 13

▶**Lesson 13·1**   *Pages 278–279*

Make a pictograph of the information in the table.

Ice Cream Bars Sold	
Day	Number Sold
Monday	45
Tuesday	35
Wednesday	30
Thursday	50
Friday	85
Saturday	100
Sunday	90

Ice Cream Bars Sold

Key ▮ = 10 ice cream bars

Monday	▮ ▮ ▮ ▮
Tuesday	▮ ▮ ▮
Wednesday	▮ ▮ ▮
Thursday	▮ ▮ ▮ ▮ ▮
Friday	▮ ▮ ▮ ▮ ▮ ▮ ▮ ▮
Saturday	▮ ▮ ▮ ▮ ▮ ▮ ▮ ▮ ▮ ▮
Sunday	▮ ▮ ▮ ▮ ▮ ▮ ▮ ▮ ▮

▶**Lessons 13·2 and 13·3**   *Pages 280–283*

Make a bar graph of the information in each table.

1.

Area of Metro Counties	
County	Square Miles
Washington	3,000
Ramsey	6,500
Hennepin	9,000
Cooke	7,500
Beaver	2,000

2.

Carnival Rides		
Ride	Children	Adults
Roller Coaster	32	58
Ferris Wheel	45	63
Bumper Cars	68	25

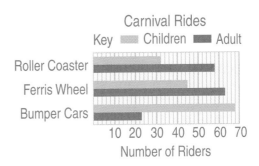

Extra Practice Chapter 13

▶ Lessons 13·4 and 13·5 *Pages 284–287*

Make a line graph of the information in each table.

1.

Number of Businesses in Springfield	
Year	Number
1994	250
1995	300
1996	375
1997	400
1998	475

Answer is on page 468

2.

Rainfall in Scottsdale		
Season	Predicted Number of Inches	Actual Number of Inches
Spring	8	11
Summer	6	3
Fall	4	5
Winter	6	3

Answer is on page 468.

▶ Lesson 13·6 *Pages 288–289*

Use the graphs to answer questions 1 and 2.

Graph A

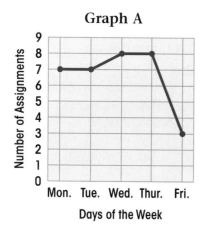

Graph B

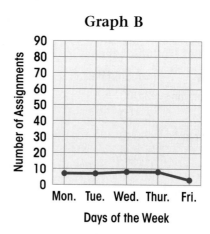

1. The teachers want to send home a graph showing the parents that they do not give too much homework in one week. Which graph should they use and why? Graph B

2. The students want to send home a graph showing the parents that the teachers do send home a lot of homework in one week. Which graph should they use and why? Graph A

Extra Practice Chapter 13

▶**Lesson 13·7** *Page 290*

Use the information in the circle graph to answer each question.

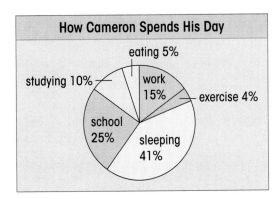

How Cameron Spends His Day

eating 5%
studying 10%
work 15%
exercise 4%
school 25%
sleeping 41%

1. How does Cameron spend most of his day? sleeping

2. What percent of his day is spent in school and studying? 35%

3. How many hours a day does Cameron work? 3.6 hr

4. How many hours does Cameron sleep each night? 9.84 hr

▶**Lesson 13·8** *Pages 292–293*

Find the mean of each set of numbers.

1. 24, 15, 18, 27 21

2. 45, 93, 100, 38, 20, 88 64

3. 11, 13, 15, 17, 19 15

4. 8, 35, 40, 2, 16, 25 21

▶**Lesson 13·9** *Pages 294–295*

Find the median and the mode of each set of numbers.

1. 27, 89, 65, 101, 48, 89, 32 65; 89

2. 7, 16, 3, 95, 21, 12 14; none

3. 5, 5, 4, 3, 1, 7, 7, 3, 2, 9, 5, 1 4.5; 5

4. 31, 72, 89, 31, 38, 21, 89, 72 5.5; 31; 72 and 89

Extra Practice Chapter 13

▶**Lesson 13·10**   *Pages 296–297*

Use the histogram to answer each question.

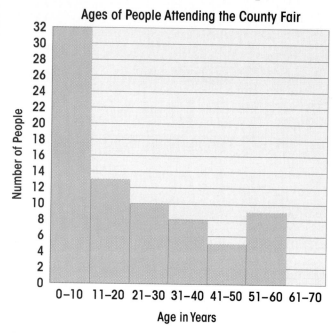

Ages of People Attending the County Fair

1. Most people attending the fair were in what age group? 0–10 years

2. How many people attending the fair were between 21 and 30 years old? 10 people

3. How many people attending the fair were 30 years old or less? 55 people

4. How many people attending the fair were 41 years old or older? 14 people

▶**Lesson 13·11**   *Page 298*

A bag contains 7 white marbles, 15 green marbles, 6 red
marbles, 2 yellow marbles, and 10 blue marbles. You choose
one marble without looking. Find the probability of each event.

1. choosing a red marble $\frac{3}{20}$

2. choosing a white marble $\frac{7}{40}$

3. choosing a green marble $\frac{3}{8}$

4. choosing a blue or white marble $\frac{17}{40}$

Extra Practice Chapter 14

▶**Lesson 14·1**   *Pages 304–305*

Change each measurement. First, decide whether to multiply or divide.

1. 36 inches = ▨ feet
3

2. 3 miles = ▨ feet
15,840

3. 9 yards = ▨ feet
27

4. 16 feet = ▨ yards
$5\frac{1}{3}$

5. 5 yards = ▨ inches
180

6. $\frac{1}{3}$ foot = ▨ inches
4

7. 108 inches = ▨ yards
3

8. 42 inches = ▨ feet
3.5

9. 1.5 yards = ▨ inches
54

10. $\frac{1}{3}$ yard = ▨ inches
12

11. 1.1 miles = ▨ feet
5,808

12. $\frac{7}{8}$ mile = ▨ feet
4,620

▶**Lesson 14·2**   *Pages 306–307*

Change each measurement. First, decide whether to multiply or divide.

1. 3 pounds = ▨ ounces
48

2. 3 tons = ▨ pounds
6,000

3. 64 ounces = ▨ pounds
4

4. 2.7 tons = ▨ pounds
5,400

5. 2.5 pounds = ▨ ounces
40

6. 8 ounces = ▨ pound
$\frac{1}{2}$

7. 1,000 pounds = ▨ ton
$\frac{1}{2}$

8. $\frac{1}{8}$ pound = ▨ ounces
2

9. 200 ounces = ▨ pounds
12.5

10. 5.2 pounds = ▨ ounces
83.2

11. $1\frac{1}{8}$ pounds = ▨ ounces
18

12. $\frac{1}{2}$ ton = ▨ pounds
1,000

Extra Practice Chapter 14

**Change each measurement. First, decide whether to multiply
or divide.**

1. 6 quarts = ■ pints
   12

2. 5 gallons = ■ quarts
   20

3. 70 pints = ■ quarts
   35

4. 128 fluid ounces = ■ quarts
   4

5. 6 pints = ■ fluid ounces
   96

6. 50 pints = ■ quarts
   25

7. 44 quarts = ■ gallons
   11

8. 80 fluid ounces = ■ pints
   5

9. 2.5 gallons = ■ quarts
   10

10. 1.5 quarts = ■ pints
    3

11. 8 pints = ■ gallons
    1

12. 10 quarts = ■ gallons
    2.5

**Change each measurement. First, decide whether to multiply
or divide.**

1. 5 hours = ■ minutes
   300

2. 240 hours = ■ days
   10

3. 540 minutes = ■ hours
   9

4. 9 years = ■ months
   108

5. 90 seconds = ■ minutes
   1.5

6. 3 years = ■ weeks
   156

7. 63 days = ■ weeks
   9

8. 364 weeks = ■ years
   7

9. 390 minutes = ■ hours
   6.5

10. 12.5 years = ■ months
    150

11. 9.5 days = ■ hours
    228

12. 102 months = ■ years
    8.5

Extra Practice Chapter 14

▶Lesson 14·6 *Pages 314–315*

Find the elapsed time.

1. 5:15 P.M. to 7:40 P.M.
   2 hours 25 minutes

2. 9:36 A.M. to 11:10 A.M.
   1 hour 34 minutes

3. 3:23 A.M. to 9:45 A.M.
   6 hours 22 minutes

4. 4:52 P.M. to 1:13 A.M.
   8 hours 21 minutes

5. 7:32 P.M. to 12:00 midnight
   4 hours 28 minutes

6. 6:10 A.M. to 10:04 A.M.
   3 hours 54 minutes

7. 8:39 P.M. to 3:13 A.M.
   6 hours 34 minutes

8. 5:21 A.M. to 8:48 A.M
   3 hours 27 minutes

9. 4:29 P.M. to 11:11 P.M.
   6 hours 42 minutes

10. 3:15 A.M. to 2:19 P.M.
    11 hours 4 minutes

11. 1:46 A.M. to 7:29 A.M.
    5 hours 43 minutes

12. 2:13 P.M. to 9:00 P.M.
    6 hours 47 minutes

▶Lesson 14·7 *Pages 316*

Add or subtract to find the new temperature.

1. The temperature was 55° in the morning. By noon, it rose 15°. What was the temperature at noon? 70°

2. The temperature was 42° It fell 18° during the night. What was the temperature at the end of the night? 24°

3. In the afternoon, the temperature was 85°. It fell 6° five hours later. What was the temperature five hours later? 79°

4. In the morning, the temperature was 35°. By noon, the temperature fell 10°. What was the temperature by noon? 25°

Extra Practice Chapter 15

▶ **Lesson 15·2**   *Pages 324–325*

Change each measurement. First, decide whether to multiply or divide.

1. 4 kilometers = ■ meters
   4,000

2. 800 meters = ■ hectometers
   8

3. 950 centimeters = ■ meters
   9.5

4. 7,400 millimeters = ■ meters
   7.4

5. 60 millimeters = ■ centimeters
   6

6. 45 decimeters = ■ meters
   4.5

7. 4 dekameters = ■ meters
   40

8. 800 millimeters = ■ meter
   .8

9. 3.4 kilometers = ■ meters 3,400

10. 790 centimeters = ■ meters 7.9

▶ **Lesson 15·3**   *Pages 326–327*

Change each measurement. First, decide whether to multiply or divide.

1. 3.8 kilograms = ■ grams
   3,800

2. 400 grams = ■ decigrams
   4,000

3. 7.5 grams = ■ milligrams
   7,500

4. 5,000 grams = ■ kilograms
   5

5. 890 centigrams = ■ grams
   8.9

6. 4,600 milligrams = ■ grams
   4.6

7. 9,000 grams = ■ kilograms 9

8. 6.2 grams = ■ milligrams 6,200

▶ **Lesson 15·4**   *Pages 328–329*

Change each measurement. First, decide whether to multiply or divide.

1. 6 liters = ■ milliliters
   6,000

2. 5,000 liters = ■ kiloliters
   5

3. 20,000 milliliters = ■ liters
   20

4. 9.6 kiloliters = ■ liters
   9,600

5. 3.5 kiloliters = ■ liters
   3,500

6. 3,400 milliliters = ■ liters
   3.4

7. 4.8 liters = ■ milliliters 4,800

8. 100 liters = ■ kiloliter .1

Extra Practice Chapter 16

▶**Lesson 16·2** *Pages 340–341*

Use a protractor to measure each angle.

1. 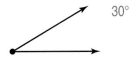 30°

2.  152°

3. 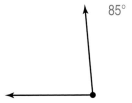 85°

4. 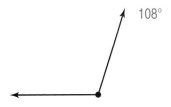 108°

▶**Lesson 16·4** *Pages 344–345*

Find the measure of the unknown angle in each triangle.

1. 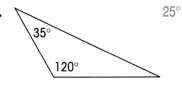 25°

2. 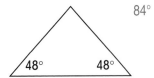 84°

3. 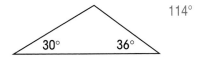 114°

4. 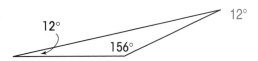 12°

5. 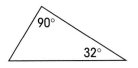 58°

6. 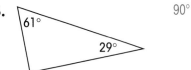 90°

Extra Practice Chapter 16

▶ Lesson 16·6 *Pages 348–349*

Find the perimeter of each figure.

1.

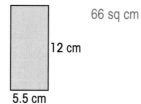

13 m
8 m   8 m
13 m

42 m

2.

4 yd
3.5 yd   3.5 yd
5 yd   5 yd
6 yd

27 yd

3.

3 in.   3 in.
2 in.   2 in.
5 in.

15 in.

▶ Lessons 16·7 and 16·8 *Pages 350–352*

Find the area of each figure.

1.

4 in.
7 in.

28 sq in.

2.

12 cm
5.5 cm

66 sq cm

3.

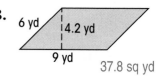

6 yd   4.2 yd
9 yd

37.8 sq yd

4.

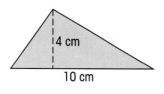

5.6 ft

31.36 sq ft

5.

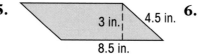

3 in.   4.5 in.
8.5 in.

25.5 sq in.

6.

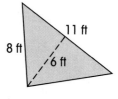

4.5 m
2 m

9 sq m

▶ Lesson 16·9 *Pages 354–355*

Find the area of each triangle.

1.

4 cm
10 cm

20 sq cm

2.

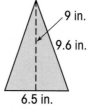

9 in.
9.6 in.
6.5 in.

29.25 sq in.

3.

11 ft
8 ft   6 ft

33 sq ft

Extra Practice Chapter 16

▶ **Lessons 16·10 and 16·11** *Pages 356–359*

Find the circumference of each circle. Find the area of each circle.

1.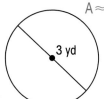
C ≈ 9.4 yd
A ≈ 7.1 sq yd
3 yd

2.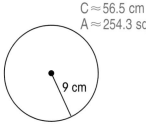
C ≈ 56.5 cm
A ≈ 254.3 sq cm
9 cm

3.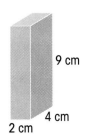
C ≈ 26.7 ft
A ≈ 56.7 sq ft
8.5 ft

4. radius = 5 ft
C ≈ 31.4 ft.
A ≈ 78.5 sq ft

5. diameter = 13 in.
C ≈ 40.8 in.
A ≈ 132.7 sq in.

6. diameter = 8.2 yd
C ≈ 25.7 yd
A ≈ 52.8 sq yd

▶ **Lesson 16·13** *Pages 362–363*

Find the volume of each prism.

1.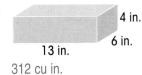
4 in.
6 in.
13 in.
312 cu in.

2.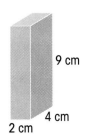
72 cu cm
9 cm
4 cm
2 cm

3.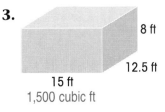
8 ft
12.5 ft
15 ft
1,500 cubic ft

▶ **Lesson 16·14** *Pages 364–365*

Find the volume of each cylinder.

1.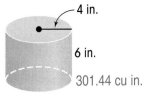
4 in.
6 in.
301.44 cu in.

2.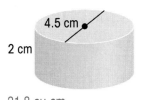
4.5 cm
2 cm
31.8 cu cm

3.
13 ft
5 ft
255.125 cu ft

Extra Practice Chapter 17

Add.

1. $^-6 + {}^-2$ $^-8$
2. $^+8 + {}^+7$ $^+15$
3. $^-5 + {}^-1$ $^-6$
4. $^-4 + {}^-7$ $^-11$
5. $^-5 + {}^-1$ $^-6$
6. $^+6 + {}^+9$ $^+15$
7. $^-9 + {}^-4$ $^-13$
8. $^-2 + {}^-6$ $^-8$
9. $^-1 + {}^-3$ $^-4$
10. $^+8 + 0$ $^+8$
11. $^-4 + {}^-3$ $^-7$
12. $^-12 + 0$ $^-12$
13. $^-7 + {}^-3$ $^-10$
14. $^+12 + {}^+7$ $^+19$
15. $0 + {}^-13$ $^-13$

Add.

1. $8 + {}^-6$ $^+2$
2. $^-7 + {}^+9$ $^+2$
3. $^-5 + {}^+3$ $^-2$
4. $4 + {}^-10$ $^-6$
5. $^+6 + {}^-3$ $^+3$
6. $^-4 + {}^+5$ $^+1$
7. $^-9 + 0$ $^-9$
8. $^+2 + {}^-8$ $^-6$
9. $^-3 + {}^+7$ $^+4$
10. $12 + {}^-15$ $^-3$
11. $^+11 + {}^-7$ $^+4$
12. $^-9 + {}^+9$ 0
13. $^-1 + {}^+7$ $^+6$
14. $^-12 + {}^+8$ $^-4$
15. $^+10 + {}^-2$ $^+8$

Subtract.

1. $^-7 - {}^+3$ $^-10$
2. $^+6 - {}^+10$ $^-4$
3. $^-2 - {}^-9$ $^+7$
4. $^+3 - {}^+5$ $^-2$
5. $^+14 - {}^+7$ $^+7$
6. $^-4 - {}^-4$ 0
7. $^-1 - {}^-6$ $^+5$
8. $^+15 - {}^-3$ $^+18$
9. $^-5 - {}^+6$ $^-11$
10. $^-12 - {}^-12$ 0
11. $^-4 - {}^+8$ $^-12$
12. $^+20 - {}^+9$ $^+11$
13. $^+2 - {}^+12$ $^-10$
14. $^+9 - {}^-8$ $^+17$
15. $^-3 - {}^-10$ $^+7$

Extra Practice Chapter 17

Lesson 17·5   *Pages 382–384*

Multiply.

1. $^+2 \times {}^-5$ $^-10$
2. $^-4 \times {}^+3$ $^-12$
3. $^+9 \times {}^+6$ $^+54$
4. $^+9 \times {}^-7$ $^-63$
5. $^+8 \times {}^-6$ $^-48$
6. $^-8 \times {}^+3$ $^-24$
7. $^+4 \times {}^-9$ $^-36$
8. $^-3 \times {}^-9$ $^+27$
9. $^-6 \times {}^-4$ $^+24$
10. $^-5 \times {}^+8$ $^-40$
11. $^-5 \times {}^+9$ $^-45$
12. $^+12 \times {}^-1$ $^-12$
13. $^+7 \times {}^+4$ $^+28$
14. $^-8 \times {}^-4$ $^+32$
15. $^+11 \times {}^+5$ $^+55$

Lesson 17·6   *Pages 386–387*

Divide.

1. $^+16 \div {}^+4$ $^+4$
2. $^-12 \div {}^+6$ $^-2$
3. $^+27 \div {}^-3$ $^-9$
4. $^+49 \div {}^-7$ $^-7$
5. $^-24 \div {}^-8$ $^+3$
6. $^-20 \div {}^-2$ $^+10$
7. $^-18 \div {}^+3$ $^-6$
8. $^-15 \div {}^-1$ $^+15$
9. $^-35 \div 5$ $^-7$
10. $^-30 \div {}^-5$ $^+6$
11. $^+48 \div {}^+6$ $^+8$
12. $^-64 \div {}^-8$ $^+8$
13. $^-54 \div {}^+9$ $^-6$
14. $^+32 \div {}^-4$ $^-8$
15. $^+55 \div {}^+11$ $^+5$

Lesson 17·7   *Pages 388–389*

Solve.

1. The temperature was 5 degrees above zero at noon. It dropped 6 degrees. Then, it rose 3 degrees. What was the temperature after all the changes?   2 degrees above zero

2. In the All-State football game, Terry gained 6 yards. Then, he lost 18 yards. What was Terry's total loss or gain?   loss of 12 yards

3. The Blue Giants gained 6 yards, lost 2 yards, and then gained 9 yards. What was the team's total loss or gain?   13 yards gained

Extra Practice Chapter 18

Simplify each expression.

1. $40 - (10 + 2)$ 28

2. $6(8 - 2)$ 36

3. $(5 \times 3) + 4$ 19

4. $(8 + 6) - 3$ 11

5. $(9 \times 4) - 16$ 20

6. $12(7 - 5) + 1$ 25

7. $74 - (42 - 5)$ 37

8. $(11 \times 9) - (6 \times 11)$ 33

9. $4(8 + 5) + 5$ 57

Simplfy each expression. Remember to multiply or divide first.

1. $18 + 2 - 12$ 8

2. $41 - 7 \times 3$ 20

3. $24 \div 6 \div 2$ 2

4. $50 \div 2 \div 5$ 5

5. $6 \times 8 \div 4$ 12

6. $19 - 7 + 13$ 25

7. $26 - 8 - 2$ 16

8. $14 \times 3 + 1$ 43

9. $9 + 6 \times 3$ 27

Solve each equation.

1. $x + 7 = 15$ $x = 8$

2. $y - 8 = 2$ $y = 10$

3. $15 = t + 3$ $t = 12$

4. $w + 19 = 40$ $w = 21$

5. $24 = c - 8$ $c = 32$

6. $f + 4 = 10$ $f = 6$

7. $29 = h + 9$ $h = 20$

8. $j - 12 = 3$ $j = 15$

9. $46 = p + 8$ $p = 38$

Solve each equation.

1. $\frac{m}{6} = 4$ $m = 24$

2. $8s = 56$ $s = 7$

3. $\frac{w}{3} = 5$ $w = 15$

4. $48 = 6t$ $t = 8$

5. $9 = \frac{x}{7}$ $x = 63$

6. $7v = 49$ $v = 7$

7. $17 = 2r$ $r = 8.5$

8. $14e = 42$ $e = 3$

9. $120 = 12d$ $d = 10$

Extra Practice Chapter 18

▶**Lesson 18·6** *Pages 404–405*

Solve. Use the formula $d = r \times t$.

1. Cara took a train to Boston. The train's rate was 56 mph. She rode the train for 5 hours. How far did she ride the train? 280 miles

2. Chen drove 192 miles in 4 hours. What was his average rate of speed? 48 mph

▶**Lesson 18·7** *Pages 406–408*

Solve each equation.

1. $7a + 5 = 26$ $a = 3$
2. $\frac{m}{4} - 2 = 6$ $m = 32$
3. $32 = 3c + 8$ $c = 8$

4. $\frac{w}{9} + 15 = 18$ $w = 27$
5. $17 = \frac{x}{3} + 10$ $x = 21$
6. $5h - 6 = 14$ $h = 4$

7. $16 = 5r - 14$ $r = 6$
8. $15y - 12 = 33$ $y = 3$
9. $\frac{v}{4} + 12 = 19$ $v = 28$

▶**Lesson 18·8** *Pages 410–411*

Solve. Use the formula $c = r \times d + f$.

1. Leroy rented a lawn mower. The rental cost $8 per day plus a fee of $25. He paid a total of $49. For how many days did he rent the lawn mower? 3 days

2. Seung paid $100 to rent a ladder. It cost $12 per day plus $4 for the renter's fee. For how many days did she rent the ladder? 8 days

Reference Pages: Multiplication Table

Look at the multiplication chart below. It is easy to find the product of any two numbers on the chart. Find one number in the first column going down. Find the second number in the top row going across. Move across from the first column and down from the top row. The box in which the row and column meet contains the product of the two numbers.

x	0	1	2	3	4	5	6	7	8	9
0	0	0	0	0	0	0	0	0	0	0
1	0	1	2	3	4	5	6	7	8	9
2	0	2	4	6	8	10	12	14	16	18
3	0	3	6	9	12	15	18	21	24	27
4	0	4	8	12	16	20	24	28	32	36
5	0	5	10	15	20	25	30	35	40	45
6	0	6	12	18	24	30	36	42	48	54
7	0	7	14	21	28	35	42	49	56	63
8	0	8	16	24	32	40	48	56	64	72
9	0	9	18	27	36	45	54	63	72	81

Reference Pages: Formulas

▶ Percents Formulas

Percent = Part ÷ Whole
Part = Percent ÷ Whole
Whole = Part ÷ Percent

Sales tax = Tax rate × Cost
Total cost with tax = Cost + Sales tax

Discount = Discount rate × Price
Sale price = Original price − Discount

Commission = Commission rate × Sales
Gross salary = Base salary + Commission

Percent increase/decrease = Difference ÷ Original number

▶ Algebra Formulas

Order of Operations
   1. Multiply and divide from left to right.
   2. Add and subtract from left to right.

Distance = Rate × Time
Rate = Distance ÷ Time
Time = Distance ÷ Rate

Cost = Rate per day × Number of days + Renter's fee

Reference Pages: Tables of Measures

▶ Customary System

Length

1 foot (ft)	= 12 inches (in.)
1 yard (yd)	= 36 inches
1 yard	= 3 feet
1 mile (mi)	= 5,280 feet

Capacity

1 pint (pt)	= 16 fluid ounces (fl oz)
1 quart (qt)	= 32 fluid ounces
1 quart	= 2 pints (pt)
1 gallon (gal)	= 4 quarts

Weight

1 pound (lb)	= 16 ounces (oz)
1 ton (tn)	= 2,000 pounds

Time

See below.

▶ Metric System

Length

1 kilometer (km)	= 1,000 meters (m)
1 hectometer (hm)	= 100 meters
1 dekameter (dam)	= 10 meters
1 meter	= 1 meter
10 decimeters (dm)	= 1 meter
100 centimeters (cm)	= 1 meter
1,000 millimeters (mm)	= 1 meter

Capacity

1 kiloliter (kL)	= 1,000 liters (L)
1 hectoliter (hL)	= 100 liters
1 dekaliter (daL)	= 10 liters
1 liter	= 1 liter
10 deciliters (dL)	= 1 liter
100 centiliters (cL)	= 1 liter
1,000 milliliters (mL)	= 1 liter

Mass (weight)

1 kilogram (kg)	= 1,000 grams (g)
1 hectogram (hg)	= 100 grams
1 dekagram (dag)	= 10 grams
1 gram	= 1 gram
10 decigrams (dg)	= 1 gram
100 centigrams (cg)	= 1 gram
1,000 milligrams (mg)	= 1 gram

Time

60 seconds (sec)	= 1 minute (min)
60 minutes	= 1 hour (hr)
24 hours	= 1 day
7 days (d)	= 1 week (wk)
52 weeks	= 1 year (yr)
12 months (mo)	= 1 year

Reference Pages: Geometry

Perimeter of polygons = sum of the lengths of all sides

Rectangle

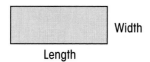

Area = length × width

Parallelogram

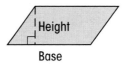

Area = base × height

Triangle

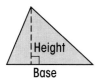

Area = $\frac{1}{2}$ × base × height

Circle

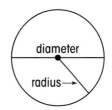

Diameter = radius × 2
Area = π × (radius)^2
Circumference = π × diameter
Circumference = π × 2 × radius
π ≈ 3.14

Rectangular Prism

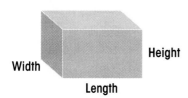

Volume = length × width × height

Cylinder

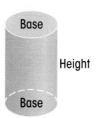

Volume = π × (radius)^2 × height

Reference Pages: Table of Squares

Number	Square	Number	Square	Number	Square	Number	Square
1	1	26	676	51	2,601	76	5,776
2	4	27	729	52	2,704	77	5,929
3	9	28	784	53	2,809	78	6,084
4	16	29	841	54	2,916	79	6,241
5	25	30	900	55	3,025	80	6,400
6	36	31	961	56	3,136	81	6,561
7	49	32	1,024	57	3,249	82	6,724
8	64	33	1,089	58	3,364	83	6,889
9	81	34	1,156	59	3,481	84	7,056
10	100	35	1,225	60	3,600	85	7,225
11	121	36	1,296	61	3,721	86	7,396
12	144	37	1,369	62	3,844	87	7,569
13	169	38	1,444	63	3,969	88	7,744
14	196	39	1,521	64	4,096	89	7,921
15	225	40	1,600	65	4,225	90	8,100
16	256	41	1,681	66	4,356	91	8,281
17	289	42	1,764	67	4,489	92	8,464
18	324	43	1,849	68	4,624	93	8,649
19	361	44	1,936	69	4,761	94	8,836
20	400	45	2,025	70	4,900	95	9,025
21	441	46	2,116	71	5,041	96	9,216
22	484	47	2,209	72	5,184	97	9,409
23	529	48	2,304	73	5,329	98	9,604
24	576	49	2,401	74	5,476	99	9,801
25	625	50	2,500	75	5,625	100	10,000

Reference Pages: Square Roots of Perfect Squares

The number that was squared is called the square root.

$$9^2 = 81 \qquad \sqrt{81} = 9$$

Perfect Square	Square Root	Perfect Square	Square Root
1	1	256	16
4	2	289	17
9	3	324	18
16	4	361	19
25	5	400	20
36	6	441	21
49	7	484	22
64	8	529	23
81	9	576	24
100	10	625	25
121	11	676	26
144	12	729	27
169	13	784	28
196	14	841	29
225	15	900	30

Glossary

add   put numbers together; find the total amount

angle   figure formed by two rays with the same endpoint

area   the amount of space inside a figure

base salary   salary before adding commission

canceling   dividing a numerator and a denominator by the same number

capacity   how much space is in a container

circumference   the distance around a circle

column   numbers placed one below the other

commission   payment based on a percent of sales

composite number   number with more than two factors

cross products   the results of cross multiplying

Customary System of Measurement measurement units used in the United States

data   information gathered from surveys or experiments

decimal   a number that names part of a whole

decimal places   the places to the right of a decimal point

decimal point   the dot in a decimal; a decimal point has digits to its right

degrees (°)   units used to measure temperature

denominator   the bottom number in a fraction

diameter   the distance across the middle of a circle

difference   the amount obtained by subtracting; the amount by which one number is larger or smaller than another

digits   the symbols used to write numbers: 0, 1, 2, 3, 4, 5, 6, 7, 8, and 9

discount   amount that a price is reduced

dividend   the number to be divided

divisible   can be divided without a remainder

division   the process of finding out how many times one number contains another

divisor   the number to divide by

elapsed time   the amount of time that has passed between two given times

equation   a mathematical sentence stating that two quantities are equal

equivalent fractions fractions with different numbers but equal values

estimate to quickly find an answer that is close to an exact answer; to make a good guess

even numbers numbers that end in 0, 2, 4, 6, or 8

exponent tells how many times to use a number as a factor

factors the numbers that are multiplied to obtain a product

fraction a form of a number that shows part of a whole

gram the basic metric unit used to measure mass (weight)

graph a visual display that shows data in different ways; includes bar, line, and circle graphs

greatest common factor (GCF) the largest factor that two or more numbers share

gross salary commission plus the base salary

histogram a graph that shows how many times an event occurred

horizontal written across the page from left to right

integers numbers in the set {..., −3, −2, −1, 0, 1, 2, 3, ...}

invert to reverse the positions of the numerator and denominator of a fraction

least common multiple (LCM) the smallest multiple that two or more numbers share

length how long an object is

like fractions fractions that have the same denominator

liter the basic metric unit used to measure liquid capacity

lowest terms when only 1 divides evenly into both the numerator and denominator of a fraction

mean sum of the data divided by the number of data; also called average

median middle number when data are ordered from least to greatest

meter the basic metric unit used to measure length

metric system the system of measurement based on the number 10 that is used in most countries

minus the symbol or word that means to subtract

mixed decimal a number with a whole number and a decimal

mixed number a number made up of a whole number and a fraction

mode number or numbers that appear most often in a set of data

multiples possible products of a given number

multiple unit pricing the cost of one item or one unit measure of an item

multiplication a quick way to add; repeated addition

multiply to add a number to itself one or more times; 2 + 2 + 2 + 2 = 8 or 4 x 2 = 8

negative integers integers to the left of zero on the number line

number expressions a number or numbers together with operation symbols

number line numbers in order shown as points on a line

numerator the top number in a fraction

odd numbers numbers that end in 1, 3, 5, 7, or 9

opposites two numbers that are the same distance from zero on the number line but are on opposite sides of zero

order of operations the specific order to do the four basic operations when more than one operation is in an equation

parallelogram a quadrilateral whose opposite sides are parallel; examples are rectangles and squares

parenthesis ( ) marks around an operation that should be done first

partial product the number obtained by multiplying a number by only one digit of a two or more digit number

percent a part of a whole divided into 100 parts

percent decrease percent less than an original number

percent increase percent more than an original number

perimeter the distance around a figure

pictograph a graph that uses pictures to represent data

plus the symbol or word that means to add

polygons plane figures with three or more sides; examples are triangles, quadrilaterals, pentagons, hexagons, and octagons

positive integers integers to the right of zero on the number line

prime number number with only itself and 1 as factors

probability the chance that an event will occur

product the final answer to a multiplication problem

proportion a statement that two ratios are equal

protractor a tool used to measure angles

quotient the number obtained by dividing one number into another; the answer in a division problem

radius the distance from the center of a circle to its edge

rate a comparison of two amounts with different units of measure

ratio a comparison of one amount with another

regroup   (in addition) to rename and then carry a tens digit to the place on the left when adding; (in subtraction) to rename and then carry a tens digit to the place on the right when subtracting

remainder   the number left over in a division problem

rename   to show a number another way; to show place value, 28 can be renamed as 2 tens + 8 ones

rounding   changing a number to the nearest ten, hundred, thousand, or so on

sale price   price of an item after the discount is subtracted

sales tax   a tax that is a percentage of the price of an item

scale   a ratio that compares the size of a drawing with the size of the original object

scale drawing   a picture that shows the proportional size of actual objects

simplify   to write a shorter or easier form of an expression; or to find its value

solution   the value of a variable that makes an equation true

solve   to find the answer to a problem

space figure   a three-dimensional figure that has length, width, and height

square   product of multiplying a number by itself

square root   number that was squared

subtract   to take away one number from another; to find the amount that remains

sum   the amount obtained by adding; the total

unit price   the cost of one item or one unit measure of an item

unlike fractions   fractions that have different denominators

variable   a letter that stands for a number

vertical   written as one thing under the other

volume   the amount of space inside a three-dimensional figure

weight   how heavy an object is

whole numbers   0, 1, 2, 3, 4, 5, 6, 7, and so on

Index

W

Weight (mass)
   customary measurement, 303, 306–307
   metric measurement, 326–327
Whole numbers, 3, 4
   adding, 25–41
   comparing, 12–13
   dividing, 85–105
   multiplying, 63–83, 158
   even and odd numbers, 5
   ordering, 14–15
   place value, 6–9
   rounding, 18–20
   subtracting, 43–61
   in word problems, 16–17, 21, 166–167

Z

Zeros
   in multiplication, 78–79
   in quotient, 98–99
   in subtraction, 56–57

Photo Credits

Overflow Annotations

Extra Practice   *Chapter 13 Lessons 13-4 and 13-5*

1.

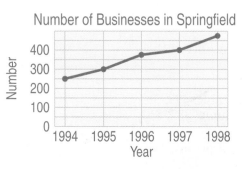

2.

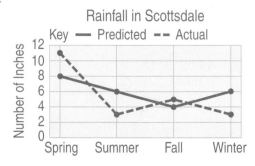